Dying
Cure

For all who have endured the living hell of acute drug-induced akathisia

Dying for a Cure

a woman's battle with antidepressants,
misdiagnosis and madness

Rebekah Beddoe

With a Foreword by Professor David Healy

Hammersmith Press
London, UK

Revised edition first published in Great Britain in 2009 by
Hammersmith Press Limited,
496 Fulham Palace Road, London SW6 6JD, UK
www.hammersmithpress.co.uk

First published 2007 in Australia by Random House Australia Pty Ltd

Author's note

I've written this book based on medical and pharmaceutical records,
diary entries, four years of research, and memories – of my own and of
those courageous enough and caring enough to travel this treacherous
journey with me. Except for those of my immediate family and myself,
the identities of people have been changed. Descriptions of places
have been altered also.

British Library Cataloguing in Publication Data:
A CIP record of this book is available from the British Library.

ISBN 978-1-905140-25-1

Designed and typeset by Julie Bennett
Cover image by Veronica Rooke of Fishbitten Designs
Production by Helen Whitehorn, Pathmedia
Printed and bound by TJ International Ltd, UK.

Mixed Sources
Product group from well-managed
forests and other controlled sources
www.fsc.org Cert no. SGS-COC-2482
FSC © 1996 Forest Stewardship Council

Acknowledgements

A gigantic and heartfelt thank you must go to the following people:

Georgina Bentliff of Hammersmith Press, London. For your unapologetic determination to allow the other side of so many stories to be told. For investing your faith in me and my story and allowing it to be told beyond Australian shores.

Pam Solomon for your dedication and success with UK publicity.

Bob Fiddaman of the popular blog *Seroxat sufferers stand up and be counted*, for your utterly selfless efforts in chasing up information for me relevant to the UK.

Claire Ward for your encouragement and your lovely supportive on-line review of my book in an effort to assist bringing it to the UK.

Photographer and graphic artist Veronica Rooke of Fishbitten Designs for your commitment and talent in getting the cover just right.

Professor David Healy . . . how do I count the ways? For the work you do at large, unwaveringly and with impeccable integrity and selflessness, raising awareness of the inadequately publicised true limitations of antidepressant treatment and the reality of what's actually known about depression's cause: discoveries you have made both while commissioned as consultant for the pharmaceutical industry, and since. Your efforts could quite possibly have saved my life, or at the very least have returned to me my health. Hence, no amount of thanks seems quite adequate. On a more personal level, I am utterly honoured by your agreement to support this book by contributing your foreword, and by your consistent willingness to help me, with what must have been at times, pestering little requests for UK-specific info.

I must also reiterate my thanks to all those integral to the conception and production of the Australian edition:

My lecturers Christine Balint and Liam Davison. Daniel Williams of TIME magazine.

Dr Jon Jureidini of Healthy Skepticism.

My agent, Pippa Masson. The team at Random House Australia, who published, edited and publicised the book for the Australian market.

Nigel, for having the strength and tolerance to revisit again and again this horrendous time in our lives. Mum, for all the practical support you offered, and for forgoing your privacy in allowing me to use your diary entries. My darling Jemima, for your maturity in understanding why Mummy has had to spend so much time at the computer and for helping here and there with the care of your little sister (without complaining too much) as I've worked on this lastest edition of the book. For being the exceptional little girl that you are.

Foreword

The Oscar-nominated movie *The Changeling* starts with a clip saying it is a true story – not just 'based on' a true story. In it the horrors of psychiatry are portrayed, pretty much as they have been since *One Flew over the Cuckoo's Nest*, through the forced administration of Shock Therapy (ECT) – even though the heroine's incarceration happened 10 years before ECT was invented. When the historical detail is so flagrantly wrong, presumably what's going on is based on a calculation that ECT inflicted in this way will best epitomize the fears of today's viewers about psychiatry. But in fact forced treatment with ECT is now vanishingly rare. In regular psychiatric practice, insiders, both staff and patients, are much more likely to fear forcible and indefinite medication with long-acting antipsychotic injections – a treatment that is more clearly brain damaging and more likely to turn a person into a zombie than ECT.

It is, however, in outpatient, or voluntary, or primary care treatment, with drugs like antidepressants, that the greatest amount of damage is done to the greatest number of people; these are the real abuses, the real dramas. While ECT when given punitively, as has happened in the past, might be compared to rape as an instrument of war, in countless outpatient and primary care settings an abuse quite comparable to the sexual abuse of children or sexual harassment happens – much more common than wartime rape and at least as destructive.

The pink section papers of a Mental Health Act aren't in evidence when we are prescribed an antidepressant. We are free to walk out the door after a consultation, and we think as a consequence that there is nothing to worry about. But these drugs are available on prescription only, and when we go for treatment we are linked inescapably to the prescriber. In the ordinary course of events for most of us, going to the doctor is like going to the bank manager or the head teacher – we feel only a few inches tall, absurdly grateful for the smallest signs of favour, and often completely forget what we had meant to say. This situation is compounded if things begin to go wrong after some treatment starts, when the doctor may quickly seem like our only way out. We become ever more dependent on him, and ever more grateful. We are unaware we are heading into a medical version of Stockholm syndrome – the puzzling state where hostages are often close to being in love with those who have taken them hostage. If the difficulties we develop are caused by the treatment and the doctor doesn't recognise that what he has done or is doing is wrong for us, then we become almost hostages to fate.

It can be extraordinarily difficult for any of us, doctors or patients, to distinguish between the almost identical anxieties, insomnias, and morbid thoughts that antidepressant treatments can cause, even in healthy volunteers, and the anxieties, insomnias and morbid thoughts that may stem from the illness or problem we took to the doctor in the first instance. It becomes effortless for the doctor to blame any developments or worsening on our original problem, rather than the treatment. With much less going for them, surgeons did just this – blamed the victim – faced with the evidence of memory problems after cardiac surgery; psychotherapists did it in the face of evidence that memories of abuse were sometimes false; and psychiatrists routinely do it when patients get hooked on antidepressants or tranquilizers or get tardive dyskinesia or diabetes from antipsychotics.

In addition to things getting worse for us when a treatment goes wrong, we can become isolated astonishingly quickly. If we approach someone for help, we have first to risk the stigma of being seen to have a mental problem and then also to risk being stigmatised as a loser. We risk incomprehension – even if we approach mental health professionals, none of whom are likely to take our side rather than the doctor's. We risk the next prescription being increased to root out the lingering traces of our illogical thinking. No one will call this a reprisal. If, for some reason, we are listened to and treatment stops and we get worse, no-one is likely to counsel patience to help see us through what might well be a withdrawal syndrome.

The ultimate bind is that our questions will be put in the weighing scales against the scientific answers and found wanting, and what self-respecting doctor in an era of evidence-based medicine will want to be seen to go against the evidence. Can all the guidelines be wrong? There is no-one on our side who is likely to point out that the so-called scientific evidence has been carefully constructed by pharmaceutical companies, who suppress trials that don't suit their interests, and who selectively publish data from trials so that even a trial that has shown a drug fails to work and can trigger suicide can be transformed into a trial that shows unparalleled evidence of efficacy. No one to point out that pretty well all the trials published in even the best journals are likely to be ghost-written. No-one to point out in the case of the antidepressants that pharmaceutical companies have moved dead bodies around in a manner that may well be fraudulent. No-one to point out that lawyers and others looking after the interests of pharmaceutical companies regularly take advantage of medical innumeracy to hide even more dead bodies simply by constructing trials so the results will not be statistically significant.

As in other areas of abuse, if we wait for the abusers to recognise the problem we are likely to wait forever. As in so many other areas, from Enron to sexual abuse, it is likely to be women who will blow the whistle. And this is the background against which Rebekah Beddoe's *Dying for a Cure* needs to be read. She outlines a drama of seduction, increasing personal confusion, family bewilderment, and finally survival against the odds. But she is also offering a manifesto. What she describes will seem unbelievable to many – although not to those who have been through the 'system'. Could it happen here in Britain in 2009? Absolutely. Countless dramas of this sort happen in British clinics every day – and not just within the mental health domain. Any area of medicine that has a large number of currently on-patent pharmaceuticals, for respiratory or cardiac or other conditions, can be infected in the same way. The truth is that as 2009 slides into 2010 and beyond we are increasingly less likely to get good medical care – by which I mean when a doctor cares enough about his or her patient to put their welfare first even if this means taking on an employing organisation, or the medical or scientific establishment.

Dying for a Cure calls out for a movie to be made of it – but we are likely to be waiting a long time for some future celebrity Director prepared to take on this challenge. What stops them? In contrast to ECT, the problems found in *Dying for a Cure* are so difficult because they are ones in which we are all complicit. This makes for very uncomfortable viewing But if movie directors are not prepared to take on this challenge, as a matter of honour they should desist from making movies like *The Changeling* or *Girl Interrupted* that indirectly play a part in perpetuating the kind of abuse that Rebekah Beddoe outlines so vividly here.

Professor David Healy
Director,
North Wales Department of Psychological Medicine,
UK
2009

Prologue

The yin, the yang
The good, the bad.
Give, take.
Life, death
For every positive somewhere lurks a negative.
I was given the ultimate gift – a beautiful baby girl. Shortly
after, something stole my mind . . .

ONE

'Results in two to five minutes,' the instructions on the test read. Two lines: pregnant. One line: not.

I watched as the moisture crept across the test strip. One pink line materialised in the control window, partnered very rapidly by another in the test window. I was pregnant. 'Two lines: pregnant.'

I stared at that stick until the toilet seat cut into my bare thighs and snapped me out of my stupor.

Just weeks prior, I'd been offered a permanent position in a multinational computer company where I'd been working under contract for a number of years. The competition from a group of longer-standing, more qualified male candidates had been cut-throat, but I had been selected. It was a real triumph – not just for me but for all women, I felt – to have made it in such a male-dominated profession.

I'd been steadily chipping away at reaching precisely this professional position for a number of years. In my early twenties, after arriving home from a two-year-long overseas working holiday, I took a position as an administration officer for a large building services company. Though it was steady, relatively enjoyable work, it was completely unfulfilling. I'd noticed pretty quickly that the company had a need for someone to deal with their computer faults, so I took some night classes studying computer hardware. Once up to speed, I volunteered to help with any computer-related problems and soon enough I was recognised as the unofficial information technology coordinator. With this new set of skills I was eligible to apply for work requiring more credentials and it was then I was selected to work on contract for my current prestigious IT company.

This strategy was a fairly typical one for me. I was always on the lookout for opportunities to seize, challenges that would give me the chance to prove what I was capable of. The benchmarks I set for self-approval were high in any given situation and I would not be satisfied unless I reached or exceeded them. I had come to expect my circumstances would always be improving and that I would move onwards and upwards. My life was neatly contained and controlled. I was in charge of my own destiny. But my momentum was about to be halted.

It was horrifying to discover that while I was smiling and accepting my promotion I was also pregnant.

I'd been having premenstrual-like symptoms – bloating, cramping – for weeks. I'd had lots of spotting as well, but each time I was sure my cycle was about to begin everything would subside again. I knew this wasn't the normal way for my body to behave, but pregnancy was, selectively, the furthest thing from my mind.

A huge wave of nausea at work one day yanked my head out of the sand. It became clear that ignoring the possibility of pregnancy would not make it go away. That mode of thinking had landed women in loads of trouble for centuries, I was sure. I excused myself and made a beeline for the nearest pharmacy.

In addition to the store-bought test, an ultrasound a couple of days later confirmed I was already eight weeks pregnant.

How had I wound up in a situation I had dreaded all my life? A situation so sickeningly similar to that of my mother. She had favoured my right to life over her right to happiness at an age too young to have had to make such a life-altering decision. I now envisaged my personal and professional life following that same route fraught with heartache and struggle. My choices restricted at every move. My gold-paved path to the future turning to mud.

I held out telling my boss for as long as I could, but my belly soon started to show and I knew the announcement was unavoidable.

He was clearly rattled by the news, but took it better than I had predicted. I was expecting him to renege on the job offer altogether and hand it to the runner-up. Instead, he said he would see what he could do about getting me some time off after the birth; there was no entitlement to maternity leave until twelve months of permanent employment had been served.

I couldn't help wondering, though, what he was really thinking. Was he kicking himself for going against advice and hiring the only female applicant? He'd gone out on a limb and I'd let him down. I left that meeting with my tail between my legs. I'd just lived up to every male chauvinist generalisation ever voiced about women striving for equal opportunity: 'There's no point selecting her for promotion. She'll only go off and have kids one day.' What a scourge to the sisterhood.

I was overcome with relief when, the following day, my compassionate boss advised me that he had managed to negotiate six months of leave for me, without pay, upon the arrival of my baby. Things seemed not quite so dire. I would have been in the role nearly half a year by then and I imagined I should have a good grasp of things. I felt certain that six months after the birth I could handle putting my baby in day care. In fact, I was pretty sure I'd be climbing the walls by then and itching to get back to work. My partner Nigel's response was not so encouraging. His knees literally buckled when I gave him the news – lucky the arm of the lounge chair was there to break his fall. I knew expecting him to want to celebrate was unrealistic, but for him to react as if I had just told him his life as he'd known it was ending was what I was dreading.

My early job at the building services company had proved to be quite a beneficial venture: not only had it opened the door to a career in computers, it had also united me with Nigel, a then trainee project manager in the engineering department.

As we were both single and similarly aged, matchmakers on the staff had put plenty of pressure on us to go on a date. I hadn't been particularly interested in him. He was good-looking, that was for sure – in a wholesome and almost school-boyish kind of a way. But he was slightly younger than me and from the little that I'd come to know of him since working in the same building, he wasn't my type. Or at least what had been my type: a professional sportsman, an artist and a police detective, to date. Their lifestyles had initially held great appeal and intrigue, and their overt self-confidence was highly attractive. But after a year or so, each man's charisma had begun to lose its charm, in the end revealing nothing much more than self-absorption and ego, which eventually smothered any spark of my interest in them.

One particular Friday the word was passed around that drinks would be held after work at a local bar rather than the lunchroom, as was usual. Nigel and I were the first, and as it turned out, the only ones to arrive. A coincidence? I think not. As we chatted over a drink, then later over dinner, Nigel began to take on an unexpected allure. He was genuine and serious and modest. He was interesting too, an accomplished sailor and extreme water-sports enthusiast. There was no showing off though – just a simple, straightforward recounting of his passions. In fact, he preferred to talk about me, a refreshing change from what I'd been used to. He made me feel important and valued. On each successive date I felt increasingly illuminated in his company.

Our relationship went steadily from strength to strength, and we never ceased to amaze each other with our similarities. We both seemed older than our years, and took life very seriously. We each lived by a code of hard work and self-sufficiency, but also strongly believed in the importance of volunteering our services to those less fortunate. We shared the same moral and ethical values, spiritual beliefs, and professional and personal aspirations. We both loved to be healthy and active. Neither of us had to try to impress the other, neither of us had to pretend we were anything other than our true selves. There was, for both of us, an unfamiliar substance and purpose to this relationship.

After seeing each other for six months we decided to rent a unit together.*

During the ensuing couple of years we did talk about a future of mortgage, marriage, children – to occur strictly in that order and only when we were completely financially secure. First, we both had careers to build.

Just as I'd not planned to be pregnant at twenty-seven, Nigel hadn't dreamt of an initiation into fatherhood at twenty-five.

---

*In Australia a residential 'unit' refers to one of usually six to ten single-level dwellings that share one common block of land, often facing one another with a shared driveway down the centre, They are most commonly situated in densely populated suburban regions of large cities

I didn't actually verbalise that I was pregnant. I couldn't quite get myself to utter the words. Instead, I laid the envelope containing the films of the ultrasound in Nigel's hands, placed the positive stick-test on top and waited for the penny to drop. After grappling with the realisation for a few moments he said, 'But is it still early enough to do something about it?'

I heard his murderous words as though spoken by a stranger. Surely, after all this time sharing my life, he would know that such a thing was beyond consideration for me. I glared but could not speak. His 'what'd I say?' expression compounded my disgust and I ran to the bedroom.

I had feared this – history repeating. My father deserted my mother when she became pregnant with me. He already had children and didn't want another. Mum was left with little but her Catholic conscience and, fortunately, the stoicism and resourcefulness necessary to survive profound hardship. Without Mum's resilience I dread to think where we could've ended up. Given more privileged circumstances Mum could have become anything, somewhere in the realm of judge or politician, I'd always imagined (she'd often told me she'd planned to study law). Even with all the adversity, she graduated from teachers' college. Not quite the esteem her intelligence, aspirations and tenacity could have achieved for her, though. My arrival made sure of that.

I knew I was strong but I doubted I had quite her level of resolve. I didn't want to have to have it. Until this moment I hadn't believed in fate or predetermined reasons for things. I'd always considered such explanations for life's adversities were a way for people to absolve themselves of blame when they'd screwed up. But now I began to wonder if events in my life were influenced by some 'greater power'. Maybe this *was* happening for a reason; so I could appreciate how much of her life Mum had to sacrifice to ensure I was provided for. Even when she'd tried to gain my sympathy, I don't think I'd taken enough notice. So now, it seemed, God was doing the talking.

Nigel and I did not talk further that night. Nigel's personality is a classic example of still waters running deep, but boy, right then I yearned to see a ripple. In fact, I needed a cascade of expression to flow so that the same could come from me. We could talk and yell and cry.

Then he could see that killing my baby in the name of convenience was not an option for me. Mum could have done that, but she hadn't. I owed the same to the helpless being inside me.

Over the subsequent days, the tension between us became stifling. Nigel, deploying his typical conflict-avoidance strategy, tried to talk about anything other than the pregnancy. He'd pay me an excess of compliments and try to engage me in light-hearted banter. Deep in denial, he must have somehow thought if he could distract me from what was getting to me I might forget all about it and things would be a-okay once more.

He came home one night to find me curled in a ball on our bed in the dark. I rocked and wept. As if aware of the magnitude of my distress for the first time, he sat beside me and tentatively stroked my back.

'I don't want to be alone, Nige, but I have to keep this baby.' There, it was said. I just hoped he'd be the one to offer to move out.

After a drawn-out pause, he said softly, 'I'm never going to leave.' I was giddy with relief.

I was now free to bask in the anticipation of having a child. My daydreams became overrun with romantic notions of motherhood. My thoughts would run away with visions of the six months I would spend at home with my babe, waking to her cute gurgles instead of the alarm, enjoying afternoon naps with her swaddled in my arms, treating myself to coffee with friends; the days slipping by as I immersed myself in the bliss of parental discovery.

I discovered a website called *Pregnancy: Week by Week*, where I could click on any week of gestation to read about the details of a developing fetus. Each day at work I'd resist like crazy the desire to sneak a peek, until on Friday at lunchtime, in a secluded conference room free from colleagues' queries and badgering telephones, I'd get comfortable with my sandwich and cup of tea and log on to behold in awe what was happening in my belly.

The look of my ripening shape pleased me no end and I loved it when others referred to it. Perhaps that was because Nigel rarely did. He seemed unable to see past the weighty responsibility thrust on him as soon-to-be carer and provider for two dependants. No wistful daydreaming for him; he became consumed with bolstering the security of our future.

'We'll need to get some financial advice. We need to buy a house, we can't be renting with a new baby. And your car, we'll need to sell your car. You won't get a pram in a hatchback.'

Perhaps I was expecting too much for Nigel to rejoice in our unplanned situation, just yet anyway. After all, it wouldn't seem as real to him as it did to me. How could it? To him she was still abstract, but my baby and me, we were one and the same.

I would have loved for him to share in my joy, but I wasn't about to push him – no way. He hadn't left and that was paramount. At least we had something to build on. So, as though it was an illicit love affair, I kept my romantic musing between myself, my child and the internet.

One gloriously unforgettable evening in June 1999, I got to meet my precious child. After ten hours of screams, grimaces, pleadings, headlocks, and a heaven-sent epidural, my baby began her individual life. 'A girl, she's a girl!' Nigel called, before I'd had the chance to see. And for the first time it struck me as strange that I'd thought I'd always known.

Jemima. Seeing her, holding her. Oh, no words suffice. Nigel, who'd been by my side unfalteringly through the labour, seemed as exhausted as I was. 'I can't believe she's ours,' he said, his tears of elation cancelling my fears he wouldn't bond with his daughter. 'My family.' He shook his head as if it was all simply too wonderful to bear. '*My* family.' I felt that to love him more than I did at that moment would be near impossible. Our rapture was interrupted by the midwife whisking Jemima away for all her required medical bits and pieces. Nigel, along with my mother and her partner, who had both waited patiently throughout the labour, followed her to where Jemima would be washed and weighed. I was left alone in the delivery room, bloody, sweaty and restrained by my epidural-affected legs. If I craned my head at the right angle I could just see her squirming little body being lifted from the scales into the bath. She was screaming. She needed her mum. I'm here, baby. I haven't left you. I'm just over here.

The nurse presented her, spruced and bundled, to me for another quick hold before she was admitted to the special-care nursery. The lovely olive complexion she was sporting was in fact a touch of jaundice that would require twenty-four hours of UV light in a special crib. I masked my anxiety and resentment at the thought of strangers, medically trained or not, being my child's caregivers before I had been given the chance. The extension of me that I had been nurturing for nine months was taken and so was my say in what was going on. The abrupt, complete separation was almost unbearable.

I lay awake that night in the unfamiliar surrounds of the hospital room, ears tuned to the endless cries from the nursery at the far end of the ward. Which one was Jemima's? I wanted to go to her, show that I had nothing to do with them separating us. Instead, I did as I was told and stayed helplessly, sleeplessly, in bed.

She was brought into my room early the next morning, still sleeping, tightly wrapped in the fleecy bunny rug I'd bought months earlier. I had often tried to picture her in it, had imagined bundling her up and holding her close. And now there she was, the real thing: gorgeous, perfect . . . and a complete stranger. I extended my hand to stroke her cheek, then retracted it. How did I know if that was what she wanted? How would I provide what this helpless, completely dependent individual wanted; what she needed? My confidence and optimism wavered as it hit me for the first time what caring for this unique, fragile, unpredictable little person might entail.

She awoke, crying. With trepidation I picked her up. I tried to convince her, 'It's okay, Mummy's got you.' She was inconsolable. I offered her a feed; she rejected it. I held her closer to my body. 'Hey, relax. You're with your mummy now.' Don't your instincts tell you that?

Nothing went according to plan over the next few days in hospital. I seemed not to be blessed with the motherhood magic I'd heard so much about: the gift that was supposed to descend from nowhere the minute your baby was born; the sixth maternal sense that enabled you to pacify her angst, discern a hunger cry from a tired cry, and equipped you to breastfeed as if it was the most instinctive and natural of all abilities.

Once we get home things will settle, I assured myself. Familiar surroundings and a natural routine will make all the difference.

Alas, it made little difference. My self-doubt only intensified in the absence of round-the-clock instruction and encouragement from hospital staff. Through no fault of anyone I had little support once discharged. Family was scarce. I was a single-parented only child and Nigel had only his father and younger sister in his immediate family. His mother, sadly, had died before we'd had the chance to meet. As a project manager for a fire protection company, Nigel now worked ten-hour days. Mum still had her full-time teaching career, and none of my close friends had any children as yet – they were all still working full-time too.

Perhaps things would have been different had Jemima been a more content baby. I'd had realistic expectations that babies spend a large amount of their time crying, but it seemed that unless I kept Jemima in constant soothing motion her ear-piercing protestations were relentless. That meant she needed to be strapped to my chest as I walked about, or rocked back and forth in her pram, or jigged constantly in my arms or her bouncinette. I acquired painful tendonitis in my wrist from the hour-long bouncing ritual that it took to pacify her to sleep at night.

Breastfeeding was such a trial too, but I couldn't quite put my finger on what was wrong. It took us forever, twice as long as I'd seen it take other mums. I'd been told by the nurses to demand feed (when Jemima wanted a feed then that's when she was supposed to get it), but she seemed to be demanding more often than should be expected. Wasn't I supplying what she needed? Was my milk no good?

Perhaps she was sick. When she was about eight weeks old I took her to see the local GP.

He agreed with my suspicions and suggested I take her to a paediatrician. He phoned and made me an appointment on the spot. There'd be a three-week wait.

✦✦✦✦✦

I'd just managed to settle Jemima to sleep for one of her twenty-minute cat-naps – one of the two that would constitute her entire day's sleeping – when I heard our front gate swing open. The doorbell didn't ring; I'd disconnected it to prevent such callers from waking Jemima. I thought about ignoring whoever it was, as I'd become quite accustomed to doing with both the phone and the door, but realised my outline could most likely be spied through the stained-glass panels. I lifted myself gently from the couch, taking great care not to alert Jemima to my movement.

I relaxed when I discovered the visitor was my good friend Celeste.

'Oh, thank goodness it's only you.' I ushered her inside with a hushing finger pressed to my lips.

'*Only* me? Gee, thanks a lot,' she joked in a whisper.

'I didn't mean it like that. Come on, we'll go sit in the bedroom so we can talk properly.' Celeste stopped to admire Jemima before following me down the hall.

'You sleep her on her belly?' she quizzed, once in a non-restricted-voice zone. 'I thought these days it was the back or nothing, you know, with the risk of cot death and everything. Not that I'd know,' she added hastily, probably remembering how little new mothers enjoyed being questioned on their methods, particularly from those without children.

'For her it's either the tummy or nothing, I'm afraid. She's particular about little things like that. And I tell you, I'm so worn out lately that if she's prepared to sleep, I ain't about to argue with her about how to do it.'

'No, I guess not. I'm sorry to land in on you like this, but I've tried leaving a couple of messages, and then when you didn't turn up to Amy and Grant's engagement on the weekend, I wondered if you were okay. Everyone missed you there, you know.'

'Yeah, I felt terrible cancelling at the last minute, but I just couldn't get myself in the mood. I'm so busy with Jemima, and so tired. I didn't know it was possible to be this tired.'

'Are you getting any time to yourself?'

'Only when she sleeps, and then that's when I sleep.'

'Bek, that's no good. You've got to get some time to yourself.'

'That's really easier said than done.'

'What about Nigel, is he helping?'

'He's terrific, when he's here. Just let me give you an example of what it's like, though: if Nige and I want to eat together, and in peace, then I can only cook meals that can be eaten with a fork. We each have to keep the other arm free to take turns nursing Jemima. The second she's put down she screams blue murder.'

'God, that sounds terrible.'

'It is, Lessie, it is.'

'She's not sick or something, is she?'

'Not with anything outwardly obvious, but I took her to the GP the other day and after witnessing her in action he thinks there might be something causing her pain. He's advised me to take her to a specialist. This is going to sound really awful, but I almost hope he's right. At least then it would be treatable. There'd be a reason for why she's so unhappy, a reason other than that I'm just a terrible mother.'

'You're not a terrible mother, Bek. Don't say that. Listen, I really think you need to get out of these four walls for a while. Come with me now. I'll take you shopping.'

'That's sweet of you, Less, but I really don't feel like it.'

'We'll wait until Jemima's woken. Come on, it'll be fun. How long since you've had yourself a decent latte?'

'A while,' I conceded.

'Well, I think it's about time, then. Don't you?'

'Oh, all right. Thanks, Lessie. You're a good friend.'

The paediatrician determined Jemima's array of behaviours might be due to reflux: an involuntary regurgitation of swallowed milk that burns the digestive tract. I walked from her surgery with new optimism, clutching my order for *Prepulsid* and *Zantac*, two prescription medications that I prayed would cure Jemima of her discomfort and me of my conviction that I was a lousy, defective parent. But, after one

11

week, when the medicines had failed to help, a landslide of broken hope dragged me deep into confusion and disillusionment.

'Just hang in there,' said the paediatrician. 'Your baby's barely three months old. In time her digestive tract and stomach will mature and this problem is likely to clear up by itself.'

In *time*? I couldn't carry on a minute more like this. I couldn't endure any more of this kind of time.

I returned to the GP and, teetering on the verge of tears, expressed how I felt. He suggested Jemima and I spend a few days in the mother and baby unit of Elm Court, a local general hospital. It was a place where new mothers could go for a bit of respite and learn some everyday coping strategies. I would be taught settling techniques for Jemima, as well as receiving therapy for myself. Nigel could stay too, if he liked.

Although I felt a swirl of resistance at resigning myself to the fact that I needed outside help with mothering, I imagined it would probably be in Jemima's and my best interests to swallow my pride and book in. After all, if a few days in hospital would help me be the mother I was determined to be, then it would be worth it.

With the referral the doctor handed me a small box of tablets: a trial pack of *Lustral*. 'Get started on these before you go,' he said. 'They'll be able to write you a prescription for some more at the hospital.' Whoa, whoa, whoa. He's medicating me?

'What are they, first?'

'They're . . . antidepressants,' he said almost guiltily. 'They'll help set you back on track,' he rushed before I could protest. 'Just take one a day, preferably in the –'

'So you think I'm depressed?'

'You could have a touch of postnatal depression.'

I hadn't thought about it that way before. 'But how will they make me feel? Are there side effects, are they addictive?'

'They only have an effect on people who are depressed. If I was to take them, for example, I'd feel nothing. They'll just balance you out a little, get you back to feeling like yourself.'

'What about side effects?'

'Unlike the older kind of antidepressants, this new class is very safe.

12

You can stop taking them any time you like. You would have heard of *Prozac*? Well, this one is a cousin of *Prozac*. They both belong to a group of antidepressants called SSRIs.'

Depression, *depression*. The word was so foreign it might as well have come from another language. I have depression. I've become depressed. I suffer from depression. It didn't matter how I tugged, hitched, hiked or stretched it, the concept just didn't fit right. As I drove back home, I reflected on my time spent in Europe, working as a live-in nanny, not more than a few years back. For over a year I'd taken sole responsibility for the care of two small children – one aged two, the other six months – while their parents were working or socialising. Although I'd had little previous childminding experience I'd taken to the work as though it was second nature to me, loving every minute. I'd kept house, cooked and shopped for the family. I'd taken the children on outings and to playgroup twice weekly, negotiating my way around a foreign city, a foreign language and a foreign culture, and I'd relished every exciting, enriching moment. Yet now, when faced with the care of my own flesh and blood, I'd developed depression? Requiring medication, no less. I just couldn't make sense of it.

I didn't believe in quick fixes, whether it was paracetamol for a headache or medication for a psychological problem. Drugs only ever masked the symptoms while the underlying cause went untreated. I just needed a break, someone to talk to. And I'd get that at this Elm Court place. I didn't need drugs. But then, even once I'd commenced therapy, I rationalised, it was likely to be a while until I would feel the benefit. Maybe the pills would take the edge off in the meantime . . .

I was supposed to take my first dose as soon as I got home. I sat on the couch staring at the pink and blue packet in my hand, unable to take the plunge. '*Lustral*, active ingredient sertraline,' it read. It sounded ominous. My gut told me that taking mind-altering medications was not something to be considered without thought. But the doctor seemed to think it was no big deal. His haste had made me uncomfortable.

I was flabbergasted that he had simply handed me the pills from his desk drawer. I was confused. These were not vitamin supplements. They were antidepressants – agents that affected brain chemicals. He'd conducted no formal assessment, and he hardly knew me – I'd only seen him a handful of times since we'd moved into the area. He hadn't even written a prescription. I had thought handling matters of this kind would be strictly reserved for psychiatrists. Surely what my GP had done couldn't be accepted practice.

But what he had done was not only accepted practice but extremely common. In fact, 85 per cent of antidepressant prescribing takes place in general practice in Australia,[1] while as many as 92 per cent of British GPs prescribe these medications.[2] With recent campaigns for depression awareness[3] and public messages telling us mental illness will affect one in six of us at some point in our lives,[4] there's great pressure on GPs to detect and treat it.

In the 1990s, right around the time I went to see my doctor, Australian general practitioners were being urged to be more aggressive in both the detection and treatment of depression. While attending 'continuing medical education' events, they were warned that an incredible one in three patients who walked into their surgeries was suffering from a mental illness. Sponsoring the event was the maker of an antidepressant. This was just one of the many programmes designed to 'educate' doctors about depression during the 1990s, all generously funded by antidepressant manufacturers. As part of one programme, a simple screening test was developed, designed for use by GPs to detect mental illness in their patients. According to the test criteria, 49 per cent of Australians were considered mentally ill.[5] So it's interesting to note that during the period of 1990 to 2000 antidepressant prescriptions tripled in Australia. Among those aged 15–24, the rates increased tenfold.[6] Family doctors, I imagine, were feeling it was their duty to leave no stone unturned where possible depression was concerned.

My doctor's haphazard manner had left me unconvinced his diagnosis of depression was right. I put the pills away and dialled Elm Court's number.

TWO

Elm Court's mother and baby unit was situated in a comfortably appointed wing of the small suburban general hospital. The unit accommodated two kinds of patients: those there for the sleep clinic, seeking help with their unsettled babies, and others like me, diagnosed with postnatal depression.

We were greeted by Barb, who was to be my nurse during that shift. Her well-rehearsed sympathy grated on me a bit and seemed to assume a lot about my emotional state. Nigel had barely set my bags down in my room when he apologised that he really had to get back to work. His reaction, when I'd initially told him of my wish to come here, had astounded me. At first he tried to dissuade me on the grounds that I hadn't given things enough of a chance at home. Then he expressed anger at the GP for recommending anything more for me than regular involvement in a mothers' group. I'd been close to phoning Elm Court and calling the whole thing off, but then it occurred to me that his attitude might be affected by something secondary. When Nigel was twenty, his mum had died in hospital. What the doctors had dismissed as migraine headaches had turned out to be a malignant brain tumour, inoperable by the time the correct diagnosis was made. What was coming across as chagrin from Nigel could just as easily be an indirect expression of a blanket fear of hospitals, couldn't it? Making allowances for him based on this possibility, I kissed him goodbye and without protest let him leave. Still, doubts about my stay grabbed me sharply as I watched him walk out the door.

15

'I just need to get a few particulars from you, sweetie,' said Barb, motioning for me to sit. I perched on the edge of my double bed. She sat in the armchair opposite, clipboard in her lap.

'Would you like to put . . . um,' she glanced at my admission forms, 'Jemima down?' She motioned at a large cloth sling – just like the one carried by the legendary stork – suspended on a metal frame by a spring.

'She'll be okay for now,' I replied, loath to relinquish the comfort she was providing me, ironically. Barb eyed me thoughtfully, as if there was something to be made of my decision.

'I'm going to ask you some questions about how you've been feeling. Try to answer them as accurately as you can,' she said, pen poised, 'then we'll know how best to help you during your stay here.

'How would you describe your mood over the past few weeks?'

'Pretty flat, I suppose.'

She looked at me, apparently expecting more.

'Things haven't been anything like I thought they would be. I seem to swing between feeling guilty for not being the mum I dreamt of being to feeling angry at Jemima for expecting me to be.'

'Have you felt sad, teary?'

'No, just more like I'm out of my depth really, and frustrated that I can't put things right. Not very teary. I don't cry much. I wish I could cry more.'

'How has your sleep been? Any problems with falling asleep or waking during the night?'

'I usually drop off pretty quickly when I get into bed at around eleven. But after the early morning feed at about four o'clock, I struggle getting back to sleep.'

With each answer Barb would tick her clipboard.

'What about daily activities? Are you still getting out and about and doing things?'

'Not much. It all takes so much effort now. Jemima tends to cry most of the time whenever we go anywhere. I find the whole experience really stressful.'

'Sometimes babies are just responding to the way Mum feels.' There was that smile again.

16

'How have you been physically? Aches and pains? Diarrhoea? Headaches?'

'Just tiredness.'

'Appetite? Any noticeable changes?'

'I'm tending to eat a bit more than I used to.'

'Have you had any thoughts of harming yourself, or that life isn't worth living?' She looked at me earnestly.

'God, no, nothing like that.'

'Any voices or feelings of unreality?'

Any *voices*? 'No, not at all.'

She replaced the questionnaire with a blank sheet.

'Tell me about your family,' she said and proceeded to sketch out a genogram. A genogram is a chart used to depict a person's family structure. Males are drawn as a square, females as a circle, then connected with lines to indicate the nature of their relationship to each other. A set of symbols is used to convey additional information – for example, whether a couple are married or divorced, or if a child has a biological relationship to their parents, or an adoptive one. Codes and symbols are also used to represent any significant events in a person's life, such as sexual abuse or an abortion. It's really just a therapist's version of a family tree.

I watched as she drew two short slashes through the line connecting my mother and father and then again through the line that connected my father and me, indicating severed relationships.

'Right then, we're done for now. I'll let you unpack and get comfy. Would you like me to run you a bubble bath? We can mind Jemima while you treat yourself to a nice relaxing soak. You'll just have time before dinner.'

'Sounds lovely, thanks.'

'Okay, I'll let you know when it's ready. In the meantime, pop these on.' She handed me identification bands for Jemima's and my wrists. That made things seem very clinical. 'Your doctor will be by to see you in the early evening, he said. Now, he's not the one who generally practises here. The one who usually looks after our ladies is on leave, but we're assured this one's very good.'

'My doctor?' Was I to have a physical examination or something?

17

'Yes, sweetie. The psychiatrist who'll be seeing you while you're here.'
A psychiatrist!

'Don't worry,' she said, reading the shock on my face. 'It's standard procedure for anyone admitted with postnatal depression to be seen by one. If anyone's going to be able to help you, he will, okay? It's all right.'

There was that term again – depression – being tossed around. When had I received an official diagnosis, anyway? It had just been mentioned by my GP and now the staff here were picking it up and running with it. My apprehension was growing. Things seemed to be getting blown out of proportion.

I had not long finished my dinner of beef stroganoff and a glass of chardonnay. Jemima was asleep in her sling and I sat in the soft light of the bedside lamp watching television with the volume down. I was cheated from savouring the moment, though, by the nervous anticipation of meeting the psychiatrist. I didn't have to wait very long.

'Rebekah. Max Braydle,' announced a voice at my door.

So, here he was. I stood and took the business card in his outstretched hand. He sat on the bed and patted it, inviting me to join him. I'd imagined they'd have a room for psychiatric consultations but it looked as if this one was going ahead here.

His dress belied his status: polo shirt, jeans and casual shoes – an effort, I guessed, to appear non-threatening. Of fairly average stature, a tan leather belt supported his middle-aged paunch. Rich brown hair of his youth was heavily woven with silver-grey.

Was he of European origin? His voice had offered no clue. Perhaps it was his narrow rectangular spectacles, moustache and goatee that gave him an air of the Austrian psychoanalyst Sigmund Freud.

'So, what's been happening?' he began. 'You've been having a bit of a rough trot, I hear.'

I had no idea where to start. Did he mean during the past few weeks or my whole life? I was certain that even the most disturbing events in my life would seem quaint to a man who would, I was sure, have had vast experience in dealing with serious mental illness. All this fuss, for my little issues, really seemed unwarranted.

I rehashed the details I'd given the nurse earlier. I struggled to articulate the more intricate aspects of my feelings. He looked at me as if I was fooling nobody. His gaze was intense, hypnotic, like he was trying to draw out the truth.

'I haven't been myself at all,' I volunteered. 'I just can't seem to find the enthusiasm for life at the moment that I'm used to.'

'I'd like to know a bit more about your family. You're an only child, you said, raised by your mum. What's your relationship like with your dad?'

'There isn't one.'

'Has there ever been?'

'It's complicated. For most of my childhood I believed he was dead. But when I reached my teens I started to realise things weren't making sense. There were no photos, none of his possessions, and Mum shut down whenever I tried to speak about him. She had never actually told me he'd died. Apparently, after visiting Mum's dying uncle in hospital when I was about four, I formed the belief that he was my dad, and it was easier simply to let me go along with it. It also spared me the awful truth, I suppose, that after my birth my father hadn't wanted anything to do with either my mother or me. When I was about fifteen, on the advice of a school counsellor, I cornered Mum and demanded she tell me where he was buried so I could visit his grave. That's when she dropped the bombshell: he wasn't dead. From that point on, all I wanted to do was find him. Mum had no idea where he was; there'd been no contact. For the next five years I searched and searched, finally locating him when I was twenty.'

'And did you get to meet him?'

'Uh-huh. But it was messy, very messy. After Mum, he'd recommitted to his wife. She had a hard time dealing with our reunion, plus she and my dad had two sons who hadn't known anything of my existence. My dad was nothing like I had hoped, but then I guess it would have been a tough task for anyone to have lived up to the hero I'd built him up to be in my childhood fantasies. Really, though, the hardest thing of all was his apparent complete lack of understanding of the devastating impact his abandonment of Mum and me had had on us.'

'Wow, that's some ordeal. What a horrible thing for your mother to do – deny you the truth like that for so many years.'

'I won't deny that it hurt, but I've grown to understand that she only acted out of protection for me.'

'How was that protecting you?'

'Well, I suppose it was better than telling me my birth caused my father to ignore our existence in favour of his first family. That he happily raised my two half-brothers, but he couldn't even bear to look at me. How does a kid cope with that news?'

'Well, it sounds like you did have to cope with the news, after fifteen or so years of believing something else.'

I was getting tired of all this prodding for my emotional fault line. What about Jemima? What about my difficulties with managing her? What about her crying? What about my exhaustion? I raised my wrist to look at my watch. But before I got the chance Max grabbed my hand and pulled it back down, holding on to it.

'Have you ever had anyone to talk to about all this?'

'Yes,' I said, hoping it might get him to lay off a bit. 'I had some counselling.'

'I meant friends, family?'

'Well, no. I don't like to sound like a whinger.'

'So, let's see if I've got this right. Not only have you borne the brunt of some pretty hurtful and selfish behaviour on the part of both your mother and your father, and had no one to share the burden, but you feel guilty even allowing yourself to acknowledge the pain?'

Jeez, he made me sound so tragic. He searched my eyes for validation of his claims, but I dropped my gaze to deny him the chance.

'Stubborn determination to stay strong at all costs isn't always healthy, you know.'

I said nothing.

'Don't worry, we'll get there.' He gently swept my hair back to reveal my profile, tucking it behind my ear with his fingers. I stiffened and kept my eyes down.

'Rebekah.' I succumbed to the pressure to turn my face to his. 'We'll get there.'

His eyes pulled me in with their compassion, interest and empathy. Rebelling against all my efforts to hold them back, tears began flowing, continuing without pause for a full minute or more.

'What's wrong with this place!' Max flung things about, looking for something with which to dry my eyes. 'This'll do.'

He sat back down and mopped gently at my tears with a handtowel.

With his arm around my shoulders, he tenderly pulled me into his chest and held me there. I breathed in his warmth infused with the sweet smoky smell of pipe tobacco and was momentarily swept back twenty years to when a hug from my grandfather would deliver the same comforting aroma. I knew I wanted to pull away but I felt somehow disarmed.

'That might be enough for tonight, hey?' He released his arm and gave me back my space. 'We don't want to exhaust you on your first day. I'll be back to see you tomorrow. I think some medication is going to be helpful in alleviating your acute sadness.'

Oh no, not him too. 'What kind of medication?'

'Nothing too scary. Just an antidepressant.'

'How long will I need it for?'

'Oh, probably six months or so, but we'll assess that as we go along.'

'How do we know I actually need them?'

'We've all got a mechanism up here,' he said, pointing to the top of my head, 'that's in charge of producing and distributing a chemical called serotonin, which keeps us feeling balanced and content. When a person becomes depressed, like you have' – Max squeezed my hand as if to soften the blow of what he was trying to get me to accept – 'this mechanism becomes less efficient, creating an imbalance in the brain. All the medication will do is correct this imbalance.'

I wanted to know why I couldn't be tested for this imbalance before being put on medication, but I didn't want him to think I was questioning his expertise. He was the second doctor now to recommend the treatment and I was sure he must know what he was talking about. Besides, I imagined from what had transpired over the last twenty minutes that therapy with this man was going to be gruelling; my heart quickened just at the thought. If medication was going to help me endure it, then it would be a wise decision to take it.

'And these are the newer sort . . . the ones that aren't addictive or anything?'

'They're not addictive. They're very safe.'

So it was settled. I *would* be starting on *Lustral*: that evening.

Lustral (sertraline) is a drug in the same class as *Prozac* (fluoxetine), *Cipramil* (citalopram), *Seroxat* (paroxetine) and *Faverin* (fluvoxamine). They are the antidepressants known as selective serotonin reuptake inhibitors, or SSRIs. Over recent years when a person has been prescribed one of these drugs it's likely they've been told that their condition is due to a biochemical imbalance in their brain. In the case of depression the chemicals that have been implicated are serotonin and, less commonly, noradrenalin. They are then likely to have heard that psychiatric medications can correct this imbalance.

At around the time of my diagnosis, this explanation was at the peak of its popularity. When I first heard it I assumed there must have been extensive solid scientific evidence behind this theory. In fact, it was put to me with such confidence by Max, and then repeatedly backed up by the nursing staff, that I figured it must have been so unequivocally known that I didn't even need to be tested for it. But the reason I had no test is because it is simply not possible to measure serotonin (or any other brain chemical) in a living person's brain.[1] Approximations of brain-chemical levels have only ever been inferred from indirect evidence. One method, which has been tried by several researchers, is to measure breakdown products (metabolites) of brain chemicals in a person's urine and cerebrospinal fluid. The reasoning is that the metabolites will reflect the amount of brain chemical being used. However, the results of these studies have shown that although some depressed patients (about 25 per cent) have low levels of these breakdown products, the majority are well within the range of the normal population.[2]

And, of course, drugs that are intended to stimulate serotonin, like the SSRIs, actually do seem to alleviate some people's stress and low mood, giving the impression that they may restore some sort of balance.

However, as Dr Jeffrey Lacasse of Florida State University College of Social Work points out, '. . . the fact that aspirin cures headaches does not prove that headaches are due to low levels of aspirin in the brain.' It follows, he suggests, that to interpret SSRIs' alleviation of depression as evidence that they correct serotonin levels is flawed logic.[3]

Elliot Valenstein is Professor Emeritus of Psychology and Neuroscience at the University of Michigan and author of over 140 scientific articles and five books. In *Blaming the Brain: the truth about drugs and mental health*, he says:

> The evidence claimed to support the various chemical theories of mental illness is not strong, and there is much evidence that contradicts the prevailing view. I have examined the arguments for these theories with an open mind and have tried to tell a coherent and convincing story when lecturing to graduate students, but there is just too much data that indicate that the theories could not be right . . . The truth is that we still do not know what causes any mental disorder or how drugs sometimes help patients get better.[4]

So, why then have biochemical theories for mental illness been perpetuated and accepted so readily? One reason, perhaps, is because they're convenient.

Biochemical theories have been convenient for doctors. When a patient believes there is a physical cause for their mental illness, they are more likely to be treatment-compliant. People diagnosed with a psychological problem like depression are often led to believe they need to take psychiatric medication just as a diabetic, say, must take their insulin. This explanation may come in handy when getting people to swallow their pills, but it is shamefully inaccurate. When someone is diagnosed with diabetes, only after reliable diagnostic testing has determined the extent of their glucose metabolism problem are they prescribed insulin. The amount of insulin prescribed is very precise in accordance with the results. Furthermore, the patient continues to undergo frequent blood testing to ensure their glucose–insulin ratio remains optimal.

This is nothing like what occurs when a person is diagnosed with a psychological condition such as depression. No test is conducted to find out whether they actually have a chemical excess or deficiency, either before psychiatric medication is prescribed or afterwards.

Understandably, biochemical theories can also be convenient for patients and their families. Physical disorders don't carry the stigma that psychological ones do. When diagnosed with a mental illness it can soften the blow to hear, 'It's nothing you've done. It's beyond your control. It's a physical illness.' Family members are absolved of blame via this explanation, and the spotlight is taken off any family dysfunction. Sadly, though, by believing that their condition is out of their hands, the patient becomes disempowered and inhibited from contributing to their own recovery as they become reliant on doctors and drugs. Ironic really, when you consider that feeling circumstances are beyond one's control can be a catalyst for depression.

Biochemical theories have been convenient for pharmaceutical companies. They sell the medications that they claim can treat these chemical changes and they make billions of dollars a year from them.[5]

Pfizer, the makers of *Lustral*, offer these words of reassurance on their website:

> In the past, people believed that depression was merely an emotional state that made people sad. These days, however, depression is recognised as a medical condition . . . Scientists have discovered a link between the chemical changes in your brain and this 'state of mind', which makes it a treatable condition.[6]

There's no mention, however, that this 'discovery' was the result of research throughout the 1960s: tentative findings that have failed to replicate themselves in more modern, sensitive studies.[7]

Psychiatrist Professor David Healy, director of the North Wales Department of Psychological Medicine and former secretary of the British Association for Pharmacology, has spent a large part of his career researching the role of serotonin in depression.

In his book *Let Them Eat Prozac: the unhealthy relationship between the pharmaceutical industry and depression*, he writes:

... It is now widely assumed [as a consequence of drug company marketing] that our serotonin levels fall when we feel low ... But there is no evidence for any of this, nor has there ever been.[8]

Fortunately, some of the most prominent and influential psychiatric authorities are conceding it's time to move on from a decades-old concept that seems to be revealing itself as little more than a myth. In 2006 the Royal College of Psychiatrists removed from its website any mention of chemical imbalance. Its fact sheet about depression now lists several 'factors' implicated in depression including circumstances, life events, certain personality types, and heredity.[9]

◆◆◆◆◆◆

After I'd told Mum about what had happened during my visit to the GP, she'd given me a book, *Postnatal Depression: families in turmoil.* Although I had felt a rise of resentment when she'd presented it to me, the minute Max left my room I grabbed it and flicked to the section on antidepressant medication. By this stage I was becoming convinced that my aversion to taking the medication was perhaps stemming more from ignorance and overreaction than anything else, and I just needed a few more reassuring details. The book gave them to me:

Many women with PND (postnatal depression) are prescribed antidepressants. Antidepressants work by restoring the balance of brain chemicals to normal. Drugs like *Lustral* have fewer and less severe side effects than the older antidepressants, and any side effects they could have would most likely disappear in two to three weeks. Many mothers claim that the benefits far outweigh the possible side effects. Unlike *valium*, antidepressants are not addictive and are therefore suitable for long-term treatment. It generally takes six to twenty-four months before the brain relearns the right levels of chemicals to produce to lift depression. Antidepressants must not be stopped before your physician says so. Although it is a common fear, antidepressants do not change your personality. Many mothers have described how medication literally saved their lives.[10]

By all accounts a rave review.

What would have helped to make my decision a more informed one would have been some information that accurately reflected the pros and cons of taking antidepressants. Something that pointed to the fact that in three of the four trials that saw *Prozac* get its approval, 25 per cent of participants were co-prescribed anti-anxiety medication, and in trials of all the SSRIs 15–20 per cent of people dropped out when suspected adverse reactions became intolerable.[11]

But the message I was getting, everywhere I turned, was that SSRIs were not really drugs, but more like serotonin supplements. Would I refuse to take iron tablets if I was anaemic? Of course I wouldn't.

A major factor in the implication of serotonin deficiency as a cause of depression occurred in the mid 1950s when a drug by the name of *Reserpine* – used as an antipsychotic and later as blood pressure medication – seemed to be provoking depression and suicide in its users.[12] Animal studies showed that *Reserpine* decreased brain levels of serotonin as well as noradrenalin.[13] Thus, it was hypothesised that depression sufferers might have insufficient levels of these brain chemicals (neurotransmitters).

Scientists got to work devising a pharmaceutical that would elevate the levels of these neurotransmitters in the depressed. By the early 1960s the first antidepressants were being prescribed. First were the MAOIs (monoamine oxidase inhibitors) followed by the tricyclics. All acted in various ways to enhance the effects of serotonin, noradrenalin or both. But by the mid 1980s these classes of antidepressant began losing popularity with the advent of *Prozac*, the first SSRI. SSRIs were considered to have far fewer side effects, to be much easier to administer and to be far safer in overdose than their predecessors.

SSRIs exert their action not by supplying the brain with new serotonin, but by increasing the availability of existing serotonin. They do this by preventing the brain from reabsorbing (re-uptaking) any serotonin it has produced in excess. Essentially, through this re-uptake inhibition, SSRIs interfere with the brain's natural self-regulatory mechanism responsible for preventing an oversupply of serotonin.[14] (Some of the other latest antidepressants, such as *Efexor*, act by inhibiting the re-uptake of serotonin and noradrenalin.)

Helping to ease my mind about the antidepressant I was about to take was the inclusion of the word 'selective' in its name. This gave me the impression that it would have no effect on my brain other than increasing my supposedly depleted serotonin. But I was wrong. In this case 'selectivity' can simply mean that the drug has no action on one particular brain system. For example, an SSRI might act on every system other than the noradrenalin system and still be touted as 'selective'.[15]

One of the pitfalls of the older antidepressants was that they affected brain chemicals other than the ones targeted. Assisting the SSRIs achieve their reputation as a revolutionary treatment for depression was the belief that they had a unique ability to act only on the serotonin system. This claim now seems discredited.

Writer, psychiatrist and author of *Rethinking Psychiatric Drugs*, Grace Jackson comments: 'The very concept that an antidepressant might be specific for one type of brain chemical has fallen by the wayside, as researchers have demonstrated the complex interactions which exist between and among the neurotransmitter systems of the brain.'[16]

THREE

I was quietly thrilled when Max told me that because the *Lustral* would pass into my milk, I'd have to stop breastfeeding. Although it had never gone well for Jemima and me, the maternal and child-health nurse (health visitor) had urged me to persevere and I truly felt that to stop of my own volition would be doing the wrong thing by Jemima. But now, being told that I had to give it up helped me to relinquish my guilt fairly readily. If letting go of some of my ideals was what it was going to take to put things right for my baby and me, then that's how it would have to be, I told myself.

The nurses, however, didn't accept the prospect with quite so much ease. Max left my room and went to their station to tell them the treatment he was initiating. They thought asking a mother to give up breastfeeding a very young baby for the sake of medication was unreasonable. Minutes after Max had left, Barb appeared at my door.

'Are you okay with giving up your feeding?'

'I think so.' I was a bit annoyed she was encouraging me to have any say in the matter.

'He's the only doctor we've had that won't allow breastfeeding on these meds,' she said. 'The other psychiatrists say *Lustral* is the preferred antidepressant for nursing mothers. I could have another talk to him if you'd like.'

'Well, okay, maybe that would be best,' I agreed, though I felt as if I'd had a free pass for a taste of irresponsibility revoked.

'I'll see if I can catch him before he leaves.'

Barb returned a while later with a plastic medicine cup in one hand

28

and a breast pump in the other. She tipped the contents of the cup into my hand and poured me some water.

Persistent little buggers, aren't you? I thought as I eyed the two innocuous-looking white oval-shaped pills in my palm. I threw them into my mouth and, partly thanks to what my *Families in Turmoil* book had just told me, swallowed them down as if they were multivitamins.

'Dr Braydle wouldn't budge on the feeding issue, I'm afraid.' Barb's tone conveyed regret. 'Have you used one of these before?' She showed me the pump.

'I've used one similar.'

'Oh, good. That makes things a bit easier. You'll need to express the next feed.'

'What happens to the expressed milk?'

'We throw it away. I'm sorry.'

The idea of my precious milk being discarded like waste smarted a bit. But, when it came down to it, at least Max was being cautious about any risk associated with the drug being secreted into my milk.

Jemima was taken to the nursery that night so I could try to get an uninterrupted sleep. Now she was on the bottle the staff were going to take care of her late-night feed. But with my emotions all stirred up sleep would not come to me. June, the night nurse, had a soft, caring manner that made me feel safe and special. She made me hot chocolate and gave me a shoulder massage as I lay in bed. When these efforts failed to help she offered me a sleeping tablet, which Max had written up for me to have if I needed it. Perhaps the antidepressants weren't addictive, but I knew that sleeping pills were.

'But only if you take them consistently for a week or more. You won't get hooked after a couple of nights,' June assured me. 'My advice to you: take advantage of all you can while you're here. Enjoy us doing the worrying for you.'

Well, when she put it that way . . .

She was soon back with a single bright green pill shaped like a rugby ball.

'You'll be right now,' she said, after I'd swallowed it down. She tucked in my quilt and turned out my lamp.

'Enjoy,' she whispered, leaving me feeling nurtured and pampered. Within twenty minutes or so the effects of the 'sleeper' had kicked in and I slipped softly into slumber.

By the time I awoke the next morning my breakfast was waiting beside my bed. It felt like ages since I'd seen my baby – we hadn't been more than about an hour apart before. I quickly got dressed and went to collect her from the nursery down the hall. She was in one of the nurse's arms sucking merrily on a bottle when I got there. I felt a pang of jealousy. Hadn't she missed me, too?

'We thought we'd let you sleep in,' the nurse said.

I couldn't believe it. Whenever I left Nigel with expressed milk in a bottle for Jemima she'd simply refuse it.

'She'll be ready to go down again soon,' said the nurse. 'I'll come and help you with some controlled crying shortly, if you're up to it.'

Controlled crying is a technique designed to help babies settle themselves to sleep instead of relying on their parents to pacify them. The idea is to put baby down and ignore the crying for a couple of minutes, before returning and checking everything is all right without picking them up. The duration of the intervals between returning increases each time by a couple of minutes.

The unit was equipped with several small rooms just for this purpose. When it was time for Jemima's nap, which had now been scheduled every two hours, I was instructed to swaddle her tightly in her bunny rug, lay her on her back in the cot, say 'sleep time', switch off the light and shut the door. Jemima would often cough and gag from the intensity of her crying, which would abate to softer sobs each time she heard me enter the room to soothe her. ('No picking up, just a few comforting pats, then leave.') I would sit on the floor outside her door and pray that she could sense my heart was just metres from hers.

Half an hour of subjecting her to what instinctively felt like neglect was all I could take. Nurses' strict instructions or not, at that point I would pick her up.

'Rebekah, you're a silly girl – you're making a rod for your back. How's it going to be when you've got a four-year-old destroying your relationship with Nigel because she refuses to sleep in her own bed?

And all because she was able to wrap Mummy around her little finger when she was a few months old?' That was when the head nurse informed me the nursing staff would take over control-crying Jemima for me.

Jemima was allocated the room for the most resistant sleepers: a windowless, soundproof cubicle behind two thick doors. The most I had to do with her bedtime was a kiss and cuddle in my own room before she was taken by a nurse. My baby monitor was taken from beside my bed to the nurses' station and I was advised to go nowhere near her room.

Within only a few days of this routine, Jemima was going to sleep within a short while of being put in her cot. The duration of her sleeps had increased ever so slightly, as well. Could the nurse have been right when she'd said Jemima was manipulating me? Had I been all the while thinking I couldn't provide enough for Jemima, when in reality I'd been trying to give her too much?

◆◆◆◆◆◆

While Jemima napped in the nursery one morning, I was washing my face in my bathroom when I heard Max's voice.

'You in here, Bek?' I loved it when people called me Bek without waiting to be asked.

'I'll be right there.'

As I walked out he stretched out his hand and grabbed mine.

'Let's get out of this stuffy place, hey? I thought we'd go for a walk.' He sure was full of surprises.

We strolled around the undulating streets surrounding the hospital in the warmth of the spring sunshine. He held my hand, swinging it to and fro. We talked about what appeared to be nothing in particular, but a lot of it was about him. I listened to him speak of his family and his recreational pastimes – I learnt very quickly how passionate he was about his two racehorses – all the while thinking it was strange for a psychiatrist to disclose so much of himself to a patient.

We sat to rest on the brick wall of someone's house. Max reached into the garden and picked me a flower.

'It's beautiful, isn't it?' he said. 'What springs to mind when you look at flowers?'

'Beauty,' I said,'. . . love. But they're also a lure, aren't they?'

He laughed. 'Trust you to say that. They certainly do provide us with beauty. What they really are, though, is a plant's sexual organs.' I recoiled a little.

'So, Bek, tell me, when did it happen to you?'

'When did what happen?' I felt like *I'd* just been dragged into a lure.

'I think you know what I mean. It was someone you depended on, wasn't it?'

Our outing suddenly soured. I felt angry with Max; angry for cornering me like this, angry for spoiling a nice walk. It was true that I became riddled with a protective urge to cover my baby if anyone saw her being bathed or her nappy being changed. It was true that there was no way I would take the maternal and child-health nurse's advice to occasionally let my child roll around with her nappy off to prevent nappy rash because I felt it left her too vulnerable. I knew that I was trying to ensure her the defence I hadn't had when a family friend had tried to sexually 'educate' me when I was thirteen. There had been no serious molestation, just some inappropriate touching and smutty talk. I'd always tried to convince myself it wasn't a big deal.

'So, there you go,' I said, after spilling out the details as quickly as possible.

Max gripped my hand and, with expectant eyes, gave a short, sharp nod for me to continue.

'Well, no. That's it.' I explained. 'Nothing earth-shattering. Don't even know why I'm still bothered by it.'

He seemed doubtful I'd been completely forthcoming. He seemed . . . disappointed? Nevertheless, he answered, 'Perhaps because your innocence and trust were violated by a calculating predator.'

Bloody hell, the tears were rolling again. Max mopped at them with his fingertips.

'You know,' he said, 'you're even beautiful when you cry.' The words arrested my ease. Why did he say those things? He offered his hand but I didn't feel like taking it this time. We walked in silence back to the hospital.

Back at the unit we were met by a very angry nurse. 'We were just about to call the police! What did you think you were doing?'

'I just assumed . . . I . . . I was with a doctor . . .'

Max interjected, 'She was with me, I had my mobile. What are you so uptight about?'

The nurse redirected her glare at Max. 'What am I so *uptight* about? She left her baby here unsupervised, that's what.'

Oh my God! So I had.

'You're nurses, aren't you?' Max retorted. 'Surely you can look after a baby for an hour or so. I'll see you Friday, Bek. I won't be in to-morrow. Good work today.' He walked away, leaving the nurse clearly dumbfounded and insulted.

'I am really sorry, I didn't even think . . .'

'It's all right, Rebekah,' said another nurse, coming down the hall with Jemima. '*He* should have known better.'

I needed another pill for sleep that night. It was the only way I could mute the bickering in my head. My judicious self, becoming nervous about this freefall into dependence on Max, was wanting to flee back to the comfortable terrain of self-reliance. But my little girl alter ego re-sisted doing so with gusto, so reluctant was she to give up the embrace of this psychiatric pied piper.

By noon the following day, reason had triumphed over impulse and I had decided I would request a different doctor, specifically a female. I felt an objection based on gender couldn't be disputed by anyone. And also, with a woman professional boundaries would hold steadfast and I'd be able to deal with things in a more pragmatic manner.

I had no problem gaining the support of the nurses for my decision. I got the feeling Max had worn out his welcome with them after his antics of the day before. I didn't have to have any more to do with him, they said. One of them would phone him for me and then arrange for another psychiatrist to come and see me as soon as possible. It was all much easier than I'd anticipated.

Late that afternoon I was seen by Susan, a female psychiatrist. She was very formal, even detached in her conduct. There was no lounging across my bed or physical contact. She asked me some closed questions about my emotional status, agreed to keep me on the same medication Max had me on, and that was it. She was poles apart from him in her demeanour. I could barely believe they belonged to the same profession. I'd been hoping I could strike a happy medium with a therapist, somewhere in between the beguiling Max and the official no-nonsense Susan. I got the feeling she would probably manage my medication and that would be it. Oh well, there was daily group therapy as well, so that would hopefully fulfil the talking component of my counselling. I decided Susan would do for the duration of my stay, which I had been told would be about two weeks, all things going to plan.

That night I enjoyed a calming guided meditation session. At bedtime June, my favourite nurse, said she would do Jemima's night feed for me again and made me another of the best hot chocolates I'd ever had. When she offered me another 'sleeper' I declined. With the pressure of therapy with Max no longer on my mind I didn't think I'd need one. I snuggled deep under the quilt with thoughts of the coming days: the meals that would be cooked for me; the night feeds that would be taken care of; the relaxation sessions; the motherly comfort of the nurses. I assured myself that with all this support, plus the added help of the antidepressant, things should be totally different by the time I was due to go home. Closing my eyes and coaxing sleep, I ignored the niggling feeling that I'd taken the easy way out.

◆◆◆◆◆◆

Celeste had just left after visiting me for morning tea. She had brought some crossword puzzles and a selection of magazines. I was sitting on my bed flicking through a copy of *Cosmopolitan* magazine when there was a sharp knock at my door. Before I could give permission it was pushed open. Max entered, flanked by one of the nurses, one I didn't know too well. He closed the door behind him and said, in reference to the presence of the nurse, 'I thought I'd better play it safe. Just in case there are any screams to be heard.' *What?*

Then, without warning, he lunged for me, attempting to clamp me in his arms. With no clue what was going on I scurried backwards and he followed, striding on his knees across the bed. Focusing on keeping him at bay and missing that I'd reached the edge of the mattress, I tumbled backwards to the floor. I scrambled to my feet and jumped from his reach. Sitting on his heels he threw his head back, laughing heartily. 'Oh, Anne,' he said to the nurse, who was looking on in amusement, 'is this not one of the best cases of transference you've seen?'

What the hell *was* this?

'Come on,' he said, as if the joke was now over. 'We need to talk.' He swung his legs around to sit on the edge of the bed and motioned for me to join him. I stayed put where I stood, backed up to the wall.

'What's transference, Bek?'

'I don't know,' I said feebly.

'The reason you're pushing me away. But also the very reason I am the best person for the job when it comes to helping you.'

Transference occurs when a patient begins to transfer thoughts and feelings connected with influential childhood figures – typically parents – to the therapist. In psychoanalysis, transference is considered to be of great value in gaining insight into ways in which the patient might misread or misperceive other people in his or her present life. Put simply, according to Max the very problems I had with him were the ones I needed to sort out. I could use him as a medium, so to speak.

At this point Nurse Anne spoke up. 'I've known Max for over twelve years and I've seen him work wonders. You might not see it, but the way you're feeling right now is a breakthrough. If you want to set your and your daughter's future completely right, not just gloss over the surface, stick with him.'

'Don't run from this, Bek, like you've run from everything else.' Max slapped a business card on my bedside table and stood to leave. 'If I don't hear from you, I hope you have a nice life.'

I waited till the door had snapped closed before swiping the card from the table. I tore it to tiny pieces and threw it like confetti on the floor. I slumped back against the wall, staring angrily at the ripped-up bits. *Sometimes babies are just responding to the way Mum feels . . . The way you're feeling right now is a breakthrough.* The advice of the past few days played over in my head. Maybe there was more to the way I was feeling than simply Jemima being a difficult baby. *Set your and your daughter's future completely right, not just gloss over the surface . . . The very reason I am the best person for the job.*

Though I'd ordered something highly appetising, I didn't eat much of my dinner that evening. I was preoccupied chewing over something else: what the implications of keeping Max as my therapist would be. This transference stuff he was on about: did that mean he was going to try and 'become' the people in my past he was convinced had contributed to my lack of success with parenting? It all seemed a bit esoteric, and downright nerve-racking. I imagined Max was just dying to sink his teeth into my defunct relationship with my dad and what he seemed to be identifying as unresolved anger towards Mum. But wouldn't now, when I was already feeling so rotten, be about the worst time to tackle all that? If I'd sought therapy to deal directly with these issues, then okay, but I hadn't. But what if he was right and all of it was interconnected? He was the expert in matters of the subconscious after all, not me.

I reached for my handbag, but hesitated. Then I reached for it again and retrieved the card Max had given me on his introduction. I stared hard at the after-hours contact number for a few moments then, smothering all my gut feelings, I picked up the bedside phone and dialled.

FOUR

Typically, daytime at the unit consisted of a group therapy session, followed by an outing with the other mums, such as a walk with our babies to the park or the local shops for a coffee. Group therapy could probably have been more appropriately named group chat, because it was really just an hour of swapping stories with a psychologist present. But I enjoyed it, all the same. It gave me a break from Jemima and the chance to realise I wasn't alone in not coping well with a newborn. But by afternoon there really wasn't much to pass the time. What I found most frustrating was that at no stage could I get out and go for a run; something I did most days as a form of stress release. It was a bit of an addiction really – one I'd had ever since I stopped teaching aerobics in my early twenties. Nigel and I would often go together. Whether on a balmy summer's evening or a rain-doused winter's one, the rhythm of my feet on the pavement would lull me into a state of meditation. Running together had gone down the drain the minute we arrived home with Jemima, but Nige still let me go alone; he appreciated just how important it was to me. I'd practically throw Jemima into his arms the minute he got in the door from work. By the time I got back he'd be tearing his hair out and Jemima would be screaming for me and refusing the expressed milk. But I'd be less fazed than usual. A run always gave me a new lease of life, for a couple of hours anyway.

At least I had something else at the unit to look forward to every day that made missing out on my run more tolerable: my visit from Max. The nurses had seemed pretty annoyed with me when I'd told them I wanted to change my mind, again, and keep Max as my doctor. He'd returned that very afternoon. He showed no ill feeling. He even laughed about the fact that I'd tried to give him the 'sack'.

'No one's ever tried that before,' he said.

Within days Max's visits became the most anticipated event in my day. When he was with me I had no child, I had no responsibilities. I learnt how to be angry and how to blame others for hurtful events in my life. He told me I was ripping myself off by not realising the magnitude of injustice I had suffered in my past. According to him I deserved a lot more love and attention than I had ever received. Letting go of hurt and guilt while Max held me and absorbed my sobs was narcotic. He continued to talk about himself, too: his hobbies and his family. His daughter, he said, was a lot like me.

'She loves it when I give her a toe massage,' he told me one day. 'Take off your shoes and socks and pop your feet up here.' He patted his lap. 'Now tell me this doesn't feel delicious.' He gently circled each toe round and round, and stroked the sole of my foot. It felt delicious, all right.

'Are you this attentive with all your patients?' I asked him. 'It must be exhausting.'

'When I'm with you, Bek, you're the most important person in the world.'

Right out of the blue one day, he wanted me to describe an orgasm.

'Why?' I managed, once I'd shaken free of my shock.

'Why?' he echoed, as though the question was inane. 'Because to be a confident, complete mother, you need to be a confident, complete woman. That means being comfortable with all aspects of your femininity, which includes your sexuality. So, let's see if you can do it. An orgasm feels like . . . Off you go.'

I reached for some words befitting the task and realised I hadn't any. He chuckled, 'Ah, Bek, you're precious. I knew you'd struggle.' What did that show? Was I abnormal?

Max came to my rescue and helped me along.

'At first you feel that tingle . . . Yes? Yes? Am I right? And then that flush of warmth?' I nodded in agreement, feeling, and obviously looking, horribly uncomfortable and inadequate.

'Never mind.' He threw an arm around my shoulders and gave me an encouraging squeeze. 'Just means we've got a bit of work to do. I've got plenty of time.'

He introduced an exercise that I termed 'cuddle therapy'. In a standing position he would hug me: a full body embrace. He'd pull my face into the crook between his neck and shoulder, and point out just how far I'd stuck out my bottom.

'Now, do you think you could get your groin any further away from mine?' he said on my first attempt. 'I know life would be a lot easier for you if all men were eunuchs, but . . .' He gently pressed his hands into the small of my back and pulled me in close. 'There, it's only a hug – I'm not trying to fuck you.'

Each session was to start with a greeting just like this. I'd be critiqued on my ability to make body contact.

I was sure we must have been nearing the session's end late one morning, when Jemima began to cry from the irritation of a wet nappy. 'Go right ahead,' Max said, nodding his head in the direction of the baby-change table, 'don't mind me.'

I carried Jemima to the table and laid her down. I expected Max would use this break in the session's flow to end it and head back to his clinic – he'd surely have an afternoon schedule of patients, didn't he have to prepare? But he followed me to the table, hovering just behind my right shoulder. What was he up to now?

Sensing that a test of some sort was imminent, I moved slowly to unbutton Jemima's jumpsuit. Just as I'd pulled away the first tab of her nappy, Max spoke: 'Tell me, Bek, what does your clitoris look like?'

Oh, *what*? Not now, Max. Not while I'm doing this.

'Describe it to me. I want to hear what you think. Just like a rosebud,' he prompted, 'beautiful. Those delicate folds of skin.'

I stood silent, looking down at Jemima – smiling at me now, blowing bubbles – and tried to lose myself in her innocence.

'You've got no clue, have you? Never felt comfortable to explore yourself.' He said it as though it was an injustice of the greatest magnitude.

He leant into my neck and spoke directly to my ear. If I was unable to look at my own, then I at least had to look at my daughter's. The most intriguing, empowering part of the female anatomy – I had to learn to appreciate its beauty. 'Go on then,' he said, 'no time like the present.' Then, thankfully, he walked out of the door.

A little over a week into my stay, I was sitting with the other mums talking about nothing important and waiting for our group therapy to start. All of a sudden and all at once I couldn't breathe, my heart began to pound so it shook my body and I oozed a clammy sweat. The sound of rushing blood thundered in my ears. I walked briskly out of the door and in the hall broke into a sprint back to my room. I grappled for the emergency buzzer. When the nurse arrived I couldn't speak to tell her what was happening. I couldn't breathe out, I could only get short sharp gasps – in, in, in. I felt myself begin to fade and prepared to pass out. A heart attack, I'm having a heart attack.

The nurse took one look at me and said she'd be back in a second. She promptly returned with a blood-pressure monitor and a paper bag.

'Just breathe in and out,' she said, placing the bag over my mouth. I'd thought they only did that in movies. 'Try to relax. Think about your breaths . . . That's it.'

The bag worked. Within a couple of minutes I was fine.

'What happened to me?'

'Just a panic attack, that's all,' she patted the back of my hand. 'They're pretty common in depression. Anxiety and depression often go hand in hand. You just try and get some rest. I'll let your doctor know.'

Panic attack? But I don't *panic* over anything.

I thought of all the times I'd instructed aerobics to a roomful of merciless, hard-core fitness enthusiasts; of the times I'd performed in national aerobics competitions before an audience of hundreds and a panel of judges – I'd never panicked then. What about the precarious situations I'd scraped through while travelling through Europe, on many occasions alone, with little money and no grasp of the language? I'd never panicked then, either. And there was many an occasion while establishing myself in my IT job that I was put on the spot and asked to do something that stretched way beyond either my formal training or practical knowledge, far inferior to that of my colleagues. But quick thinking always saw me through. I never panicked. Never.

Now, to have been overpowered by such potent alien feelings . . . and in response to what? I suppose I could question it no longer. I really was ill.

I spoke with Mum. Did she know of anyone in the family with a history of mental illness? Not really. But her father had tended to stress and worry a lot, sometimes resorting to bouts of heavy drinking as a coping mechanism – 'drowning his sorrows' as the old saying goes – and there'd been talk in the family that his half-brother may have committed suicide. A fairly weak link, but enough, according to the staff, to point to a genetic factor in my depression.

I felt as if my whole life till then had been an illusion. Why had God set me up like this? Why had He allowed me to believe that I was strong and resolute and able to cope with just about anything thrown my way, knowing all the while I'd be brought to my knees at twenty-seven? He'd dangled the carrot of a happy future, a family, a career – only to whisk it away at the last minute. I had always believed that if a situation was unfolding to my dissatisfaction, all I had to do was change it. But now I'd been dealt something beyond my control. I needed Max more than ever.

'Well, I wouldn't wish a panic attack on anyone, but perhaps now people might start to take notice of just how much you're suffering. You come across as so together that most people, including your family and those nurses out there, haven't got a clue.' Max cradled my face in his hands and looked at me straight on. 'But we know, don't we? We know.'

'But what does this mean, Max? What's going to become of me?'

'Hey, hey, hey.' He smoothed out the worry wrinkles on my forehead with his thumb. 'The antidepressant hasn't even taken effect yet.

You've been taking it for, what – nine, ten days? They'll take at least another week, I'm afraid, maybe even two. In the meantime we'll give you something for the anxiousness.'

'And how long will that take to work?'

'About twenty minutes.'

That evening when the nurse brought me my white pills, there was a little pale yellow one with them. It was *Valium*.

It's commonly accepted that it takes two to three weeks for SSRIs to take effect.[1] Therefore, if there is any adverse change in the patient's behaviour during the initial two-to-three-week period, there is the risk of it being blamed on the disease, not the drug. It is, in fact, during the early stages of antidepressant therapy, the discontinuation of therapy and with any increase or decrease in dosage that these drugs are most likely to cause problems.[2]

Antidepressants produce the maximum elevation of serotonin and/or noradrenalin in the first one to two days.[3] Elliot Valenstein, author of *Blaming the Brain*, argues that the reason it takes several weeks to see any elevation of mood on these drugs could be because, by this time, many other brain changes are happening in response to the initial surge of serotonin or noradrenalin. 'The number of different brain changes that can occur over a three-week period of drug treatment is huge,' he writes, 'as every change produces a cascade of other changes until the complexities become unfathomable.'[4]

Since the approval of the SSRIs in the late 1980s, a host of associated reactions has presented itself to the unsuspecting medical profession and their patients. Some of them include:

- Suicidal thoughts and behaviour[5]
- Self-harm[6]
- Mania and hypomania[7]
- Panic attacks

- Impulsivity
- Anxiety
- Agitation
- Insomnia
- Irritability
- Hostility[8]
- Worsening of depression[9]
- Personality changes[10]
- Akathisia[11] (an intolerable feeling of severe, relentless, inner agitation).

By 2005, a total of sixty-one deaths associated with these drugs had been reported to the Australian Therapeutic Goods Administration (TGA) and patients had reported more than 7000 incidents of adverse drug reactions. More than half of these reports concerned *Lustral*.[12] After ten years on the US market, *Prozac* had been the subject of 39,000 adverse reaction reports to the American Food and Drug Administration (FDA).[13] Over a similar time frame, over 19,000 reports regarding *Seroxat* were made to the UK Medicines and Healthcare products Regulatory Agency (MHRA).[14]

It's only voluntary, in both Australia and the UK, for doctors to report adverse reactions to their respective drug regulators, and the MHRA accepts that not all reactions are reported.[15] In fact close to official estimates suggest that fewer than *one in ten* reportable reactions are indeed reported.[16]

Where the issue of adverse psychiatric drug-induced effects gets tricky is that many of these effects mimic those of the illness for which the patient originally sought help, no doubt at times making it difficult for a doctor to know what's what. But if a patient starts displaying behaviour that was absent prior to commencement of a new drug, or an increase in dosage, shouldn't simple common sense determine that the drug be suspected as a cause?

◆◆◆◆◆◆

A little less than a week after the panic attack it was arranged that I would return home on overnight leave; all things going well I'd then be discharged for good. It was the weekend so Nigel was at home. We didn't have any plans to go anywhere or do anything; safest, Nige and I had decided, that we just stay in and see how I fared.

My relationship with our neighbours across the driveway had never been good. Actually, they bothered all the residents in our block of units. There were five of them sharing the place. They were inconsiderate, loud and rough. They rode motorbikes and held frequent parties, treating the communal driveway as if it belonged to them. I'd complained to our property manager a couple of times but was too intimidated to ever confront them directly.

But today was different. I'd just put Jemima down to sleep and, thanks to my newly found precision with controlled crying, she'd dropped off pretty quickly. The guy across the drive started his bike. He revved the throttle hard only feet from Jemima's window. My temper flared and, quick as a whip, I was out in the driveway blocking him from entering the street.

'You did that on purpose, didn't you?' I shrieked, voice charged with hatred. 'Didn't you?' I felt fierce, powerful. He was yelling something back, but luckily it was muffled from inside his helmet. If I had made out one single slur against me I would have hit him. In fact, I was hoping I might get the chance.

Nigel yelled from the lounge room window, 'Christ, Bek, would you get inside?' The neighbour took this opportunity to zip past me and away.

I went back inside. I felt electrified.

'Man, that felt good!'

Nigel stared at me with bewildered scorn.

Towards evening, he went to the supermarket to get some things we needed for dinner. He took Jemima with him. I decided I'd start to prepare what I could and went to the drawer for the vegetable knife. A couple of days before, I had been in the depths of therapy when Max suddenly asked if I ever deliberately hurt myself. When I'd answered that I'd never even considered such a thing, he said, 'Well, you're certainly giving yourself a good go now.'

When I had looked down I saw that I'd been digging into my arm with my nails, breaking the skin.

As the knife had just squashed the tomato I was trying to slice, I was pulling it back and forth across the sharpening steel. I gently flicked my thumb over its edge to test if it was ready. It was; so ready, in fact, it shaved off a thin layer of skin. Instead of sucking my thumb to soothe it, or running it under cold water, I pressed hard on the tip, forcing the formation of a teardrop of blood. My gaze shifted downward, setting hungrily on the fine flawless ivory of my inner forearm. Suddenly, despising its purity, I swiped it through with the cold steely blade. Horror-struck, I tried to jump away from myself and dropped the knife. It clanged to the floor.

I held the bent elbow of the cut arm with my opposite hand and stared incredulously at what I'd done.

The slicing had been audible; the skin splitting open like a sausage in a too-hot pan. The richest of reds had welled in the gash, before trickling down to the crook of my elbow. It took a few seconds for the pain to register: a stinging burn at first, then a deep ache, amplifying with every heartbeat. Raspberry splotches dappled the floor.

I don't know how long I stood there without breathing before I grabbed a tea towel and pressed it to my wound. How was I going to conceal this from Nigel? I unravelled a length of paper towel and frantically wiped at the spilled blood. It smeared to an area ten times its initial coverage and locked in the ridges of the patterned linoleum. My wound, where I had accidentally brushed it against my top, had left big red smudges. I fell in a resigned heap to the floor.

Nigel motored back in the drive.

He dropped both bags of shopping when he discovered me sitting amidst a tangle of ruby-stained towel. He grabbed for the phone.

'There's no rush,' my voice surfaced through my shame. 'I wasn't trying to kill myself.' His expression turned from one of fright to repulsion. Oddly, an attempt on my life would have been easier to digest, for both of us. He turned and went to get Jemima from the car.

After cleaning the floor and tending to my wound, Nige called Elm

Court. He was told to bring me back in right away.

The nurses were very unimpressed and treated me as if I had returned with a sudden bout of leprosy.

'Show me what you've done,' said one. She spoke as though reprimanding a child and made no effort to disguise her disgust.

'I don't think we'll bother disturbing a doctor on a Saturday night for that, we'll get away with some Steri-strips. So, why would you do this to yourself?'

When people deliberately harm themselves they often give reasons such as they were sick of feeling numb and simply had to feel something, or that the act helped to transfer intangible emotional hurt into physical pain, which is easier to handle. I wished that I had some such, almost comprehendible, reason to give. It would sound less crazy than the truth: that I had absolutely no idea why I had done this. I just couldn't fight the compulsion.

Max was called to come and see me first thing in the morning, which was Sunday. I felt bad disturbing him on his day off.

'Come now, show me what you've done. You've got them all in a flap around here.' He undid the light bandage on my arm. 'Oh, not much more than a scratch. They're not used to dealing with this kind of self-expression here, Bek. From the way they carried on over the phone I thought your arm must've been hanging off. Let me just word you up.' He lowered his voice and leant in towards me till our foreheads touched. 'These guys don't cope with this kind of thing too well, but there's nothing you could do to make me shun you.'

When the nurse brought me my pills that evening, I discovered Max had doubled my *Lustral*. I was now taking 200 milligrams, along with the *Valium*.

My mind now became blitzed with thoughts of hurting and marring myself. I would sit in my hospital room and think of ways to better my maiden effort, thirsting for my own blood. A few months earlier I would have been applying that kind of ambition to my work, my fitness or the glassware I made, but now my energies were being channelled towards how well I could mutilate my own flesh.

Late one night, only a short while since the incident with the knife,

I decided to wrap my water glass in a sock and whack it on the floor. There was a muted shatter and I held my breath, waiting to see if anyone had heard. Nothing. Okay.

I went into my bathroom and looked in the sock. It was full of neat little glass squares. Safety glass. Shit. I pulled out a piece. The edges were sharp, at least. I had to dig the corner in hard and twist it back and forth as I dragged it along my arm for it to have any significant effect. Jagged top skin parted around a raw pink layer, leaking dots of blood. I was left ungratified.

There was a light tap at my door and someone entered my room.

'Rebekah?' It was June, my favourite nurse.

'I'm just on the toilet.' I attempted to sound nonchalant while desperately trying to get rid of the evidence. How was I going to hide my arm? 'I won't be long.'

She lingered outside the bathroom. What the hell did she want? Something must be up with Jemima.

I flushed the toilet, threw the glass-filled sock in the cupboard and ran some cold water over the cut. June began knocking at the door.

'Come on, Rebekah, what's going on?' It hadn't occurred to me till then that I might've been under surveillance. I was in trouble. I had no option but to open the door.

'What have you done?' Her usual warmth was gone. 'Show me. What have you done?' I gingerly turned over my arm. 'Oh, Rebekah.' She looked betrayed.

Max came back in the morning. He sat beside me on the floor between my bed and the wall, where I was trying to fool the world I didn't exist.

'You know they won't let you stay here, don't you?'

I nodded. 'I thought as much.'

'I've arranged a bed at Ashgrove.'

I looked at him in horror. I'd heard mutterings of Ashgrove. It was where they sent those from the unit who needed more 'specialised' attention. When a nurse had said that there was nothing much they could do for me as long as I was deliberately doing things that were counter-productive, I really thought she meant I'd be sent home.

'Please, Max . . . no . . .' My head dropped into my hands. 'What have I done, stupid, stupid idiot. Oh, what have I done?'

'Look, I can understand your concerns. Ashgrove's a really scary place: twenty-foot walls with armed guards patrolling them, razor-wire. You know, we have to be careful considering the types we let in there.' This attempt to lighten the mood was lost on me. He took hold of both my hands. 'Hey, you just need a bit more help than they can give you here. Okay?'

'But you don't understand. We're due to move into our new house in a fortnight. I was supposed to be home helping Nigel pack.'

'I think getting you the right help is more important, don't you? Nigel will find someone to help him.'

'But I don't want someone else packing up all my things. I *need* to be there.'

'Bek, let's just put the horse *before* the cart, shall we? We need to get your health sorted out, then you'll be fit to enjoy your new place. If you ask me, it'll be good for you to relinquish some control for once. Stop resisting.'

'Max, I'm just so scared. I think I'm really sick. I don't know who I am . . . I'm not in control. This medication, it's not working, there must be something else, something stronger. I need help, please, I need serious help.'

'We'll sort it all out when you get to Ashgrove.'

FIVE

There were no armed gunmen or high fences. In fact, Ashgrove looked like an old mansion that had been renovated and converted to a hospital. Set quite a way back from the road it had a lovely manicured front garden and a discreet welcoming sign that read: ASHGROVE, Private Hospital. I'd actually driven past it a number of times and always imagined it must have been a nursing home.

But its unintimidating appearance did not calm me. As we approached the entrance, I clung to Nigel's arm and cried. We said nothing; nothing seemed appropriate. What was happening was far beyond our realms of comprehension.

Ashgrove's interior was spacious and modern. Fresh flowers decorated the foyer and tasteful art hung on the walls. It was rather hotel-like, and if it had only been a hotel I would have been quite happy to stay.

As I filled out the admission form at reception, all I could think about was home, how much I wanted to be there, and how much I regretted complying with Max's stipulation that I did not stop in there on my way from Elm Court. I'd understood, even agreed with his reasoning that, given my aversion to the transfer, it would be best to avoid doing anything that might make it even harder. But what if I was still here in two weeks, when we had to vacate our unit and move into the new place? I might never get to see our treasured little home again; never get to say goodbye to it. My pen stopped where the form requested my signature, reluctance restraining it like an invisible hand, preventing it from surrendering me to this place.

'Just your signature, thanks,' the receptionist gently prompted. 'Rebekah? We need your signature.'

'Bek,' Nige said softly, 'come on.' Conceding defeat, I scrawled out my name.

We were asked to take a seat. A nurse dressed in a grey shirt and navy pants soon appeared to show me to my quarters. It was a private room, I was relieved to discover, on the ground level, with a single bed, telephone and en suite bathroom. A large window, with a desk before it, looked out onto a landscaped back garden. As Jemima was still so young – she had only recently turned four months – it was arranged that she could stay with me, which went against usual procedure. Ashgrove had no mother and baby unit. A hired port-a-cot was sandwiched between my bed and the wall.

Nigel was given information on visiting hours and my direct phone extension, then he said he'd have to get back to work.

'Please, just stay a bit longer?'

'I'll come back tonight,' he said, with what felt like an obligatory kiss to my cheek. I refrained from clutching at his clothing as he turned and left.

The nurse gave me a tour of the rest of the place. She showed me the large common room where morning meeting, group therapy, activities and relaxation were held. It was the only room with a television. There was an art and craft room and a few smaller rooms where psychiatrists held their consultations. There was a courtyard smoking area. The dining area was cafeteria-style. All meals were served there and, I was impressed to hear, cooked fresh on the premises. I was shown the sink and microwave where I would need to prepare Jemima's bottles. There was an urn available at all times and a large selection of herbal teas and biscuits. On a noticeboard in the hall was a timetable of scheduled outings to places like art galleries and swimming pools. It seemed as though every effort was made to make patients as welcome as possible and to keep them busy.

Nurses milled about their station enclosed behind thick glass. It was from there, it was explained, that medications would be handed out through a small, otherwise locked window at set times.

'The patients are in group at the moment, that's why it's so quiet. But you can have some time to yourself for the rest of the day to try to get used to the place. Dr Braydle will be in to see you a bit later, I would imagine.'

On our way back down the passage a very drowsy middle-aged woman in a wheelchair was brought out of a room by a nurse. I caught a glimpse through the door just before it closed. It had a hospital bed, lots of cupboards and a whole lot of medical equipment.

'What happens in there?' I asked, not sure I wanted to know the answer.

'That's the treatment room,' she said, apparently reluctant to elaborate.

Treatment room? Not medication room, not consultation room, but *treatment* room.

Back in the pretentious homeliness of my room, I sat hugging Jemima to my chest. I rhythmically rocked and sang lullabies staccato-style through snot and tears. I had a duty to her to get well again and for that I felt I had no choice but to surrender to the professionals.

At afternoon-teatime the nurse returned to ask me if I wanted to go down to the dining room for some cake. I declined and asked if I could please eat in my room for a couple of days. That went completely against the objectives of my stay here, she said.

'If we allowed people to do that we'd have hardly anyone in the dining room.'

'But I have panic attacks.'

'We have lots of people here who have panic attacks.'

I didn't want to share mealtimes with a pack of psychiatric patients. I had visions of them babbling nonsense to themselves or trying to engage me in irrational conversations. I didn't belong with those people and I certainly didn't want my baby around them.

Max came to see me briefly late in the afternoon. I noticed he was very familiar and friendly with the nursing staff, not at all the way he had been at Elm Court. I had found out a little earlier that he had a lot more involvement in Ashgrove than I had originally realised. He was slightly different towards me there, too – a little more 'proper' in his conduct. There were still hugs and toe massages, but no more private walks or lying on my bed. His visits (now consultations) were held in the designated rooms, not in my own.

At dinnertime I realised that if I wanted to eat I was going to have to drag myself to the dining room. When I got there my worries were allayed slightly. People weren't ranting and smearing their food on the walls, but instead sitting, chatting and eating in a civilised manner. There were forty or so patients, from all walks. Some were my age, but many of them, I guessed, were around forty to fifty years old. A number of them smiled empathically at me and a few made complimentary comments about Jemima. They were respectful of my wish to sit alone at the end of one of the emptier tables, where I ate as much of my spinach and ricotta lasagne as my churning stomach would allow.

After dinner there was a gentle knock at my door. It was Amelia. She was about my age, though by wearing her long black hair in plaits, she looked younger. Her sweet voice and warm smile were what I really needed right then. I had seen her at dinner sitting with a guy, also aged around thirty, and had immediately wondered what would have brought such a normal-looking pair to Ashgrove. They had seemed to know each other well.

'Hi, I hope you don't mind me interrupting you. I saw you earlier with your baby and I thought I'd come and see if you were adjusting to this place okay.'

'As best I can, I s'pose. Come in, if you like.'

Amelia didn't move from the doorway. 'Or we can go outside, sit on the verandah.' I hadn't realised patients weren't allowed to socialise in each other's rooms.

'Okay. Just give me a minute. I just need to change Mima . . .'

'Mima. Is that her name?'

'Short for Jemima.'

'Gorgeous, it suits her. My two are at home with their dad. I miss them like crazy. Whoops, bad word selection in a place like this! I mean – like hell.' We laughed. 'I'll meet you out there then if you like. You know where I mean, don't you, just off the dining room? I'll have a quick ciggy ahead of you so I'm not smoking in front of bubs. Do you smoke?'

'No.'

'That doesn't surprise me – I imagined someone as sporty-looking as you probably wouldn't. Give it time though. It can end up being a bit hard to resist in a place like this. I'll see you out there.'

Amelia told me she too had originally been diagnosed with postnatal depression after the birth of her first child, who was now four. He was only months old when she discovered she was pregnant again. She hadn't had the chance to get over the first depressive episode, she said, and it was compounded by another when her second son was born.

'How on earth did you manage? My God. A baby, a pregnancy and depression.'

'The simple answer is I wouldn't have without my saintly husband and the antidepressants.'

'What, you mean that they let you stay on medication when you were pregnant? Are you on something similar to mine?' I thought of Max insisting I had to stop breastfeeding on *Lustral*.

'I was on *Lustral* then. I'm on *Efexor* now.'

As I had by now discovered, SSRIs are prescribed to pregnant women, particularly when there has been a history of postnatal depression with previous pregnancies. The belief usually held by mothers-to-be is that the drugs are doing no harm to their unborn child. But reports to the Australian Adverse Drug Reactions Advisory Committee (ADRAC) have demonstrated that taking SSRIs during pregnancy is associated with agitation, poor feeding, stomach upsets, convulsions, tremors, fever and respiratory disorders in newborns.[1]

In 2005, a population-based Danish study found a 60 per cent increase in cardiac abnormalities among babies of mothers taking SSRIs.[2] In 2006 a Canadian study of almost 5000 women revealed that those taking SSRIs during pregnancy were twice as likely to have a stillbirth as those not taking the drugs. Women on SSRIs were also twice as likely to have a premature or low birth-weight baby.[3]

By July 2006 the FDA released a public health alert after a study revealed a sixfold increased risk of neonatal persistent pulmonary hypertension (PPHN) in babies of women who took an SSRI in the second half of pregnancy.[4] PPHN is a condition in which the lungs constrict, severely limiting their blood flow. As a result, oxygen levels become dangerously low. The FDA warns that in newborns the condition is associated with 'significant morbidity (disease and suffering) and mortality (death)'.[5] But Amelia was totally unaware of the potential harm she was doing her baby as she carried him to term, all the while taking her daily dosage of her antidepressant.

We drank two cups of tea. Then I had to put Jemima to bed, which meant bedtime for me too.

'I'll see you at the morning meeting,' she said.

'Morning meeting – see you there.' I had made a friend.

There was a detectable 'us and them' mindset at Ashgrove. As Amelia soon explained, some of the patients, especially many of the younger ones, were there undergoing drug and/or alcohol detox and rehab. The others, the vast majority, were receiving treatment for various varieties of depression and/or anxiety, from what I could gather. People from each group tended not to get to know anyone from the other group to any meaningful degree, but there were some exceptions.

Over the weeks, Amelia and I became very close very quickly, as people with shared adversity often do. We had heaps to compare notes on: our diagnoses, our medications, our families and our doctors, whom I found out came from the same consulting practice. We didn't get to do many of the scheduled activities together though. The staff were aware we were drawn to each other and therefore separated us as a teacher would separate a couple of disruptive students. Apparently spending too much time around one or two people was another thing considered to be against the objectives of our stay. But we caught up at every other possible moment during our free time.

The guy who had been sitting with Amelia on my first night in the dining room was Adam, a computer software developer. He had been in and out of Ashgrove numerous times. Almost every time he went home he'd try to kill himself. This time he'd only been admitted a few days before I'd arrived. The three of us were sitting together over morning tea when Adam, with both arms bandaged to his elbows, described his current dilemma. He'd been brought to Ashgrove straight from the emergency department of a public hospital, where he had been taken after slitting his wrists. As he lived alone, there was no one left behind to clean up the mess he'd made. There was blood all over the kitchen, he recalled – on the walls, the phone and the kettle. He chuckled as he recounted making himself a cuppa after he'd dialled for help.

Adam wasn't only a regular at Ashgrove. He was no stranger to the psych wards of public hospitals either, where, although he paid for private health insurance, he would end up when his behaviour exceeded what the private clinics were prepared to handle. He told me how they had seclusion rooms where patients were confined if they 'misbehaved', with nothing but a bed and a tiny window high in the wall. And yes, the walls were padded. And yes, patients could be restrained – buckled down to their bed by the wrists, waist and ankles. There were no such things as private rooms, he told me. There you shared a ward. He recounted the time he was in the high-dependency unit, a locked ward for patients considered acutely ill. Patients would be dropped off throughout the day and night, sometimes by medical personnel and quite often by the police. Adam had had the misfortune of getting the bed next to a female patient who spent most of her time explicitly masturbating for his benefit.

Adam was good-looking, sociable, articulate. If I'd met him at a party I'd have had no idea he had such problems. But then, that went for many of my fellow patients at Ashgrove.

It was common for Amelia and Adam to swap suicide-attempt stories. Though their conversations showed Amelia up as a novice, Adam had been labelled the least likely to succeed because most of his previous attempts had been thwarted by a comedy of errors. There was the time he'd strung up a belt ready to hang himself, only to find he hadn't hung it high enough and he had to lift his feet from the floor to try to dangle. Then the belt snapped and he landed with a thud on his backside.

And there was the plastic-bag-over-the-head incident, which seemed to be going fine until he accidentally bit a hole in the bag.

Amelia told us about the time she'd presented to emergency after an overdose, and had spat the charcoal mixture they were forcing her to drink to halt the absorption of the drugs all over the nurse.

It should have irked me to hear them tell their ghoulish tales over tea and biscuits. A few times they apologised for being inconsiderate. But actually I was lapping up the detail. Wherever possible, while taking care to appear nonchalant, I would slip in a question or two: which techniques had been complete failures and which had almost worked? Do you just go to sleep when you overdose or does it make you sick? Which pills can do the trick? If you cut your wrists, how much does it hurt, and how long does it take until you die?

I learnt that overdoses are the least successful, but that doesn't mean they won't work if you get the right combination. Wrist-cutting is effective, as long as you go deep enough, but you need a strong stomach. Sitting in a warm bath while it's done is a good idea, advised Adam, for a few reasons: it makes the veins more prominent and easier to cut; it speeds up the bleeding and gives you less time to chicken out and call for help; and it leaves less mess for the poor bastard who finds you.

A loaded gun or a moving train's usually a sure thing, of course, he said, but it takes a lot of guts to go there.

He stopped me in the hall one day on my way to morning tea.

'Hey, Bek, it just occurred to me . . . All that talk of mine and Amelia's . . . We're not . . . ah . . . influencing you, are we? I think we've probably been pretty irresponsible.'

'No, it's nothing like that. I've just got a bit of a morbid fascination, I guess. I suppose I find it like watching a horror movie or something. I'm sorry if I'm being too much of a sticky beak.'

'No, no. It's just, well, you know, we get a bit carried away at times.'

The truth was I was researching because of my own emerging suicidal drive. Preoccupations about planning my death were permeating most of my daily thoughts and taking mammoth amounts of energy to suppress. My only immediate comfort was that I could at least be saved from myself in hospital. Every patient there was treated as a potential suicide risk and the place was set up to try to ensure that any attempt would be fruitless. There were no shower-curtain rails, or anything else mounted high enough for a person to hang from. There were no sharp objects: coat-hangers were all plastic and none of the knives from the dining room was serrated. Medications were locked away and only handed out a dose at a time. Beds were checked hourly at night and bedroom doors were never to be shut. The washbasins had no plugs.

'What, you mean they reckon someone would try drowning themselves in a hand sink?' I said to Amelia one day.

'You'd be surprised. Where there's a will . . .'

And I was beginning to comprehend that will.

What the hell was this mental saboteur? What was fuelling these unhinged thoughts? I had no reason to die. I had my baby to get better for, a loving partner to go home to and a career waiting for me once I was back on my feet.

It was clear to Max I wasn't improving, but I didn't declare this latest development for fear he would rush me off somewhere more high-security. 'The *Lustral* and *Valium* combination's not quite doing the trick, is it? Don't fret, we're a long way from exhausting our options yet,' he assured me. The *Valium* got scratched in favour of a potent dose of a similar but newer tranquillising drug – *Xanax*. The *Lustral* was swapped for *Dutonin*, an antidepressant similar to the SSRIs, but stronger.

Shortly after this drug exchange I hurt myself again in the bathroom of my room. With Jemima asleep in her cot and a good hour until the next round of bed checks, I was beckoned by the disposable razor in my washbag. As a novice self-harmer I'd not before identified it as a weapon. But, just think . . . if I could only free one of the twin blades from its plastic casing surely it could do some satisfying damage. Could I pry it out with a hairpin? If I bent and twisted it would one just pop out?

'Come on, you fuckin' piece of pink plastic shit.' Crazed, I bit down on the casing with my back teeth, spitting breakaway fragments of it into the basin. With a decent strip of metal finally exposed I plunged into my arm, over and over, until my hysteria was spent. My tattered, meaty arm wept crimson syrup, a sight so repugnant through my instantaneously sobered eyes that it made me dry retch.

I picked up my bedside phone, dialled '9' and awaited an answer from the nurses' station.

Torchlight broadened as it neared my open door and swept the room, catching Jemima's face in its pass. I prayed she didn't rouse to witness her mother's disgrace. The beam halted in my lap where I cradled my arm. The night nurse inspected the damage and I awaited my scolding.

'What did you use? Where is it?'

'In the basin.'

'Do you have anything else?'

I shook my head.

'Promise?'

'U-huh.'

She left briefly and returned with a bandage, dressing it lightly around my arm. Gloving her hands in latex she proceeded to clean up and dispose of my weapon.

'I've called the locum doctor,' she said from the bathroom. 'He might take a while. Do you want to pop out to the courtyard for a smoke while you wait?'

'I don't smoke.'

'Okay then, well, I'll get you a glass of water. Just try and keep that arm elevated and maybe catch another bit of sleep. I'll wake you when he's here.'

I couldn't decide which looked more obscene, the state of my arm before the doctor had been, or afterwards, when he'd laced up my skin with bold black thread. Black, for heaven's sake, black. I'd never had stitches before but it looked to me a pretty crude job. But then he was hardly going to bother with his best handiwork, I supposed, for someone prepared to do this to themselves.

I was about to leave my room to go to breakfast when a nurse walked in. 'Just before you go, I was told to give you this.'

She handed me a sturdy elastic band and explained I was to wear it around my wrist – of the uninjured arm. I was to stretch it out and let it snap back hard against my skin whenever I felt an impulse to self-harm. Now I understood the significance of the red bands I'd seen worn by quite a few other patients about the place, and I also understood why the night nurse hadn't batted an eyelid at what I'd done.

I was flabbergasted when only a few days later Max advised me that it would be my last day at Ashgrove. Seven weeks was long enough for anyone to be shut away, he said. I could start coming to see him at his rooms once a week.

So, with a month's supply of antidepressants, tranquillisers and sleeping tablets in a big plastic bag, I was discharged.

I returned to a different house than the one I had left. While in hospital, our unit – our cosy little incubator of independence and happiness – had been handed over to strangers without me having had the chance to bid it the farewell and thanks it deserved. But it was entirely without ceremony – thanks to the emotion-neutralising properties of my new medication – that I now stepped through the door of this recently purchased property and began to refer to it as home. Nigel, with the help of a couple of friends, had done all the packing and moving in my absence. According to their taste and sense of practicality they'd stocked cupboards, arranged ornaments and placed pictures, in many instances very differently from the way I would have done. I'd missed the opportunity to set up our first owned home in a manner that would make it feel proudly, individually, Nigel's and mine. But the medication seemed to do a pretty tidy job of neutralising any lamentations in regard to this as well.

After I'd walked about and familiarised myself with the place (I'd only seen it once before, months ago during an inspection) and unpacked my hospital bag, Nigel decided it was time to tell me the news he'd refrained from disclosing while I was in hospital. He'd lost his job – he had been made redundant about a week before. I had a new baby, a new mortgage, a new psychiatric disturbance and a newly unemployed partner.

'Don't stress, Nige,' was my response, along with a chummy pat on the knee. 'That's the last thing you need right now. It's just a job, you'll get another one.'

Here, take some of my pills, you might never be bothered by anything again! Incongruously, thriving right alongside this blithe outlook remained a remorseless goading to suicide. I tried to immerse myself in as much activity as I could in an effort to stifle it, but I still graphically imagined my execution several times a day. Incitement was everywhere: the kitchen drawer, my glass studio, the oven, the bath! I couldn't even enter the garden without seeing myself hanging limp from a tree. I had no choice but to confess to Nigel what was going on. He and Mum arranged to share the job of being my minder. The cutlery and utensil drawers were cleared of anything sharper than butter knives and my medications were distributed by either Mum or Nige, dose by dose. Nigel called and told Max. Max just said we were doing everything right and that things were sure to fix themselves once I had readjusted to being back at home.

By now Mum was getting increasingly suspicious of Max and his methods. She began to keep a detailed diary of her observations. In response to her prompting, and unbeknown to me at the time, Nigel contacted the Crisis Assessment Team (CAT) affiliated with the psychiatric department of our regional public hospital to ask them to come and evaluate me independently of Max. His request was rejected for reasons that were not completely clear, but that seemed to have a lot to do with the fact that I already had an association with a private psychiatrist.

After only a couple of nights at home, I called Ashgrove.

'Please, I need to come back in. Something really bad is going to happen.'

The nurse told me to make a cup of tea and take a warm bath, and someone would call me in the morning. With my by-now somewhat vibrant history of self-harm, which is often regarded as egocentric, attention-seeking behaviour, it seemed my pleas were being considered as merely another bout of histrionics.

No one called. The next evening Nigel put Jemima to bed, then went to the study to search for a job on the internet. I said I was going for a lie-down, but instead crept out to the laundry cupboard where I suspected my pills were hidden. I found only temazepam sleeping pills, but the bottle was almost full. I snuck out to my art studio in the back corner of the yard, leaving the door ajar. I swallowed the pills in three goes, about twenty-five altogether. Lying down on the floor, pill bottle displayed in hand, I waited, hoping Nigel would find me sooner rather than later. It was my last-ditch effort, my final appeal for help.

Over four years later, in 2004, the US drug regulator, the FDA, issued this warning:

The Food and Drug Administration (FDA) asked manufacturers of [SSRIs and similar antidepressants] to include in their labelling a warning statement that recommends close observation of adult and pediatric patients treated with these agents for worsening of depression or the emergence of suicidality [suicidal thoughts/behaviour]. Health care providers should carefully monitor patients receiving antidepressants for possible worsening of depression or suicidality, especially at the beginning of therapy or when the dose either increases or decreases.[6]

This was followed by an announcement that the agency would be conducting a full analysis of all available clinical trial data to gain a better understanding of just who might be at risk.

Late in 2006 the review was complete. By pooling all the data for SSRIs and similar drugs the FDA discovered that clinical trials involving subjects with major depressive disorder and other psychiatric conditions showed a clear increased risk of suicidal behaviour for children, adolescents, and younger adults taking these medications. That older adults are also at risk could not be ruled out.

'Patients of all ages,' it required drug makers to warn, 'who are started on antidepressant therapy should be monitored appropriately and observed closely for clinical worsening, suicidality, or unusual changes in behavior [sic]. Families and caregivers should be advised of the need for close observation and communication with the prescriber.' That particular vigilance should be exercised at commencement of treatment, and with either a dosage increase or decrease was reiterated.[7]

Similar though seemingly less explicit or straightforward warnings were issued by the UK MHRA[8] and the TGA in Australia.[9]* In some cases healthy volunteers – that is, people with no history of psychiatric illness who have been screened to determine there is no indication they have any

---

*A few years earlier, after reviews restricted to paediatric trials, all three regulators issued clear warnings about children and SSRIs. In Britain, the MHRA warned that all SSRIs, with the exception of *Prozac*, are unsuitable for under 18s. The trial analysis revealed increased rates of behaviours such as insomnia, agitation, self-harm and suicidal thoughts in those taking SSRIs compared with those taking placebo. Further information can be found at http://www.mhra.gov.uk/NewsCentre/Pressreleases/CON002045

existing psychological abnormality – have become suicidal after taking serotonin-enhancing drugs. In 1999, Professor David Healy, Director of the North Wales Department of Psychological Medicine, conducted his own clinical trial to assess the effects of *Lustral* on such people. The study lasted four weeks and involved twenty volunteers. Two of them became racked with thoughts of suicide.[10]

More tragically, Traci Johnson, a nineteen-year-old healthy volunteer, killed herself in 2004 during the trial of *Cymbalta*, a new serotonin-stimulating drug. The trial was aborted.[11]

With ever-mounting evidence linking SSRIs to suicidal behaviour, supporters of antidepressants have been quick to offer explanations that might absolve the drug of any direct blame. One popular theory is that before the antidepressant has had time to alleviate symptoms completely, it has simply given the depressed patient the energy to act on pre-existing suicidal wishes that in their depressed state they were unable to summon. There's a couple of problems with this argument. For one, it seems ludicrous to suggest that a patient who retains sufficient energy to swallow their usual amount of pills would somehow lack the energy needed to execute one of the most common suicidal behaviours: the drug overdose.[12] Second, this theory does nothing to explain newly emergent suicidal behaviour in non-depressed patients taking antidepressants.

◆◆◆◆◆◆

About an hour after I'd taken the pills Nige had a break from his job-searching and went to make a cup of tea. He did a double-take when he saw from the kitchen window that a light was on in the studio. Seeing me motionless on the floor he ran to my aid, finding me conscious but extremely groggy. He called an ambulance. Although its lights and sirens were silent when it pulled into our drive it still alerted the attention of our neighbours in our quiet suburban street. When they came over to see what they could do to help, Nigel didn't know what to say or how to say it. But it turned out he didn't have to worry; the sight of me staggering out of the door with vomit down my front supported by two paramedics was enough to spare any verbal explanation.

The fluorescent ceiling lights of the hospital emergency department stabbed at my eyes, but the medical staff wouldn't allow me to shut them as they continuously asked questions and shook me to keep me awake.

'Can you tell me your name? What day is it? Do you know where you are? Come on. Do you know what day it is?'

I was taken to a curtained cubicle and made to drink a plastic sackful of that liquid charcoal I'd heard so much about. The sludgy, gritty, pitch-black mixture scraped as it went down, clogging my throat, making both swallowing and breathing difficult. Now I understood why Amelia had spat it back.

By the time they'd taken blood samples, urine samples and asked me to confirm my name and the date what felt like a hundred times, I was wide awake. Mum had been and gone. Nigel had phoned and asked her to come and take Jemima back to her place. She hadn't had much of a chance to speak to me. She had just stood, perplexed and helpless, relegated to the sidelines while the staff had buzzed about.

'She'll be in for observation tonight,' said a doctor to Nigel. 'We'll get our psychiatrist to see her in the morning. You might as well go home, mate, get some rest.'

With my nerves acutely on edge and the stark lights continuing to assault my eyes, I didn't know how I was going to bear being confined to four square metres on a too-narrow bed. I prayed that Max would be alerted soon about where I was so he could bail me out.

21 November 1999

Nigel called me at work today to tell me Bek had OD'd. I drove across town like the proverbial 'bat out of hell', arriving at the hospital without realising how I had got there.

I parked my car, but just sat there for some time waiting for the reality of the situation to sink in. Not sure how long it was exactly before I mustered up the courage and walked into the emergency department. After I'd identified myself to the triage nurse as Bek's mother she phoned through to the trauma area, then told me to wait by the locked door until someone came to let me in.

As I stood peering through the window in the door I saw Bek, in a white hospital gown, an intravenous drip in her arm and various leads connected to a monitor suspended from a mobile trolley. She was escorted by a male nurse. I tapped on the glass and she looked up at me, raising her head slightly and attempting a wave of her arm. But her movements were slow and heavy, as though in slow motion. Her expression was that of a bewildered five-year-old. Not expecting to see my face in this environment it took a moment before she realised it was me, then slowly that look of, 'I wonder what she's doing here,' crept over her face.

Her blackened lips widened to expose charcoal-covered teeth and tongue, and she mouthed the words, 'Oh, hi.' The nurse then turned and led her away, her bare feet slapping the cold linoleum floor, her jellied legs barely supporting her, exposed by the gaping hospital gown that flapped behind her. She unsteadily made her way out of my range of sight. There was something so surreal about this whole situation. I stood there wondering when I was going to wake up and find it was all a dream.

Finally the door was unlocked and I was shown into a trauma bay where Bek was propped up on a trolley. She looked at me and grinned, greeting me with a weak but pleasantly surprised, 'Hi, Mum,' as if I had dropped by for morning tea.

❖❖❖❖❖❖

I woke from a spasmodic sleep to a female voice impatiently saying my name. My head thumped in pain and I struggled to lift it from the pillow. Nausea threatened when I did.

'Sit up, please. I need to do your obs,' said the nurse, as she stuck a digital thermometer in my ear then a cold stethoscope against my chest. She scribbled something on a chart. Keeping her eyes on her work, she conversed no further. It took a couple of tries before my voice crackled into gear, 'Could I have a drink of w—' But she'd whipped the curtain aside and disappeared. As my griping stomach threatened to digest itself, I wondered if burdens on the health system got offered breakfast.

Realising it was the first time I'd not had Jemima to share my morning, I was assailed by a surge of desolation. The curtain swept open again. A slight woman with short dark hair and a what-have-we-got-here expression introduced herself.

'I'm Felicia Johnson, the resident psychiatrist. If you're feeling up to it I'd like to ask you some questions.' Her voice was soft and friendly, at least.

'Okay.'

'Are you right to stand? We'll go to another area.'

'Yep, yep, I'm fine.'

I followed her out into the hub of the emergency department, gripping my white hospital gown closed behind my back. She showed me to an office-sized room and shut the door behind us. It was scantly furnished with two basic chairs facing each other. The floor and walls were linoleum. The only adornment was a large mirror stretching the length of one wall. At least that's what I thought it was, until I realised it was more likely a two-way observation window.

'Please, have a seat.' Johnson watched me intently. An abrasive agitation, a bad energy, which had begun to build over the last week or so, buzzed about my body.

I asked if I could have a *Xanax*.

'I'll get you one when we've finished. I'll make this as quick as I can.'

She opened a manila folder with my name written in black down one edge. Holding it at an awkward angle so I couldn't easily see what she was writing, she asked me about my family structure and jotted a quick genogram. She wanted to know a bit about my past, relationships with others, my education and employment. She then rattled off a set of pro-forma-sounding questions. How would you describe your mood and how would you rate it on a scale of one to ten? Have you tried to harm yourself before? Any thoughts of harming anyone else? Ever been in trouble with the police? Do you use alcohol or any other drugs?

I'd heard people say many a time that it was only when they'd been officially diagnosed with depression that they realised they'd possibly been that way a long time without knowing it. Was that the case with me? Perhaps I was experiencing some sort of compound effect: a series of things that I just hadn't dealt with, reaching a climax. That made sense, didn't it? But wasn't there more happening with me than just depression? Depression usually made sense once you heard what a person was enduring in their life. My behaviour had stopped making sense. I wanted Johnson to delve deeper so that, like an informant helping a detective with a really elusive case, I could help her map out what was going on. I knew Max was brilliant but, even so, there could still be something he was missing, couldn't there?

But in her twenty-minute assessment there was only so much delving Johnson was prepared to do and it was clear she did not want to step on Max's toes. Just find out what's making me like this, I wanted to scream. Just find out what my chemical imbalance is and give me the drug to fix it!

'So, what do you think's going on with me?'

'Having a baby can trigger all sorts of things,' said Johnson. 'Rebekah, can you give any guarantee of your safety now or are you likely to try this again?'

'I'll try it again. I'm sure I will.'

'If you go on like this, Rebekah, you're going to leave behind a motherless baby. That's something you really need to think about.'

When Dr Johnson said she had not yet heard from Max I felt dejection so intense it made me squirm slightly at just how dependent on him I'd become. When she went on to say that Ashgrove had no beds available, I frantically wanted to retract my honesty about my suicidal intentions. I was terrified I'd be scheduled to the hospital's public psych ward.

'You understand, of course, that we can't let you go home.'

'Please, I don't want to stay here. My partner's at home. He could watch me . . . and my mum.'

'That wasn't too successful last time now, was it? No, I'm afraid, Rebekah, that would be putting unfair expectations on them. Now, I really don't want to have to make any decisions for you. If you agree to inpatient help somewhere appropriate I won't have to do that. Do you acknowledge that you need help?'

'Yes. Yes, I do, I just . . . Please, I don't want to stay here.'

'We won't do that unless we have to. It would be a shame seeing as you have private health insurance.' She stood up and opened the door. 'I'll keep trying to find another bed for you at a private clinic. I'll let you know as soon as I'm successful.'

As I was led back to the purgatory of my cubicle, I asked if I could go to the waiting area and use the phone, but was told I wasn't allowed to unaccompanied. That's when it really hit me how I was being viewed: with suspicion and distrust.

Johnson assumed it was Nigel I wanted to speak to and assured me he'd probably be in soon. I was wondering where he was and wishing he was there but, just then, I wanted to call Amelia. I thought of the people who were at Ashgrove with me and how their stories, conversations and acceptance of the unacceptable had initially unnerved me. Now I could see them just as mothers, husbands, sisters or brothers, school teachers, florists or accountants, who'd simply drifted (or been pushed) to the fringe for one reason or another – just like me. I yearned for their knowing support.

'I'll write up that *Xanax* for you now,' said Johnson, once I was safely behind my curtain.

'Thank you. Um, would I be able to get something to eat too? I think I ended up wearing most of my dinner last night.'

'You haven't had anything yet? I'll have someone bring you a sandwich.'

When Nigel did come in about mid-morning he was alone. He'd left Jemima at Mum's. I was disappointed but agreed with him that it was probably best to keep her away when I was such a mess. I was craving some sympathy from Nige but he could barely make eye contact.

He unzipped the overnight bag he'd brought to show me my fresh clothes and toiletries.

'I'd better get back to Mima.'

'Please, Nige, don't go yet. She'll be all right with Mum for a while.'

'I've got things to do as well.'

His disgust was plain. How could I make him see I wasn't in charge of what I'd done; that I'd been commandeered by some reckless, malevolent entity? I wanted to tell him it wasn't me who was hurting him. But how could he make sense of that when my actions were so deliberate? I wanted to beg him to stay, but I decided to hang on to what little remained of my pride.

'Come back soon then?'

'Tell them to call my mobile when they work out where you're going.' And with that he was gone.

I lay there in that whiter than white environment, strangleheld by loneliness, afraid to breathe for fear it would validate reality. It tore me up that Nigel couldn't bear to be near me, that my daughter was learning to relate to someone else as her mother, and that Max . . . Max, how could you leave me here? But what really left me withered and aching was the fear I'd been forsaken by myself. I shut my eyes tight and tried with all my might to detach myself from the physical and transcend my wretched state. If only I could sleep. Why hadn't the damned *Xanax* worked? The first thing I'd ask Max when I got the chance was to increase the dose.

SIX

After less than a day in the sterility of the emergency department, a bed was found for me at Fernview, a major private psychiatric hospital. Under Felicia Johnson's instructions, Nigel drove me straight there without stopping off anywhere: I wasn't allowed to have the opportunity to stash anything sharp. I was given a room in the mother–baby unit, which was quite similar in set-up to the one at Elm Court. How it differed, though, was that all the patients were there because of postnatal depression and it was staffed by psychiatric professionals.

It was clear that Fernview was to serve as a holding bay for me until I was deemed less of a suicide risk. The young female psychiatrist who spoke with me briefly each morning was simply acting as a proxy for Max because he didn't have any clinical rights there.

I loitered on the perimeter of goings-on there. The other mothers would bond with enthusiasm during group therapy over shared stories of postnatal tearfulness, sleep deprivation, feeling misunderstood and shame at not being able to cope with their child. I would sit on the sidelines wishing myself back a few months to when exhaustion and maternal inadequacy were my only afflictions.

Opposite the multi-purpose room where our group therapy was held stood an unsigned, very thick and heavy door with a narrow rectangular window down one side. Curious as to what lay beyond it, I would sometimes hang around in the hallway before the start of a session and try to peer inconspicuously through the slim glass panel. But all I managed to make out was yet another door, set about three metres inside the first.

69

Every few hours a string of four or five very sedated-looking patients would emerge, to be led by a staff member down the hallway in the direction of the smoking balcony. After ten or so minutes the guarded procession would return to be barricaded in again.

'What *is* in that room?' I finally asked another patient from the mother–baby unit.

'HDU, high dependency unit,' she explained, with a raise of her eyebrows. 'Some serious cases in there. You'd think they'd keep those kinds of people right away from the rest of us, wouldn't you?' she added. All I could think was how humiliating it was for the poor patients to have to be paraded past a group of mothers who considered them 'those kinds of people'.

On my third day at Fernview Amelia came to visit. Her husband had made her leave the kids at home.

'He doesn't like them being around these places. He almost wouldn't let me come. I think he thinks you're a bad influence,' she giggled. 'No, not really. He likes you, he's just nervous because I've been doing so well for a while now and he doesn't want anything to drag me back down.'

'Your husband's great. He cares about you so much.'

'As does Nigel for you. Hey, when you're out of here you'll both have to come over. I'll invite Adam too. Darren can have a chat with Nige, give him some partner-to-partner support, and we can do our own thing.'

'That sounds like fun.'

'Bek,' her voice took on a sombre tone, 'you really scared me when you told me what you'd done to yourself.'

'I'm sorry. I didn't mean to stir up memories.'

'No, I mean the thought of not having you, now I've got to like you so much. I don't think I could . . .' She laughed, as if she felt she should dilute her declaration. 'It just means a lot to have you in my life.' I thanked her with a hug.

'So, Amelia, you have to tell me, what medication's responsible for you doing so well?'

'I'm still on the *Efexor* and the *Xanax*, but I'm taking lithium now, as well.'

'Lithium? What, does your doctor think you're manic depressive?'

'No. Because it's a mood stabiliser they sometimes give it for depression as well.'

'How does it make you feel?'

'Just kind of numb, really.'

Numb sounded good. If I could get something to sedate me enough, I wouldn't care if it put me in a bloody coma. My anxiety was starting to get the better of me. And I wasn't sure that was all it was. I had all the physical sensations of anxiety – well, it was more nervousness really – but there was no clear trigger for the feelings. Whenever I'd been anxious at other times in my life there was something obvious preying on my mind, making me physically uptight. But this was different. This was really hard to explain.

My daily exchange with the psychiatrist rarely differed:

'How are you feeling today?'

'A bit better, thanks.'

'Any thoughts of harming yourself?'

'No.'

'Good, then. You're doing well. See you again tomorrow. If anything does change make sure you tell one of the nurses.'

I simply told her what she wanted to hear so I could expedite my return to Max's care. And that was all it appeared to take: say the suicidal thoughts had passed and I could go home; admit I was still having them and discharge would be denied. How stupid, I thought, that the suicide prevention strategy seemed to be based on not much other than the patient's declaration of their intent. Let's face it, if you'd resolved that killing yourself was what you were going to do, then you wouldn't tell anyone, would you?

When Nige came to visit he brought with him a letter. It was from my employer: a reminder that my leave of absence was drawing to a close and I was due back, full-time, in two weeks. It had been dated eight days prior. Amidst all the drama it had been sitting on the kitchen table at home, unopened.

'You could call them,' Nige suggested. 'Tell them what's going on. Max would support you. You could apply for an extension.'

'I couldn't call. There's no way I could call.'

'Well, write to them. No, you probably haven't got the time to arrange things by mail. I'll call them for you then.'

'And say what exactly? "Sorry, my wife's gone completely nuts and she's in the loony bin at the moment. Could she have an indefinite extension until she's got her marbles back?" '

'We can just tell them you're in hospital, that you're ill. They don't have to know what it is. Max will write you a letter.'

'Yeah, with the fact that he's a psychiatrist printed on the letterhead.'

'Bek, this is your career, for Christ's sake. You worked so hard for it. You can't just let it go.'

'And I'm telling you I can't handle it, okay? Just stop friggin' hassling me!'

A nurse appeared at the door. 'Everything all right in here?'

'Fine,' said Nigel curtly. The nurse looked as though she didn't believe him but she disappeared anyway.

He turned back to me. 'So, what are you saying? You're just going to throw it away?'

I stood silently staring hard at the floor, willing him to leave.

'Do what you like, Bek.' He scrunched up the letter, threw it on the bed and walked out.

I called Mum and asked her to draft a letter for me. Although she reacted similarly to Nigel at first, she could see there was no way of knowing when I'd be fit to return to work.

So, just two days before work were expecting me back they received my letter explaining that 'I have decided I really need to dedicate more than six full-time months to my baby . . . Therefore, would you please accept my resignation, effective immediately . . .'

A hard-earned and promising career, up in smoke.

◆◆◆◆◆◆

After five days at Fernview, I was discharged. A few days later I had an appointment with Max at his consulting rooms.

I was a bit reserved with him at first. I felt really let down that he hadn't been in touch since the overdose.

'I was in the middle of nowhere when they tried to call me from the emergency department. I had stacks of messages by the time my phone had reception. And guess which was the first I returned? Yours, Bek. The one about you. So, tell me, how was your stay at Fernview?'

He made it sound like I'd just taken a little holiday or something.

'How would you expect it to have been?'

'Hey, come on, don't be upset. I was miles from anywhere, had my filly running at a country meet. I can understand you being pissed off at me, though.'

'I'm not pissed off, I'm just . . .'

'Scared? I can imagine. Look, we're going to have to take a bit of a harder line with your treatment. We always go for milder options first, but if they're not working we have to rethink things.'

'I'd like to give lithium a try.'

'We're certainly thinking along similar lines. I'm going to get you to try some *Zyprexa*.'

Zyprexa (olanzapine) was then a fairly new drug, only approved in Australia for the treatment of schizophrenia. But Max was simply doing what he was permitted to: prescribing any drug 'off label' he deemed suitable for my condition. He handed me the prescription, telling me nothing other than that the sedative effects of *Zyprexa* should alleviate my anxiety and subdue my self-destructive thoughts.

It would be years before I'd discover that during FDA trials for *Zyprexa* 50 to 60 per cent of participants taking the drug dropped out, unable to tolerate it even for the six weeks that the trial lasted.[1] And it would be years before I'd discover that *Zyprexa* has the highest figure for the number of suicides in a clinical trial programme of any current psychiatric drug.[2]

At home, Mum and Nigel continued their close supervision.

14 December 1999

Medications:
Xanax, 1 milligram 4 x day

Dutonin, 600 milligrams
Zyprexa, 7.5 milligrams

Just home from spending two days with Bek. She's incredibly disturbed – frenetic and restless. She kept walking back and forth from
her glass studio to the house, forgetting all the time what she was
doing – aimless, distracted. She was clumsy and dropping things;
agitated, unable to hold a proper conversation. There's no way she
can be left alone with the care of the baby. I'll have to request leave
for the remainder of the school term. Nigel can't be expected to cope
with this alone. When I arrived the other day he was trying to push
the lawn-mower with one hand and support the baby on his hip with
the other, all the while trying to stay aware of where Bek was and
what she was up to. We had a chat and I stressed the importance
of him talking with the psychiatrist and conveying the magnitude of
the situation. Nigel has just found himself a new job – thank heavens
– and will be starting it in a few days, but Bekie simply cannot be left
in charge of a baby in her present state.

Nigel told me he'd be coming to my next session with Max. Max permitted him to stay for ten of the fifty-five minutes.

'Bek just seems to ask for something new and you throw it at her,'
said my man of few words.

'It may seem that way,' said Max, ever composed, ever charming.
'Bek is doing some pretty intensive and challenging work with me at
the moment. She's got a lot of shit to work through. It can be difficult,
almost impossible, for those not directly involved in the therapy to understand that the person often gets worse before they get better. It's a
typical response for you to feel the way you do. It's quite normal to feel
alienated, cast aside. Partners typically feel powerless, frustrated that
the therapist is assuming the carer role. It's important for you to understand these are normal feelings.'

Nigel shrugged and nodded. There was a palpable therapy silence.

'I just wish she wasn't on so much stuff.' His voice had lost its as-
sertion.

'Bek and I have been discussing some alternatives.' As he spoke Max stood and walked to the door. Nigel recognised his cue to leave. 'If she continues the way she is,' Max added, 'we might look into those further.'

Nigel reluctantly returned to the waiting area. 'That should keep him happy for a while,' said Max, with a wink.

'Mum wants me to ask if she can speak to you,' I said, knowing our time was almost up when I saw him glance at the clock on the wall behind me, out of view from the patient's chair.

'I have no intention of speaking to your mother. This,' he said, pointing at himself then me, 'is something she can keep her poisonous paws right away from.'

Max's methods were so heavily laden with Freudian influence that I'd soon realised his physical resemblance to the famous psychoanalyst probably had very little to do with coincidence and everything to do with careful styling. Right from the outset he'd made up his mind that a significant contributor to my troubles with mothering Jemima was suppressed anger towards my own mother, and that once I reconciled the latter we'd be that much closer to sorting out the former.

I'd never wanted to blame anyone for the imperfections of my childhood – not having my father, and as a result having to share Mum with the demands of her work and study. I'd been born into a difficult situation, but the only thing to blame, if anything, was circumstance. However, the trouble with only implicating circumstance, as Max had wasted no time helping me to understand, was that circumstance was very hard to hold accountable; circumstance was very hard to confront; from circumstance you could seek no apology. Blaming circumstance left matters unresolved. Circumstance needed an identity, circumstance needed a face – so we'd awarded it the face of Mum. I'd wondered why Mum was the sole nominee; what about my father? Surely he wasn't to evade blame altogether? Wasn't he actually the one most worthy of it? Perhaps it was just that Freud had little to say about fathers. Perhaps, for the purposes of the exercise, Mum was simply convenient. Perhaps we'd get to my father in due course. Perhaps it was something else entirely.

I'd never been one to indulge in self-pity – indeed, I'd been criticised before for exerting too much emotional restraint over matters worthy of a good cry. That I was now digging up painful bits of the past and reacting to them the way I should have at the time they occurred was probably very healthy. But hadn't things now shifted just a little too far? My emotions had developed a life of their own.

Pretty soon I was launching into crying hysteria at the drop of a hat – my sessions with Max became full of it. It was as if every emotion ever contemplated in my lifetime was tripping over the others, vying for acknowledgement, each accompanied by its signature torrent of tears or squall of cursing.

Though again a little too late to be of help to me, in May 2004 the Canadian Federal Health Authority requested pharmaceutical company Pfizer update safety information regarding emotional and behavioural changes suspected to be linked to their SSRI *Lustral*, as well as all the other new antidepressants. The warning, entitled 'Potential association with the occurrence of behavioural and emotional changes, including self-harm', declared that changes in behaviour, including disinhibition (impulsivity to act on thoughts or whims without regard for consequences), aggression, depersonalisation (a feeling of detachment from one's own actions), hostility, and emotional lability (loss of control over one's emotions) had been observed in clinical trials and post-marketing reports.[3]

Max would pat me on the back whenever a session culminated in a 'hostile' or 'emotionally labile' eruption. I suppose in his eyes it substantiated a conviction that I had deep-seated pain in dire need of healing; that his therapy was proving hugely successful in cleansing me of it. Meanwhile I, completely bewildered by this unbridled outpouring, began thinking Mum had messed me up in worse ways than I could ever have imagined.

'I can't get Mum off my case,' I complained to Max one day, 'wanting to know everything that's going on: what you've got to say about my condition, what goes on in our sessions. I even overheard her trying to squeeze Nigel for information about it the other day.'

Max shook his head and grinned. 'I find it hilarious how desperate your mother is to interfere in our relationship. I imagine it's killing her to think that I might be helping you to see the truth.'

I walked to his window ledge and picked up one of a number of trinkets that decorated his office, some hand-made, others shop-bought.

'Have your patients given these things to you?' I asked, feeling immediately neglectful that I hadn't yet thought to get him anything.

'Yes,' he said proudly.

I resolved to get started on a beautiful piece of glassware as soon as I got home to surprise him with in our next session. Something to do with horses; everyone knew he loved horses.

22 December 1999

This guy Braydle really worries me. Now he says he has 'no intention' of speaking to me. Why? I thought it was an accepted part of modern psychiatric therapy in this type of situation to speak with family members. Nigel knows very little of what's going on and why, and I know even less. Just as predators in the wild will target the young, the weak, the infirm, first by isolating them, separating them from the herd, from their mate, from their mother – so begins, it seems, a deliberate and calculated process of separating Bek from her family. Like a jackal encircling and luring her to a place of emotional isolation where her vulnerabilities can be exploited to the full, Braydle is claiming her. If I were to speak these thoughts aloud to anyone they'd say I was paranoid. But I get the impression this man fancies himself as a Svengali and he has Bek well and truly in his power.

Where does poor little Jemima fit into all this? Does Braydle give any consideration to her psychological and emotional wellbeing? The next thing we'll see is the suggestion that she be separated from her mother. Just wait and see.

A couple of weeks after the introduction of the *Zyprexa*, I took an overdose of my *Xanax* pills and cut my arm again. Once more Nigel took me to the public hospital emergency department, where they stitched the wound. When Max found out he added *Prozac* to my medication concoction and booked me back into Ashgrove – without Jemima.

3 January 2000

Medications:
Dutonin, 600 milligrams
Xanax, 4 milligrams
Zyprexa, 7.5 milligrams
Prozac, 20 milligrams

Bek's back in Ashgrove. That bloody Braydle's prescribed her *Prozac* now, as well, on Bek's request, it seems. He's told her it will increase the effects of the other medications eightfold! I phoned her this morning, said I'd be in to see her with the baby in thirty minutes. She said that suited as it would give us time between her group session and lunch. When I arrived she was totally surprised to see me. She was very 'absent'. Took little notice of Jemima. Noticed there was blood on the phone by the bed. Must have cut herself again. Tried to broach subject of Braydle and the amounts of medications. She got awfully touchy, told me in not so many words to mind my business, then hurried me on my way, saying she had things to do before lunch. Poor Nige looks like death. I'm just waiting for him to be the next one to crack. Lucky I'm on break so I can have the baby.

5 January 2000

Going in to see Bek daily with Jemima, making sure I get in there in time to coincide with the baby's feeds. I heat up her food in the kitchen's microwave, get everything prepared and bring it all back to Bek's room. I always have to put Jemima into Bek's arms and make her do the feeding. Jemima was just lying in her arms today like a limp doll and I had to keep reminding Bek she was there so she wouldn't drop her. She was so uninterested and disconnected – just barely going through the motions. I had Mum with me today – she witnessed Bek roughly change the baby's nappy and then walk away and leave her on the bed. On the way home in the car Mum commented on how concerned she was that Bek was so offhand and rough with the baby.

78

Within a few days Amelia was back in Ashgrove too. She'd tried to OD again. It seemed too coincidental and I couldn't help but wonder if she'd done it so she could be back there with me. Whatever the reason, I was rapt she was there. Our partners, however, were not so keen. A couple of weeks before, Amelia and her husband, Darren, had had us over for dinner. It was a night that had left the men with reservations about the virtue of Amelia's and my friendship. We had acted like tipsy adolescents, sneaking off to the patio at every available moment to smoke cigarettes, giggle and whisper, leaving the men with the children and the washing-up, and concerned that we were happily withdrawing to our own maladjusted world.

Fortunately Nigel and Darren had got along very well and had begun to form a bond of their own. Darren offered Nigel support and insight from the point of view of someone who'd had years of living with his wife's psychological instability. But for Nige it was bittersweet. To have someone of similar nature and circumstance to talk to was great, but catching a glimpse of what he might be in for rattled him.

When Amelia had overdosed this time, Darren had tried to persuade her psychiatrist to admit her to a different hospital – he'd known I was back at Ashgrove because Nigel had been talking to him – but the authority to determine her treatment was simply not his.

To add to the coincidence of Amelia being there, Adam was also readmitted. There were quite a few other young people there this time as well. One of them was Nathan. He was a bit younger than me, tall with very masculine, Mediterranean good looks. Amelia, Adam and I welcomed him into our circle. Nathan explained he was a model and did catalogue work for the likes of Hugo Boss and Calvin Klein. His work sometimes involved travel to the States and Europe. Luckily for him, he said, his agent was a 'jewel' who was very successful at negotiating contracts for him even though he was up against local competition and suffered from frequent bouts of depression. I didn't quite understand why overseas companies would go to the expense of flying someone in from Australia, but then I knew nothing about how the modelling industry worked and I just assumed he must have been incredibly popular. His agent would often call him on his mobile phone, which he was never without.

I was having the time of my life during this admission to Ashgrove. I felt I'd become the outgoing, carefree, vivacious person I'd always wanted to be. Life was great. Never mind the incongruity of believing things had never been better while still cutting myself, sharing fantasies of suicide with Adam and Amelia, and showing little regard for Nigel or Jemima. Nige would visit religiously each evening, and either he or Mum would bring Jemima in to see me at least once a day. Nigel's distress was expressed only by his deeply furrowed brow. His visits usually consisted of fifteen to twenty minutes of uncomfortable silence, as words to describe how he and Jemima were being affected by my behaviour escaped him and small talk seemed ludicrously inappropriate. I couldn't wait for him to leave.

'I mean, if he doesn't want to come here, then why does he?' I asked Nathan. 'When I was down he was pissed off at me. Now that I'm doing all right and getting on with things he's pissed off again? Who could be bothered? If he can't accept me for who I am, he can just get stuffed for all I care.'

Max would visit me at least once daily. He'd obviously heard from the nurses about Nathan's and my rapidly developing friendship. 'You'd do well to avoid him,' he said. 'He's not the kind of influence you need around right now.'

'What kind of influence?' I said, thinking whatever it could be, Max was just being silly and overprotective. He wouldn't elaborate and I paid the warning no heed.

One night our circle of four went out to a Chinese restaurant for dinner. Patients were supposedly prohibited from driving either to or from Ashgrove, but Adam had his car in the visitors' car park. The staff weren't particularly concerned with where we were going or how we were getting there. The only restriction we had was to be back by 11 pm.

'Oh, and no alcohol,' added the nurse as we signed ourselves out.

We'd finished our meal and, with still an hour till curfew, decided to carry on to a pub. Ignoring the nurses' advice not to, Nathan and I bought some drinks, then left Amelia and Adam at the bar while we went to play the poker machines. Upon our return I was startled to see Amelia and Adam looking awfully intimate – were they kissing? As though taking their lead, Nathan bent down and began kissing me. I didn't resist. My mind seemed no longer guided by right, wrong or compromise – only impulse and action.

The following day Nathan wasn't at the morning meeting. When it had finished I went to look for him in his room. It appeared to have been vacated. I went and asked Adam if he knew anything and was told Nathan had been chucked out for failing his morning urine test. 'You didn't know, did you?' said Adam.

'Know what?' I asked, puzzled.

'He was in here for heroin detox.'

Mid-morning a nurse came to my room and handed me an envelope.

'Nathan asked for this to be passed on to you.' Inside was his phone number and address. He had told me he lived in a suburb quite close to my own, but now I realised that he lived not more than a five-minute drive away.

One evening, as I prepared for bed, Amelia burst through my door, looking panicked.

'Adam's got a razor,' she panted, grabbing my hand and dragging me down the hall to his room. The sight that met us was pitiful. Adam walked slowly towards us, eyes vacant, face forlorn, presenting his lacerated wrist to Amelia like a sacrificial offering. I immediately turned and ran to the nurses' station, banging loudly on the thick shockproof window. Nurses came running and I directed them to Adam. That night he was moved to high-dependency – a shoebox-like room adjoining the nurses' station with a small observation window.

Neither Amelia nor Adam would speak to me after that. Apparently, by alerting the staff, I'd breached some unspoken psych patient code.

10 January 2000

Medications:
Dutonin, 600 milligrams
Xanax, 4 milligrams

Zyprexa, 7.5 milligrams
Prozac, 20 milligrams

Bek rang today. Told me she'll be in Ashgrove for a few more weeks
and is having electroshock treatment! I expressed my horror at this
and said what she really needed was her medication reviewed. When
I saw her the other day she said she can't stop thinking about killing
herself. What doesn't add up is that she doesn't come across as
depressed – if anything she seems to be swinging the other way. Told
her I thought one of the drugs is making her obsess about suicide.
But it's falling on deaf ears. Spoke to Nige about ECT. Sensing he's
prepared to try anything. Asked him to at least speak to Braydle and
see if something else can't be done first. I've made an appointment
to speak to Dan Reubans [Mum's GP, and mine when I still lived with
Mum]. Don't know where else to turn.

Max put it to me that because we'd pretty much exhausted other options, we had little choice but to try electroshock therapy (ECT). So
this was one of the 'alternatives' he was referring to the day he spoke to
Nigel, was it? I was initially a bit stunned because I thought the practice
had been outlawed along with lobotomies.

'Now, stop thinking *One Flew Over the Cuckoo's Nest* 'cause I know
you are,' he said. 'Things have come along light years since then. You'll
have a general anaesthetic. You won't know a thing about it. ECT's
one of the most tried and true treatments there is for depression. It's
amazing how dramatic a change it can make in some people for whom
medication's been completely useless. And the best bit is that it works
right away, no waiting for weeks and adjusting dosages and all that.'

Max gave me a prepared Informed Consent Statement. At the bottom
of a lot of print he had marked a cross where I was supposed to sign.

'Have it ready for me tomorrow,' he said, 'and we can get the ball
rolling.'

The Mental Health Act, applicable to the region in which I lived,
states that a patient must give informed consent before a course of ECT
is given. The patient is considered to have given informed consent if he/

she agrees to treatment after being given 'sufficient information about a treatment and [he/she] agrees that the treatment can go ahead'.[4] A voluntary patient, which I was, can refuse treatment, withdraw consent or get a second opinion. However, if ECT is considered 'urgent' by the treating psychiatrist, then he or she does not need their patient's informed consent to go ahead. What 'urgent' means is not defined in the Mental Health Act or the Clinical Practice Guidelines of the Department of Human Services.[5] Therefore, whether a person gets a say in whether or not he or she is given ECT will depend very much on the opinion and attitude of the single psychiatrist involved.

Better protections against the potential for inappropriate administration of ECT exist in the UK. Here, a patient can still be given ECT without consent if deemed urgent; however, the doctor prescribing the ECT must state in writing that the patient is unable to give informed consent, and this statement then has to be supported by two other mental health professionals. In addition, 'urgent' is explicitly defined as being immediately necessary to save the patient's life or prevent serious deterioration of the patient's condition.

I was barely able to focus long enough to make my bed in one hit let alone digest information in a legal document. But it didn't matter – if Max said I needed ECT, if Max said ECT would help, if Max said ECT wasn't scary, then I would have ECT.

Mum caught me before I had the chance to give the signed form to Max.

'Call and speak to the Chief Psychiatrist at the Department of Human Services,* Bek, please, before you do anything,' she begged me. 'Stop thinking *One Flew Over the Cuckoo's Nest*, Mum. It's not the dark ages any more. Max says things have changed heaps.'

'Bek, please.'

I knew I'd get no peace unless I did as she asked.

'All right, Mum. I'll call them, him, whoever. What is it? The head
. . .'

'The *Chief* Psychiatrist. Here, here's the number.' She handed me an

---

*An Australian governmental department assigned the responsibility of monitoring psychiatric practice

information leaflet about ECT with the relevant phone number high-lighted in fluorescent pen. 'Make sure they know what medication you're on. Call today.'

'All right, Mum.'

I did call the office of the Chief Psychiatrist and ask if ECT was dangerous. I was told that although many people are apprehensive about ECT it is relatively safe and effective for many sufferers of depression. Good; now I could tell Mum what she wanted to hear without having to lie.

11 January 2000

Phoned Bek today. She reckons the Chief Psychiatrist said he'd be happy for ECT to be given to his own daughter. Had an appointment with Dan Reubans. His face was ashen when I told him the extent of Bek's illness. I wish he was still her GP. He's known her for so long he'd be able to put her current state into better perspective. He was concerned about the ECT, though he said that Bek may have her psychiatrist backed into a corner with nowhere to manoeuvre with medication. He was clearly shocked when I told him what she was taking and asked if I was sure she was on all that concurrently. 'She'll end up on a mortuary slab' were his words. Asked to find out if she was at least having the drugs paused while she had the ECT as they 'most definitely should be'. Relayed this info to Nige and urged him to talk to Braydle before first treatment. Dan asked if I can try and get Bek to come in to talk to him.

Before breakfast one morning the treatment room at Ashgrove was prepared for my arrival. I would be taken there every second day for the following two weeks, though I have no recollection of it: the ECT obliterated my memory of that entire period. But this is likely to have been what happened each visit: a general anaesthetic would have been administered through a vein in my arm. When that had taken effect I would have been injected with a drug to reduce secretions in my mouth, closely followed by another to suppress my muscle movement and stop my body from uncontrollably thrashing about. I would have been artificially respirated. Next, electrodes would have been placed on my temples and approximately 140 volts of electrical current would have passed through them, triggering my brain to have a major seizure.

In his book *Toxic Psychiatry*, psychiatrist Peter Breggin gives this account of ECT's action and effect:

> The shock induces an electrical storm that obliterates the normal electrical patterns of the brain. The period of extreme bursts of electrical energy is often followed by a briefer period of absolutely no electrical activity. The brain waves become temporarily flat, as in brain death, and it may be that cell death takes place at this time. As the course of shocks progresses, the patient's apathy, memory loss and confusion increase. Judgement and general mental function become impaired. Sometimes the patient becomes temporarily giddy or artificially high. This generalised mental and emotional dysfunction is called an acute organic brain syndrome or delirium – the brain's typical response to severe stress or damage. Less frequently, extreme states of delirium develop in which the patient appears grossly psychotic with hallucinations and delusions.[7]

Though Max had put me at ease by telling me that movie depictions of shock therapy from fifty years ago bore little resemblance to today's updated version, Breggin disagrees:

> There is no reason to believe that modern shock is safer. The electrical stimulation must, in fact, be stronger nowadays since the patients are sedated and sedation makes it more difficult to convulse the patients . . . Nowadays shock doctors are very sensitive to public and professional opinion, and therefore they maintain that the treatment is relatively harmless and that its method of action is unknown. But in the first couple of decades of use, many shock authorities boldly declared that the treatment works precisely by damaging the brain and that brain-cell death is the key to successful treatment.[8]

11 January 2000

Medications:
Xanax, 1 milligram 4 x day
Zyprexa, 7.5 milligrams
Dutonin (possibly reduced during ECT)
Prozac (halted during ECT)

First ECT administered. Nigel had arranged to get into the clinic first thing and try to speak to Braydle before he rushed ahead with it. Nige says when he got there, about 6.30 am, Bek was already in a wheel-chair being taken to have it done. Nige was never given a chance to say a word. Took Jemima in to Bek in the afternoon. She can't remember anything about the ECT. I took her a framed photo of Jemima to put by her bed.

13 January 2000

Medications:
No change

Bek's had second ECT. Spoke to her by phone at 9 this morning. Told me she had a lovely photo of Jemima by her bed and did I know how it got there! Bek's friend Celeste called this morning to ask if it would be okay to visit her. Told her to meet me here at home and we would go in together around 3 pm. At 1 pm, Bek turned up here at the door! Fellow patient Adam was waiting outside in his car. Nathan had been staying at Adam's and was in a 'bad way'. She was on a mission to get him to the hospital for detox. She was talking rapidly, behaving frenetically. Not real sure of the purpose of the visit. Said she'd fed some line to the staff at Ashgrove that Jemima was in hospital so no questions were asked, it seems. She wasn't interested in seeing Jemima, probably just wanted me to back her story.

Dying for a Cure

15 January 2000

Bek's had her third ECT. I'm staying with her and the baby while she's on weekend leave from Ashgrove. Nigel's sailing in the Bay Challenge. Bek's VERY restless. Spent a lot of her time on the phone with Amelia, Adam and Nathan. She appears unaware of social mores: dressing inappropriately for mixed company, lack of modesty and decorum. I cooked a BBQ for tea, with one eye on the baby and the other on Bek.

16 January 2000

Bek went for a run in the morning. Insisted on going out when she got back and drove car despite my pleas to let me take her wherever she wanted to go. Got the feeling she didn't want me to know. Wouldn't say where she'd been upon return. Told her Jemima had been unsettled and missed her. Had little impact. Nigel drove her back to Ashgrove this evening.

17 January 2000

Fourth ECT. I sense a feeling of panic in Bek – making frenetic plans for her future. She's been sending for prospectuses for study! Displaying denial and avoidance of motherhood. Tried to talk her into enjoying her baby and mothering role – there's plenty of time for career plans. Encouraged her to pursue the glassmaking and relax. Said she felt trapped and parenthood made it worse. Urged her to speak to Braydle for counselling about it, with Nigel.

18 January 2000

Visited Bek with baby. She was totally preoccupied with Amelia and Adam and others. It was like we were intruding.

23 January 2000

Fifth and sixth ECTs have been administered. Nigel called, upset, this evening – just as he was getting ready to take Bek back to Ashgrove she had walked out (she's been home on weekend leave again). Drove down to their place and found her wandering the streets.

Had a serious talk with her, said we need to get an opinion independent of Braydle. Gave ultimatum: come with me to a public hospital NOW or see Dan at his surgery tomorrow. She agreed to see Dan.

24 January 2000

Medications:
Prozac, 20 milligrams
Xanax, 4 milligrams
Zyprexa, 7.5 milligrams
Dutonin, 600 milligrams
Sleeping pills (temazepam?)

Braydle saw Bek this morning. Discharged her from Ashgrove and doesn't want her to see him for another three weeks. I don't get it – is he distancing himself? She's worse than I've seen her: excited, agitated, erratic. To see Dan this evening.

pm

Bek admitted to Dan she feels 'unsafe'. He wants her to see someone other than Braydle. Tried to get her in to see a 'trusted colleague' back at Fernview, but found out he's away for two weeks. Explained that we can't wait. He's asked Bek to come and see him every day in the meantime. Bek didn't put up a fuss at Dan's suggestion but I suspect she's just playing along to keep the peace. Dan says there is nothing we can do to force her to sever ties with Braydle. Ultimately it's entirely up to her. I've got to be back at school tomorrow, Celeste to come and sit with Bek. Bek staying the night here tonight, Jemima home with her dad.

26 January 2000

Nigel rang. Bek's left home for a trial separation. He said she packed up a few belongings in the boot of the car and drove off alone. She'd been drinking. Nige and I have rung around her friends, no one's heard from her. Will keep trying to track her down. What does she think she's doing? What about her baby?

SEVEN

'I can't believe how easy that was. I would've been out there all night making a bloody idiot of myself. Probably would've asked an undercover cop and got arrested.'

'Doesn't take long until you know where to go and what to look for.'

'So those people handing out the syringes, are they always there? What's their story?'

'Just trying to stop needle-sharing, I think. Has this car got an interior light?'

'Somewhere, not sure where though. Nigel usually drives this one.'

'On second thoughts, don't worry about it. Those houses aren't far away. Someone might be able to see in. Moonlight'll have to do.'

'Don't spill any.'

'Stop talking then and I won't.'

I watched Nathan carefully measure the fine white powder onto a spoon, add a small amount of water, and heat the mixture from underneath to make it dissolve.

'So, that's how it's done. I'd always wondered. God, it's beautiful here, isn't it? Shame we weren't a bit earlier, could've watched the sun set over the water. How are the houses around here, huh? Bloody mansions. This is my favourite suburb. Always wished –'

'Hey, Bek, can you take a breath? Quiet a minute, you're making me nervous. Here, help me draw this into the needle, like I showed you.'

'Okay . . . there you go. Is that enough?'

'It'll do for now, thanks. Can you just hang on to it for a sec?'

Nathan took off his belt and looped it around his arm. I helped him pull it tight, just above his elbow.

'Now, just hold the syringe directly upright, can you? That's it. Give it a couple of flicks with your finger. Good. Now push a bit out the end. Tiny, tiny, that's it. Okay, give it here.'

Nathan pierced his bulging vein and pushed the syrupy substance into his blood. In what seemed like less than a second, his eyes rolled back and his body slumped in an unconscious heap against the dashboard.

'Shit! Nathan! Oh, shit.'

I jumped out of the car, ran around and opened the passenger door. I slapped the back of his hand, then his face, speaking his name, but not yelling for fear of drawing attention to us. It was clearly futile. I tilted his head back against the headrest. Blood back-washed into the syringe as I plucked it from his arm and put it on the dash. Once satisfied he was at no risk of suffocating or choking, I returned to the driver's seat. I sat for a moment chewing hard on the tip of my forefinger, eyes fixed on the spoon resting on the car's centre console and its remaining glistening pool of liquid heroin. Then, in a decision that under normal circumstances would have been inconceivable to me, I reached for a fresh syringe.

28 January 2000

School secretary paged me in the middle of class today for an urgent phone call. It was Nathan's mother. Told me Bek and he were delivered to her doorstep in the early hours of this morning in the back of a police car. Bek's car was stopped in the middle of the main coastal road with the headlights on. Bek was in the driver's seat, Nathan unconscious next to her. They had both been taking drugs. What, I don't yet know. Can't express how sick I feel about this. I stood there with the receiver to my ear and could barely speak. The second I hung up the phone I started dry retching. Pat just gave me a knowing nod and told me to go and do what I had to do, that she'd take care of my class. Poor kids, seeing me race out panicked like that with no explanation, then the principal stepping in. Nathan's mother expressed great concern for Bek. She was quite emotional. Only wants what's best for her, she said, and that isn't her son. She told me the two of them had taken off at about midday today to an appointment for Bek with a plastic surgeon! Gave me the address. Went over there and found them in the foyer. Bek was extremely pale. I put them both in the car and drove Nathan home. Bek needed me to stop several times so she could vomit. Took her home, put her to bed. Will try and spare Nigel from as much of this as I can.

pm

Just got home from taking Bek to see Dan. The crook of her arm is severely bruised. She tells me it was heroin, just as I'd feared. Dan said we must find her another psychiatrist. He spent four hours on the phone trying to find a hospital bed for her. Tried Fernview again. They phoned Braydle, without our knowledge, and told him what we were planning, then they refused to admit her! Dan then called a Dr Roosfeld, a friend and colleague. The downside, he says, is that he only has clinical rights at one very small hospital. Luckily, though, it's just around the corner from here. He wants to meet Bek there in the morning to assess her at 9 o'clock. I've arranged to take the week off. Don't know how much longer the understanding is going to hold up at work. Nige knows Bek was staying with Nathan and he's really crushed. So far he knows nothing about the drugs. I've just put Bek to bed. Says she wants to cut, cut, cut!

29 January 2000

Nige just phoned to tell me he's off to stay with friends for a while, taking Jemima with him. I don't like the sound of it. There was a lot of resignation in his voice. I pleaded with him not to do anything rash.

I hadn't known that Max had been notified that I was on the lookout for a different psychiatrist. If I had, I would have been on the phone to him at the first chance I got, pleading that I was doing it only under duress from Nigel and Mum and that I had no intention of listening to anything another psychiatrist had to say. The plan was simply to go along with whatever this new guy wanted, hopefully getting the whole thing out of the way by the time I saw Max again at his rooms, still more than a fortnight away. But it wasn't to be quite as simple as that.

After I'd spent the night with Mum, she drove me to Roosfeld's hospital. The place was small and old and smelt like a nursing home. Until a few months prior, it had been a general hospital, providing only limited services to a mainly geriatric clientele. But when a nearby mental health facility closed down it had taken the patients who couldn't be sent home.

A nurse showed me to a consulting room and told me Roosfeld would join me shortly. Mum sat with me and tried to talk away my negativity about being there. When Roosfeld arrived he asked Mum to sit in on the consultation, which I really resented.

Mum told him briefly about the events of the past few months and then about the amount of medication I'd been prescribed. He said flatly that there was no way he could see what he was dealing with while I was on 'all that stuff '. If I wanted his help I'd have to come off it all first, and that would have to be done as an inpatient.

'No,' I said emphatically. 'There's no way I'd cope.'

'I'd hardly say you're coping now, from what I've just heard. And have you looked at yourself in the mirror lately? You look terrible. There is no way I can know if I'm talking to the drugs or the person when there's this much medication involved. Gosh, look at what we have: two antidepressants, *Dutonin* and *Prozac*; a tranquilliser, *Xanax*; an antipsychotic, *Zyprexa*; and sleeping pills. No, I would need to have a clean slate and we could always build up from there. If we needed to.'

I hated him. Where had this self-righteous fool been during the last decade? Hadn't he heard about chemical imbalances? I didn't want to go backwards with some non-drug therapy from the sixties. I needed to try more drug options if anything. And how dare he contradict Max's treatment.

'I'd at least have to stay on something for the anxiety. There's no way I can do without something for the anxiety.'

'All right, we could talk about keeping up the Xanax, but we'd start reducing the antidepressants immediately. The *Zyprexa* would be next. I've no idea what you're on that for.'

If only I had had faith in Roosfeld's advice. Little did I know his recommendations and observations were the soundest, safest, most accurate I would hear. If I had listened, this story would have been much, much shorter.

He told us to go home and think about it, and if we decided to go ahead just to come back that evening. The minute we were in the car I told Mum to forget about it. I think she had cringed at Roosfeld's frankness and had wished he hadn't been so upfront so soon with his plans to take me off everything. She desperately wanted me to give him a go. She tried everything that afternoon to persuade me, from reasoning to bribery and eventually to threats. She confessed her fears that Nigel was a whisker away from leaving me and taking Jemima.

'You could lose them both, you know, the way you're going!' Her frustration broke her temper. She grabbed me by both shoulders, faced me head on and said with forced control:

'If you continue like this you could lose your baby. Don't you realise how dire this is?'

I shook free of her grip and headed for the door.

'And I tell you what,' she added, out of sheer desperation, 'I'll have no qualms supporting Nigel in a bid for custody if you don't start –'

I fiercely slammed the door and set off running, expending the fury that had so nearly just compelled me to hit my mother. And if I had started, would I have stopped? I feared not.

I hadn't recognised Mum's final statement as a bluff armouring her fear, but instead saw it as one of the most hurtful things a mother could threaten her daughter with. By the time I had come to rest propped against a lamppost a few kilometres down the road, I began to recognise it as a distinct possibility, and started thinking in overdrive how I could get away with a stay in someone else's hospital without Max cottoning on. I decided I could make it work because Roosfeld and Max had no apparent professional contact. When Mum had asked if he would be wanting to access Max's records, Roosfeld had said he'd rather be able to make up his own mind. So, I returned to Mum and, to her outwardly evident relief, yielded. I was taken back to Roosfeld's hospital that night.

Upon check-in I was asked to empty my bag of anything sharp and to give an assurance I wasn't hiding anything else to harm myself with. The nurse left with my hand mirror and some hairpins. When she brought me my medications that evening the antidepressants were cut by half.

The stay there was gruelling. As the antidepressants started to leave my system, I began to feel horrible. My anxiety intensified and for no apparent reason I would descend into intense crying spells. I had even more trouble than usual trying to sleep, and when I did I had awful, vivid nightmares. I became hypersensitive to light and sound. I couldn't eat because I was constantly nauseous. Despite all this, each day I'd tell staff I was fine. I wanted to give no reason to be kept there beyond the end of the week. I interpreted these symptoms as a re-emergence of my depression, which only reinforced my view that Roosfeld had no idea what he was doing.

Contributing to the popularity of SSRIs (and related antidepressants) is the belief that they are non-addictive, a belief to which even Roosfeld seemed to adhere, and a belief drug companies seem only too happy to circulate. 'There is no evidence that *Zoloft* [*Lustral*] is addictive,' asserts its patient information leaflet, for example.[1] But anyone thinking that's an assurance that stopping an SSRI will be easy should think again: in reality it can be a nightmare. Over the past eight to ten years an active online community has emerged, sharing experiences of withdrawal and offering advice to people who want to quit SSRIs – advice that might have been invaluable to me, had I known of its existence. Regarding sertraline (*Lustral*, also known as *Zoloft*):

Thank God for finding this site and your messages. I have been on sertraline for just over a year. [My doctor] advised a reduction of half of what I was taking for two weeks, then half again every other day for a week . . . It wasn't too bad at first . . . but by the third day my side effects have been: constant dizziness, irritability, disturbed sleep, racing thoughts . . . strange feeling in my chest, as if I am about to have a panic attack . . . lack of concentration, tired . . .crying . . . vulnerable/scared, anxious and have suicidal thoughts when the crying starts. [My] GP told me . . . that I could stop *Lustral* without any side effects. Took the last one on Thursday and by Sunday I felt like I was about to have a breakdown. Felt scared, shaky, utterly hopeless, crying, couldn't concentrate.

Regarding citalopram (*Cipramil*, also known as *Celexa*):

I started to wean off *Celexa* three weeks ago . . . I feel serious tingling and numbness throughout my body, dizziness, rapid heartbeat, and chest pain. It is very difficult to concentrate, and I find myself reacting strangely to normal events – laughing at inappropriate things and overreacting. It is so good to hear that my withdrawal symptoms are experienced by others. You all even use the same words I use when I try to describe it: numbness, dizziness, electric shocks, headaches, hot flashes, inability to concentrate, rapid heartbeat, mood swings, etc. I also have been shivering and am really sensitive to light. Went down from 20 mg to 10 mg for two weeks then stopped. Had intense mood swings and anger, then this week started with palpitations and chest pain, plus that awful electric shock feeling. Just knowing other people have had these symptoms is a HUGE relief.

And paroxetine (known as *Aropax*, *Paxil* and *Seroxat*):

Twenty-two days off *Seroxat* and counting . . . has been a roller-coaster ride going from 20 mg to nil and would not recommend it! Weeks two and three were worst – daily mood swings from hysteria and anger, down to tears and despair. I have been on *Seroxat* for about 11 months, the past two I have been reducing down from 50 mg. I am now only on 5 mg and still feel dizzy all the time and get those head judders. I am also suffering with terrible mood swings and I have zero tolerance with my family. In fact, these symptoms are causing me to feel anxious that I am mad and dangerous. Would love to hear from anyone as feeling quite desperate.[2]

Paxilprogress.org, a website offering advice on how to manage withdrawal from all major SSRIs, gets about two million hits a month.[3]

Because the symptoms of SSRI withdrawal can mimic the symptoms the drug was prescribed for in the first place, there is a huge risk of withdrawal being mistaken for relapse.

I made no secret of my hatred for Roosfeld's hospital, made worse by the fact that there was very little to do there to distract me from how terrible I felt. 'Even if you only have to go there to sleep,' said Mum, 'Bek, please hang in there.' Extending her summer break, she'd pick me up each morning after breakfast and medications and drop me back in time for the evening equivalents. There was no contact from Nige.

2 February 2000

Have been picking up Bek from Roosfeld's each day. Bringing her home for lunch. Took her to the pool for a swim – she seems to need the intensive activity to burn off all the restless energy. Took her for a walk in the park. But today – today was horrendous. When it was time to take her back to the hospital she begged me, she yelled, she cried, she tried persuasion of every kind to stop me. She called me everything under the sun. Said I don't understand what she's going through, how cruel Roosfeld is, how terrible it is to have to go without her medication. That it's like being in a prison. When she lay on the ground in the driveway screaming hysterically, clinging to my legs, begging, pleading with me to please not take her back to that place, I thought I was going to break. But I knew I had to get her back there. This is probably her last chance, her only chance to get away from that bastard Braydle, to get her life back.

But Roosfeld was less able to resist my pleas. After only four days, before he'd had the chance to withdraw me from all he'd have liked to, he let me go home, though only after I agreed that I would see him twice a week at his rooms.

To my surprise Nigel turned up to take me home. Very luckily for me, a spell away from the situation and the intense persuasion of his friends had boosted him with a new determination to stick things out. Postnatal depression is transient, they had worked hard at reminding him. One day this will all be nothing but a nasty memory. They'd helped him to distance himself enough to gain some rational perspective – they were right, everything he'd heard, everything he'd read said that postnatal depression can sometimes last a year or more, but it will end; every bit of literature, anyone he'd spoken to, promised that. *Transient, transient* – whenever he needed strength the word became his mantra. So he had returned, suspending his current feelings towards me and replacing them with the recollection of all that was, not so very long ago, so wonderful between us. But instead of gushing gratitude, as was probably warranted, I was bereft of care. The only time we spoke during the half-hour trip home was when I asked Nige to stop in at a chemist.

'What for?' he wanted to know.

'I just have to collect a prescription for some *Xanax*,' I lied.

'But they just gave you some at the hospital. I saw them.'

'Yeah, but not enough,' I said, detesting his scrutiny. 'Only a few days' worth. I can't risk running out of them. They're all I've got.'

Too energy-depleted to argue, Nige pulled up at the pharmacy near home. I went in and used one of Max's old prescriptions to get *Prozac*. Good, now I could increase the dosage to what it should be.

I dumped my bag on the lounge-room floor at home and went to the kitchen to put on the kettle. On the table was a stack of mail addressed to me that had accumulated while I'd been gone. I picked up the first envelope, opened it and scanned the enclosed contents. It was from the child sponsorship charity I volunteered for, asking me to work some shifts in support of one of their major annual fundraisers. It was a cause for which I held great passion, and typically I'd respond to such a request by offering as much of my time as I could spare. But now I carelessly scrunched up the page and tossed it aside. I walked my fingers through the remaining stack – mobile-phone bill . . . bank statement . . .

What's this one? From Max's rooms? I tore it open as fast as my hands would allow. It read:

> Dear Rebekah, I understand that you no longer require my services and that you are currently in hospital under the care of another psychiatrist. If required, I would be happy to send any relevant records to your new treating psychiatrist. I wish you well. Max

No! Oh God, what have I done?

'How did he find out about Roosfeld?' I screamed at Nigel, thrusting the letter in his face.

'How did who find out about Roosfeld?'

'Max, of course. Like you fucking don't know. That was the plan, was it? Get Bek out of the way while you organise her fucking life. Was it you and Mum, or just Mum?'

'Bek, I've got no idea how he found out.'

'Well, anyway, you've got what you wanted. He's dumped me. Happy now?'

For a few moments I worked at composing myself, then I took our cordless phone away from Nigel's earshot and dialled Max's rooms. I recognised the voice that answered as his wife's. She worked a few days a week on reception.

'Hello, it's Rebekah Beddoe speaking, one of Dr Braydle's pa –'

'Yes, Rebekah.' She was curt.

'There seems to be a misunderstanding. I've just received a letter from him saying that he thinks I no longer want to be his patient, but that's not the case.'

'Rebekah, you've made it quite clear you're no longer interested in seeing Max. You've been missing appointments.'

'What?'

'We can't keep you on as a patient if you miss appointments – it's as simple as that. There are other very sick people who are missing out –'

'I haven't missed any appointments. My next one's more than a week away.' My voice was raised and quivering.

'You're no longer Max's patient, Rebekah.'

'Let me speak to Max,' I demanded. 'Put me on to Max!'

'Goodbye, Rebekah.'

I threw the phone to the floor, splitting its casing in two. I leant into the wall, thumping at it with my fists, crying through clenched teeth. Nigel came in, took a wide berth around me, and quietly began to pick up the pieces of phone.

Suddenly and hopefully I realised that I must still have the appointment card in my purse or my bag and I began searching for it frantically.

'A-ha,' I declared, when I finally retrieved it. 'I knew it! It's not till the fourteenth. Here, it says so, in that bitch's own handwriting.'

Nigel just nodded as he reassembled the phone.

I sat at the computer to write Max a letter explaining the whole misunderstanding. It was obvious his wife and keeper was not going to put my calls through. I was baffled by what had happened but was theorising that Mum must have played some part in it. But why had Max reacted so abruptly and why was his wife making things up about me missing appointments?

In fact, Mum had had nothing to do with Max finding out about Roosfeld. He had somehow been informed, very rapidly, by his network of colleagues.

Max phoned me the day he received my letter. I burst into tears, explaining that I had only ever wanted him as my doctor and begging to be allowed an appointment. He agreed and scheduled me in that week.

Seeing Max again was nothing like I'd anticipated. There was no mistaking an uncharacteristic aloofness about him. I knew immediately something was amiss when instead of greeting me in the waiting room when it was time for me to go in, he simply called my name from the doorway of his office. He told me to take a seat, but he remained standing. He lifted from his bookcase a thick hardbound text. Opening it to a page he had marked, he placed it in my lap. He pointed to the heading

'Borderline Personality Disorder' and told me to read.

> A Borderline Personality is characterised by a pervasive pattern
> of instability and maladaptive behaviours that often prohibits the
> person from leading a constructive and successful life. Typical
> behaviours of this disorder are self-mutilation, attention-seeking
> suicide attempts, promiscuous sexual behaviour and substance
> abuse. A person with this disorder generally has a difficult time
> in maintaining interpersonal relationships, which are inclined to
> be torrid and dysfunctional. They are often distrustful of people
> close to them as a result of abuse, neglect or abandonment as a
> child and will make frantic attempts to avoid rejection. They are
> prone to hysteria, outbursts of rage and fluctuating moods and
> can suffer from paranoia and delusions.[4]

This disorder tends to be regarded with disdain by psychiatrists, due to
its reputation as 'difficult'. As claimed by psychotherapist Dana Becker
in her book *Through the Looking Glass*, 'There is no other diagnosis
currently in use that has the intense pejorative connotations that have
been attached to the borderline personality disorder diagnosis.'[5]

After finishing the passage I looked up at Max, 'You don't think that
I –'

'I do,' he jumped in. 'There's at least five criteria you meet: the self-
harm, the suicide attempts, your relationship with Nigel and Jemima,
the drugs, your moods.'

I stared at him, incredulous. He'd never been one to label, yet now
here he was chafing at the bit to brand me with this, this tragic-sounding
condition that I knew I didn't have.

I searched frantically for the compassion usually brimming in his
eyes, but it was dead. My heart swelled with pain, which I instinctively
snap-froze and stuffed in a remote chasm somewhere deep inside. I
asked him for some prescriptions to tide me over then walked from his
office for the last time. He made no effort to keep me there, even though
it was forty minutes short of the session's end. So much for there being
nothing I could do to make him shun me.

EIGHT

I had no desire to continue seeing Roosfeld – I remained terrified about how bad I would be off medication – so I went back with Nigel to see Dan Reubans. The psychiatrist at Fernview, with whom Reubans had originally tried to get me an appointment, had returned from leave. Upon Dan's urgent request, he agreed to see me. He observed and spoke to me for fewer than about ten minutes when he excused himself, picked up the phone and spoke with the psychiatrist in the neighbouring suite.

'I really don't mean to fob you off,' he explained, 'but postnatal issues are really not my forte. You'd do far better to have a word with Dr Maarsten next door. He says he can see you now.'

Dr Maarsten looked after patients in Fernview's mother–baby unit, the ward I had stayed on a couple of months earlier. He was about forty years old, tall, with dark hair waxed obediently back from his forehead. He had wayward eyebrows which I bet, considering his otherwise conservative look, he probably wished he could wax into shape too. His office was spartan, austere, embellished only with framed degrees and various other qualifications – not at all the comfy haven of Max's – and the minute he spoke, his cool, insipid voice told me he had a demeanour to match his decor. I did not want to become this guy's patient. Acknowledging, though, that I was bankrupt of bargaining power, I foraged for consolation in apparent pluses: he worked in a major psychiatric hospital with a dedicated unit for mothers and their babies, and he had specialist training in postnatal mental illness.

Maarsten sat in his Argyle-knit jumper and beige trousers, watching me closely as I paced about the room, propping myself intermittently on my chair, before jumping up and moving about again. I was ranting about everything being hopeless and how I was going to die, hysterically begging him to help and really Maarsten wasn't able to perform a proper assessment.

'Can you verbalise what it is you are feeling right now?' he asked slowly and deliberately. I didn't like him. I didn't know if I could trust him. He wasn't Max. I wanted Max!

'Is she always this anxious?' He deferred to Nigel in the hope of getting some sense.

'Sometimes she's worse than others,' Nige offered. 'She's all over the place now, though.'

I was admitted to the mother–baby unit on the spot. Nigel went home to collect Jemima and pack me some clothes.

28 February 2000

Medications:
Prozac, 20 milligrams

Bek's been admitted back to Fernview, with the baby. She's under the care of a Dr Maarsten. Dan didn't know him or his reputation personally but he's in some senior position there. He's stripped the medication right back to just *Prozac* – which Bek admitted she'd increased again almost as soon as she'd left Roosfeld's place – and has said that if Bek really feels she can't cope she can have some *Valium*. She seems to have accepted that okay, though I don't think she'd be capable of challenging anything at the moment even if she wanted to. I'd still rather she wasn't on anything, but at least this is better than it has been. Oh, thank God, perhaps things are finally going to start looking up.

Nigel's still very badly bruised about the whole thing with Nathan. Had him over for dinner last night and gave him a bit of a pep talk. He's not very happy that Bek's back in hospital but he's very glad she's away from Braydle. And I'll certainly second that. I think it's best that she's in there because at least the rest of us can get some semblance of order back in our lives. And it's a good thing she's going to be made to be with her baby under professional supervision.

Maarsten had a nurse photocopy me some handouts with techniques for combating panic attacks and reducing anxiety levels. They instructed how to slow your breathing to three counts in, three counts out, and how to use positive self-talk and visualisation. There was a relaxation class held in the unit every morning that he told me I must attend. I asked for some *Valium* or *Xanax*. He told me that first I needed to try to get a handle on things myself. But I couldn't make him understand. It wasn't like I was nervous about *something*. There was no identifiable trigger for this anxiety, this agitation, this bad energy that had been fluctuating through me for the past few months. It was just there, planted, sometimes more intensely than others. It filled my body with friction; a nasty driving force that at its most nagging compelled me to move about in order to get some relief.

There was never any mention of 'akathisia' from Maarsten as he struggled to understand the elusive cause of my agitation. Drug-induced akathisia is typically recognised as a side effect of the older type of antipsychotic drugs (neuroleptics) used, among other things, for treating psychosis. But it is also now associated with newer psychiatric drugs including SSRIs.[1] Mild akathisia can give the feeling of being over caffeinated. But, in its severest form, drug-induced akathisia is a living hell; an absolutely unendurable feeling of being tortured from the inside out. It strikes the patient physically and mentally. One of the best clinical descriptions of drug-induced akathisia I've ever read comes from Australian psychiatrist Andrew Firestone in a letter to the *British Medical Journal*:

Akathisia is often mistaken for anxiety and can even present as insomnia. Mental and physical symptoms shade into one another in akathisia in a way foreign to normal experience. The characteristic restlessness is often accompanied by mental distress; while a terrible sense of dread may be felt as abdominal discomfort. To experience this for the first time, unaware that this is a readily corrected drug side effect, is frightening. Depressed or psychotic patients can consider suicide, mistaking akathisia for further deterioration.[2]

Peter Breggin very accurately describes it as like being tortured from inside your own body by your own nervous system. Other than in rare neurological disorders or in the aftermath of epidemics of encephalitis lethargica, akathisia is drug-induced and always iatrogenic (caused by medical treatment).[3] The problem was labelled akathisia when it was observed by two German psychiatrists in 1955.[4] According to David Healy in *Let Them Eat Prozac*, this is an unfortunate choice of terms as akathisia translates to mean simply 'the inability to sit still'.[5] Although compulsive walking, shuffling of the legs and rocking from foot to foot are the most outwardly obvious symptoms, they don't even begin to indicate the extent of suffering caused by akathisia. The *Collins Dictionary of Medicine* defines akathisia as: 'The inability to sit still quietly because of uncontrollable movements caused by drugs.' There's not a mention of the neurological torment it causes on the inside.

For some unfortunates, often those who have taken psychiatric medication over many months or years, the affliction can become chronic.

Not more than about a week after my admission to Fernview, I was battling to surface from a cesspool of vivid, brutal obsessions. As I brushed my teeth a depraved savagery spurred me to smash them from my mouth; as I brushed my hair, to rip it from my scalp in bloody clumps. It wanted to gouge, stab, bite. It wanted pleadings for mercy. Thus far it only had me in its sights, but how long until it recognised Jemima as more vulnerable prey? I would not go near her alone. Her nappies would stay soiled, her little tummy empty, until Nigel or Mum was present; if the savagery struck at least they could intervene.

I spent every waking moment in the communal kitchen or lounge area, anywhere I could have company. At night I would beg the nurses to take Jemima from my room and sleep her in the nursery.

The more I withdrew from my child, the more intent the staff became on making me interact with her. Maarsten ordered me to spend at least one half hour alone with her each day. Knowing this equated to leaving my baby in the care of a wild and ravenous beast, I pleaded with him to reconsider. He pressed his fingers to his mouth as he silently debated how to deal with one of the most serious incidences of a depressed mother rejecting her child he'd seen in a while. He finally agreed to nurse supervision – 'to begin with,' he clarified.

I told Maarsten of the compelling urges to cause myself pain. I reiterated, 'I knew just *Prozac* wasn't going to be enough.'

He agreed, and added regular doses of clonazepam, a drug similar to *Valium*, but stronger and more addictive.

Prozac has long been thought to cause exactly the kind of feelings I was trying to describe to Maarsten. As far back as 1990 American clinical researchers Teicher, Glod and Cole were hypothesising about how antidepressants induced suicidal thoughts, after they observed that six people participating in a *Prozac* trial developed intense, violent suicidal preoccupations after brief exposure to the drug.[6]

One year later, in 1991, another pair of researchers, Rothschild and Locke, reported three cases of patients who made serious suicide attempts while taking *Prozac*, then recovered when it was stopped. To determine if *Prozac* was the cause, the three patients resumed taking the drug under close observation. They developed exactly the same urges and distressing feelings that had precipitated their original suicide attempts.[7]

Teicher and his colleagues considered the responses might have been due to a specific serotonin reaction caused by a sudden increase in serotonin transmission. Upon further evaluation they proposed specific clinical mechanisms by which antidepressants can induce or exacerbate suicidal tendencies. These included:

- paradoxically worsening depression
- inducing akathisia

- inducing panic attacks
- switching patients into manic states
- inducing an obsessional state
- producing a personality disorder with borderline features.

These findings were published in a 1993 edition of the journal *Drug Safety*. In the same article the researchers state that their 'observations suggest that antidepressants may *redistribute* [italics mine] suicide risk, attenuating risk in some patients who respond well, while possibly enhancing risk in others who respond more poorly.'[8]

Yet it has taken well over a decade for information regarding the links SSRIs have with akathisia and suicide to get into general circulation.

When David Healy conducted his *Lustral* 'healthy volunteer' study (mentioned in chapter five) it was to see whether SSRIs could make emotionally stable people 'better than well'. When two of the female subjects became obsessionally suicidal he was determined to discover just how this completely unexpected result had occurred. Nothing on the pre-trial personality or social-functioning tests had indicated any abnormality in either subject. If anything their results had shown lower than average traces of depressive thinking. But neither subject had actually become depressed on *Lustral*, so what had made them want to kill themselves? Neither of them suffered akathisia either, but both had become markedly disinhibited (impulsively acting on thoughts or whims without regard for consequences), so perhaps that was it?

After an exhaustive analysis of their findings, the cause of the women's abrupt emergence of suicidal thinking continued to elude Healy and his team. Something that was emphasised by the consequences of the study was the potential long-term injury that can be caused by making someone suicidal. Both study subjects remained disturbed several months beyond the study's end; both seriously questioned the stability of their personalities. Their view of themselves had been severely shaken. Incredibly, even though the entire incident had occurred over a relatively short period of time (four weeks), both women had trouble accepting that it had been the drug, and only the drug, that had caused their experience. 'Even I,' writes Healy, 'watching from the outside and committed firmly to the idea that when this happened on drugs, it was caused by the drugs, found myself pulled by a strange attractor. Surely, someone in whom this had happened must have something wrong with her to begin with, some disorder in her personality.'[9]

◆◆◆◆◆◆

After more than three weeks in hospital, Maarsten was keen to send me home. He read my opposition as a lack of confidence due to having spent too much time in hospital since Jemima's birth and not enough time at home learning how to be a mother. I was becoming 'institution-alised', he said. The more I resisted, the keener he was to get me out of there.

I didn't even make it through the first few days at home before I took to my arm again with pieces from a smashed glass. Nigel forced me to phone Maarsten.

'Why did you do that to yourself?' he asked.

'I told you it would happen,' was all I could say.

Sounding exasperated, he asked me to put Nigel on the phone.

'Does it have to be with the baby?' I heard Nigel ask. 'All right. I'll get them back in there tonight.' He slammed the phone down into its cradle, swiped the car keys from the table and plucked Jemima from her high chair.

'I gotta get outta here for a bit,' he said without looking at me. 'You'd better get your things packed again.'

1 April 2000

Medications:
Prozac, 20 milligrams
Clonazepam, 1 milligram 4 x day

Went to visit Bek today, unannounced. The other mothers had gone out for a walk but she wasn't allowed. Yesterday she'd gone to the

pharmacy across the road and come back with a razor. She'd been
with another patient at the time who alerted a nurse to what she'd
done. She's now not allowed to leave the premises and Maarsten's
trying to get her into the high-dependency ward there. That would
mean she'd be in without Jemima and, I have to say, in a way that
comes as a bit of a relief. I know I'm getting nervous about Bek being
around the baby at the moment and I'm pretty sure Nige is too. But
it's going to make things logistically hard to manage. If Nige takes any
more time off in this new job he's likely to lose it. Tried calling around
some child-care centres today but there are no places. Waiting on a
call back from the local council about the possibility of family day care.
Bek's old work friend Nancy has generously offered to have Jemima
on her days off. Told her that would be a huge help in the meantime.
Celeste has said that she would do what she could too, if required.
Bek's got a couple of wonderful friends in those two.

Nigel came into the hospital and took Jemima home. I was escorted by
a nurse up the hallway of the mother–baby unit, about to discover first-
hand what lay beyond the two heavy doors that had intrigued me on my
first stay at Fernview.

All the other unit mothers, bar one, watched silently as I was ban-
ished to the other realm. Conspicuously keeping to herself was the one
who'd turned me in.

The nurse pressed a PIN code into the panel on the first heavy door
and ushered me through into a small hallway. Not until the first door
had clicked shut did he unlock the next.

Inside was a small common area with two sofas and a coffee table. Six
bedrooms opened off it, as did a couple of shared bathrooms. The nurses sat
within what could best be described as a small central viewing room. No
other patients were to be seen. Presumably they were all in their rooms.

Although the HDU was on the top floor, it had the distinct feel of a
bomb shelter. The only windows, which were in the bedrooms, were
made of some sort of reinforced frosted glass and they didn't let in
much light, nor could they be opened to let in any fresh air. The artificial
lighting, which thankfully was not fluorescent, was always turned low,

giving a constant feel of evening. The only television was mounted high in one corner of the common area on an angle that made watching it for any extended period of time uncomfortable. The constant drone of the air conditioning unit made it impossible to hear it anyway.

My room was scantily furnished with a single bed and wardrobe. The linoleum floor continued halfway up the walls. One small high-set window taunted of a world beyond the hospital walls, which was rapidly leaving me behind.

I was ordered to upend both my overnight bag and handbag on the bed and the nurse sifted through my belongings, confiscating anything with which I could conceivably do any harm to myself. That included my credit and ATM cards, driver's licence – even my tube of toothpaste was locked away: when I needed it I had to ask. Patients in HDU were cut off from the rest of the hospital. The days were long and eventless. The only thing to break the monotony was being escorted out onto the balcony of a neighbouring ward a few times a day for a smoke. Amelia had been right: by now I was relishing my cigarettes – much to the dismay of all those who knew me – and I would chain-smoke three in the fifteen minutes before being led back to my room.

Mum, who felt that taking up smoking paled into insignificance against the background of other things I was doing, was happy to keep up my supply. Nigel, who didn't discriminate much between nicotine and any other drug, considered my new-found habit completely repugnant.

Before I had ever had any personal experience with psychiatrists I had imagined they would be experts in human behaviour. I expected they would be highly skilled in reading body language, interpreting subconscious action and deciphering the nuances and idiosyncrasies in a person's expression and character, which would enable them to get to know their patient better than the patient knew themselves. I had thought that they would prescribe drugs only as a last resort for those who were so mentally ill they were beyond rationalisation.

In *Toxic Psychiatry* Peter Breggin explains why the reality of my psychiatric treatment was so different from how I had thought it would be:

> Many people continue to think of the psychiatrist as the wise, warm and caring person who will help them tackle their problems. But the modern psychiatrist may have no interest in 'talking therapy'. His or her entire training and commitment is more likely devoted to 'medical diagnosis' and 'physical treatment'. He or she may look at you with all the empathy and understanding of a pathologist staring through a microscope at germs and then offer you a drug . . . The next time you go to a psychiatrist, you may find yourself in the office of someone who has never been taught how to talk with you about your problems . . . Nor has he or she been trained to understand personal and family conflicts.[10]

Gil Anaf, president of Australia's National Association of Practising Psychiatrists, is concerned that the new generation of psychiatrists is 'being exposed less and less to the good results of [psycho]therapy and more and more to the average results of medication'. Soon, he laments, 'it's going to be the norm to prescribe, as if there's never been anything else.'[11]

Maarsten was obviously a 'new generation' of psychiatrist. He seemed in his element when I was in the HDU. He'd breeze in, ask me how I was and observe me for a minute or so, then spend the rest of the time speaking to the nurses about me. Sometimes he would then phone and speak to Nigel too, without my knowledge.

In addition to *Prozac* and clonazepam, he introduced *Mellaril* (thioridazine), explaining that it would calm me. Encouraged by this promise, I ardently welcomed its prescription. *Mellaril* is one of the older-style antipsychotic drugs discovered in the fifties – the type of tranquillising drugs injected into violent psychotic patients to subdue them. As explained a little earlier, these drugs are notorious for causing akathisia in its most severe form. Antipsychotics are typically prescribed for schizophrenia and mania associated with bipolar disorder. They include *Largactil* (chlorpromazine), *Mellaril* (thioridazine), *Stelazine* (trifluoperazine) and *Haldol* (haloperidol).Some of the newer antipsychotics, known as atypicals, are *Zyprexa* (olanzapine), *Seroquel* (quetiapine), *Clozaril* (clozapine) and *Risperdal* (risperidone).

Whereas the SSRIs work to increase the availability of the brain chemical serotonin, antipsychotic drugs work predominantly by suppressing the effects of another of the brain's chemicals, dopamine. It has been hypothesised that an excess of dopamine is the cause of psychosis. But this, just like the serotonin theory of depression, is speculative since it is not possible to measure dopamine levels in the brain.

Peter Breggin and David Cohen in *Your Drug May Be Your Problem* explain that these drugs have no specific effects on delusions or hallucinations, but that they 'work' by blunting the highest functions of the brain in the frontal lobes and closely connected basal ganglia. They describe how these impairments result in relative degrees of apathy, indifference, emotional blandness and conformity. 'It is no exaggeration to call this a chemical lobotomy.'[12] Antipsychotic drugs are also referred to as 'neuroleptics', which translates literally to 'brain seize': brain (neuro) leptic (seize).

In relation to the SSRIs, Breggin and Cohen describe a mechanism known as down-regulation, by which it is possible that the brain 'fights back' in response to the abnormal increase in serotonin caused by the drug. Starting with the first dose, writes Breggin, the cells that produce serotonin may begin to shut down and stop releasing serotonin. Additionally, it may be that the brain compensates by becoming less sensitive to the effects of serotonin.[13] With antipsychotic drugs, which aim to decrease the effects of dopamine, it is likely that the brain readjusts by upregulating, making the dopamine system hypersensitive.[14] With prolonged treatment the brain may actually begin to physically change. Neuroscientists are discovering that long-term therapy with psychoactive drugs has the potential to alter not only the function but the anatomy of the human brain.[15]

These changes can result in some devastating neurological disorders. As well as akathisia, antipsychotic treatment commonly causes another hideous condition known as tardive dyskinesia.[16] Tardive dyskinesia (TD) involves irreversible abnormal movements of any of the involuntary muscles of the body. It is often characterised by repetitive involuntary movements of the tongue, face, mouth or jaw: for example, protrusion of the tongue, puffing of the cheeks, puckering of the mouth, or chewing movements.[17] It can also affect the hands, arms, feet and torso and sometimes impairs speech. The drugs actually suppress the condition as it is developing and it may not be discovered until the dosage is reduced.[18]

I have met some people who will be permanently affected with TD. One very beautiful 35-year-old mother of two, who was treated with an antipsychotic to quell mania, now speaks as though she is spastic, and her head and hands constantly shake with Parkinsonism.

With these drug-induced effects in mind, plus the ones mentioned earlier regarding akathisia, just try now to conjure up the stereotypical image of the mental patient: jigging from foot to foot, pacing back and forth furiously, pushing their tongue through their teeth, eyes twitching . . .

In addition to these 'movement disorders', antipsychotic use is associated with: weight gain; hyperlipidemia (an abnormal increase in blood-fat levels, often leading to coronary heart disease); diabetes;[19] respiratory disorders; and respiratory disease.[20] It is also known to cause raised prolactin levels (a hormonal imbalance that can lead to infertility);[21] a potentially fatal blood abnormality (clozapine);[22] and neuroleptic malignant syndrome, a potentially fatal disease of the brain with effects similar to those of severe viral encephalitis.[23] The results of an extensive, six-year-long study published in the June 2004 issue of the *Archives of Internal Medicine* reinforce a long-standing suspicion that antipsychotic drugs can damage the heart. The study revealed that patients treated with antipsychotics were at a threefold increased risk of sudden cardiac death – the elevated risk existing even among those on low doses.[24]

Many believe that the newer antipsychotics, the atypicals, are more effective than their older counterparts and are less likely to cause such serious side effects. However, a team of researchers at Oxford University conducted a comprehensive review of fifty-two clinical trials, involving more than 12,500 participants, comparing the new antipsychotics with the old ones, and determined that: 'There is no clear evidence that atypical antipsychotics are more effective or are better tolerated than conventional antipsychotics.'[25]

Antipsychotics have been described as some of the most lethal drugs in medicine.[26] 'With the possible exception of chemotherapies . . . it would be difficult to identify a class of medications as toxic as the antipsychotics.'[27]

Incredibly, one prominent clinical researcher and antipsychotic enthusiast admits, 'Neither normal volunteers nor patients find antipsychotics pleasant; in both populations they are associated with a plethora of unpleasant subjective effects . . .'[28] Such an open acknowledgement prompts the crucial question: in whose interests, then, are these drugs prescribed?

Beyond casting doubt on Max's diagnosis of borderline personality disorder, Maarsten held back on speculating what I was suffering from. In a desperate search for some answers, the microscope was turned again on other members of my family in hope of some clues. There was my grandfather and his drinking as a form of stress release – had he been depressed? Then there was his half-brother's suspected suicide. My father would also sometimes drink heavily, so could that mean he was masking depression?

I declared these suspicions to all who asked and it ended up being documented that I had a strong family history of mental illness. This piece of conjecture only served to conceal further what was really going on with me and bolster the foundations for more erroneous conclusions to be drawn.

Mum and I were intent on searching for evidence of a possible hereditary cause for my state of mind because we, like many others, thought that scientists were closing in on finding the genes responsible for mental illness. In the case of illnesses like schizophrenia I thought the gene had been discovered.

The strongest evidence supporting a hereditary link in mental illness has come from studies comparing fraternal and identical twins. The findings have shown that if one identical twin has been diagnosed as schizophrenic then the other twin has a 35 to 50 per cent chance of also developing the disorder. In the case of same-sex fraternal twins the rate was shown to be much lower, at around 7 to 14 per cent. This is generally accepted as strong evidence of a genetic factor in schizophrenia.[29]

However, Jay Joseph, clinical psychologist and prolific author on the subject of genetic research in psychiatry, writes:

> As three generations of critics have argued, the twin method is an environmentally confounded research technique which is unable to disentangle possible genetic and environmental factors. Thus, any conclusions in favour of genetic influences on psychiatric conditions . . . derived from [this] method should be disregarded.[30] . . . No genes have been found that cause the major psychiatric disorders. Unfortunately, it is widely believed that such genes have been discovered.[31]

Prominent psychiatric genetic researcher Kenneth Kendler voices the collective disappointment of scientists, whom the discovery of genes responsible for psychiatric illness has eluded for more than two decades, in a 2005 article published in the *American Journal of Psychiatry*:

> The strong, clear, and direct causal relationship implied by the concept of 'a gene for . . .' does not exist for psychiatric disorders. Although we may wish it to be true, we do not have and are not likely to ever discover 'genes for' psychiatric illness.[32]

So why, then, do the general public believe the exact opposite to be true? According to Jay Joseph, a major reason is that the media tend to report 'gene discoveries' for abnormal behaviour and psychiatric disorders, but pay little attention to, or fail to report entirely, replication failures and retractions.[33] Therefore people are led to believe that initial positive reports, which later turn out to be unsubstantiated, are actual gene findings.

In Fernview's HDU there was great incentive to behave and comply and get out quickly for good behaviour. The mood in there was oppressive. Patients stayed in their rooms, only coming out for meals, to use the bathroom, or to be taken for a smoke. The staff-to-patient ratio was 1:2 – three staff and six patients. Most of the nurses were men, with the occasional female filling in a shift here and there. Wayne, who unfortunately was rostered on most days, had a sadistic streak. He seemed to find it satisfying to play little games, such as waking up patients for no apparent reason or 'forgetting' to inform us that the dinner trolley had arrived until the food was cold. He was prone to forgetting our cigarette breaks too. He liked to do things that would make patients' behaviour look bizarre to the other staff, knowing full well it was likely to delay their discharge back to the regular ward.

At the start of one of his shifts, with no legitimate reason he demanded that all patients store their bags in a shared locker in the common area. That night when I requested access so I could get ready for bed, he refused. When I challenged him on it he pulled a packet of paracetamol out of his pocket and placed it on my bedside table. 'I might just have to let your doctor know, then, about your undisclosed medication stash and your intent to overdose.'

I knew full well that the next stop for 'rebellious' HDU patients was the nearby psych ward at a major public hospital. That night I slept in my clothes.

I learnt the only way to get out of HDU was to do exactly what I was told and what was expected and to try my hardest to convince Maarsten I was improving. Luckily, I wasn't on the *Mellaril* for long. It made me feel very nauseous so Maarsten withdrew it. He introduced *Epilim* instead. *Epilim* is an anticonvulsant drug used for the treatment of epilepsy, but it is also commonly used in psychiatry for its mood-stabilising and antipsychotic properties. Incidentally, *Epilim* can heighten the effects of SSRIs.[34]

After a few days on the new drugs my mood appeared to brighten. Maarsten, appearing quietly pleased with himself, released me from HDU to the mother–baby unit for a while, before sending me home.

While I'd been in hospital Nigel had managed to arrange some part-time child care for Jemima through our local council family day-care programme; his dad, who was semi-retired, had been helping out the rest of the time. Once home, I made no efforts to reduce the hours Jemima was in care. I was happy to have the time to myself. Feeling quite motivated and content, I saw someone else looking after Jemima as an opportunity to plan for my future and pamper myself. I began applying for courses in order to return to study, and phoning up friends I hadn't spoken to in ages. I got back into making my glassware and, no longer satisfied to keep it as just a hobby, I applied for a stall at an elite craft market. Within about six weeks I received a letter informing me of my success.

After a couple of months had passed with no sign of depression, everyone was thinking – hoping – that I was recovering. Nigel was quietly optimistic; *transient, transient* – for the first time he began actually to believe it. His enthusiasm soon swung back to concern, though, when my every day was spent having manicures or facials, going to movies or clothes shopping with friends.

I got back in touch with Amelia. All of a sudden life seemed way too short to be at odds with anyone. I'd invite her to come and stay often, weekends and week nights, with no consideration for Nigel. We'd stay up late talking and drinking Kahlua and Coke. Sometimes, like kids at a slumber party, we'd sleep out under the stars in our sleeping bags.

I had re-established contact with Nathan too (again, why be at odds with anyone?) and we'd phone and chat sometimes while Nigel was at work.

8 June 2000

Medications:
Prozac, 20 milligrams
Clonazepam, 1 milligram 4 x day
Epilim, 1400 milligrams

Dying for a Cure

Xanax, 750 micrograms 3 x day
Valium, 2½ milligrams 4 x day

Little Mima Puddleduck's first birthday party today. She was fantastic, loving every minute of being the centre of attention, with blue icing from her Winnie the Pooh birthday cake smeared from ear to ear. She was only to be outdone by Bek as the life of the party. The champagne started going down in copious amounts at lunchtime. Then she started on bourbon and Coke around 2 pm. Nigel did his best to cope with her overt baiting and to maintain a pleasant atmosphere for everyone, but so many of her loud remarks were downright inappropriate and embarrassing for everyone. She was the only one laughing. Most of the guests said their goodbyes and left as soon as the candles were blown out. Celeste was in tears when she said goodbye – something Bek had said. Her parting comment to Bek was, 'I don't know who the hell you are any more.' Neither do the rest of us, Celeste. Neither do we.

NINE

After working ten-hour days, Nigel would often come home to an empty house. I'd arrive somewhere around dinner time, usually after spending the day with friends, dragging Jemima around with little regard for her napping or feeding routines. While she was in child care I'd sometimes secretly visit Nathan.

Though he was exhausted and at times felt lonely and neglected, Nige was remarkably tolerant of my behaviour at that time. At least I hadn't been self-harming, and at that point he probably felt he could bear just about anything if it meant he was spared the horror of standing by helplessly, watching me turn on myself.

19 August 2000

Medication: no apparent change

I had Jemima with me today. She was not her usual self. By evening she was hot and unsettled. I couldn't pacify her. Gave her paracetamol and rocked her in my arms until she eventually fell off to sleep. I slept alongside her port-a-cot. She awoke a few times during the night.

20 August 2000

Little Mima not drinking or eating this morning. Asked Bek to take her to the doctor today, to keep her warm indoors and give her plenty of fluids.

I'd only taken Jemima to the emergency department in an effort to placate Mum, which I openly admitted to the triage nurse as she quizzed me about Jemima's symptoms. As I sat waiting for our turn to see the doctor, fully engaged in an animated discussion with a young girl whose boyfriend had broken her arm, I failed to detect Jemima's rapid deterioration. It was the triage nurse, from across the other side of the room, who'd noticed Jemima slump more and more heavily against my chest, her breathing become increasingly shallow and laboured, and her skin turn a deep searing red. When I stood to go outside for a cigarette with my new-found friend, the nurse tapped on her glass screen and called me over. 'I'm going to upgrade your daughter's status and get her seen to quickly,' she said.

I thanked her in the same manner I would someone who'd held open a door for me and continued outside for my smoke.

When I walked back in my name was being paged – the doctor was waiting for Jemima. A series of tests revealed pneumococcal disease. It had infected her blood. Within hours she could have been dead; she had narrowly escaped meningitis. She was immediately put on a penicillin drip and admitted to a ward, where she and I would stay for the next three days.

'She's a very lucky little girl to have got to hospital when she did,' the medical registrar said, patting me on the arm. 'Just as well her mummy's so on the ball.'

21 August 2000

I was furious to learn that Bek had taken Jemima out to lunch yesterday with her mothers' group friends. That poor little mite was so ill. She was taken to casualty and admitted to hospital today. Her temperature was 41°C. She's been put on a drip and is awaiting test results. It is patently obvious that Bek is not responsible enough in her present state to take care of her baby. It's just not sinking in! Does Nigel not realise just how irresponsible she is? He can't afford to rely on her to do the parenting.

When Nigel hadn't been able to locate me that afternoon, after trying both the home phone and my mobile, he called Mum to see if she knew where I was. It was the first he learnt of Jemima going to hospital. He headed straight there, incredulous that I'd failed to let him know what was going on. By the time he'd arrived Jemima was already upstairs in the paediatric ward, and when he got to her room she was standing up in her bed clinging to the side railings, crying inconsolably. The moment she saw her dad she pleadingly reached for him. She was dressed only in a nappy, and her arm was heavily bandaged and tethered to a drip. Nigel looked about the ward: all the other children had meals; Jemima had none. I was nowhere to be found.

After pacifying his daughter, he went to the nearby nurses' desk and asked for me to be paged. Nearly half an hour had passed and Nigel was just beginning to fear I'd deserted when I came sauntering in the door, coffee in hand.

'Oh, hi.'

'Where the hell were you? You just left her here?'

'I went to the cafeteria, I wasn't gone long.'

'So you just left her here?'

'She's all right. She's fenced in.'

I leant in to kiss him but he put a halting hand to my chest and stepped backwards, his face pained and disbelieving. How was I not seeing the gravity of this situation?

'They told me she's got pneumococcal. Isn't that deadly?'

'I think it can be. But she's here now. Chill.'

Leaving his hand in place, Nige stared hard into my face, into my eyes, beyond them – hunting, scouring, for a remnant, a trace of the person he'd wanted to share the rest of his life with; for the dedicated mother of his child. A sign, he silently willed, just give me a sign you're still in there.

I slipped past him and lifted Jemima from her bed, snuggling my face against hers and saying, 'It's okay, Daddy. Don't be so sewious. Mummy is here now and she's gonna get me some din-dins.'

Wrapping my arm around Nigel's waist I pulled him into a family embrace. His shoulders dropped and his expression softened, the corners of his mouth lifting to reveal something of an involuntary smile. Standing stone still, he seemed to be wishing time would do the same, as he drank in this reminder of all we used to be, and all he so dearly wanted to restore.

◆◆◆◆◆◆

1 September 2000

Medication: no change

Bek and Nige arrived here this morning unannounced, after shopping for an engagement ring! Bek casually blurted out, 'What are you doing on the ninth of December? It's a Saturday.' I replied that at that stage I didn't know. 'Why?' ''Cause we're getting married and I need to know if you can mind Jemima.'

All I could say was 'Oh.' I was trying to appear cool but feeling strong mixed emotions. I know she doesn't mean to be so cruel as to imply that I am only needed for baby-sitting, but it cuts like a knife. I was really taken aback, but tried not to show it. There was no hint in Nigel's expression as to how he was feeling about this. Totally misinterpreting my apprehension and hesitancy Bek snapped, 'That'd be right! Stupid me thinking you might actually be happy for me about something.'

She had proposed to Nige the other day out of the blue. There's no real surprise in that — it's been a case of expect the unexpected for some time now. But I wonder what on earth Nigel is thinking? Does he believe Bek's on the home strait to recovery? Sure, she hasn't physically harmed herself in a little while, but she's clearly still a long way from being right. This is just another example of her impulsivity, and who knows how she'll feel about it tomorrow or next week? Perhaps it's wishful thinking on his part, that marriage will be the fix-it-all and that Bek will then settle in to being a wife and mother. He can't possibly be that naïve. Maybe it's his conscience or his fulfilment of family expectations. I can only guess. I suppose it's not really my place to be quizzing him about his decisions. I know this should be great news, a cause for champagne and celebration, but all I can feel is bewilderment and apprehension. On top of the whirlwind engagement and marriage, she's talking about applying to study nursing next year. Where does Jemima figure in all this? Bek tells me she plans to keep up two full days of child care for Jemima so she can have time for herself. To do what, I wonder: gallivant around doing as she pleases, flitting from one thing to the next? I worry so much about her driving around in that car with the baby in the back. She's had three minor car crashes (all her fault) in as many weeks.

I called and spoke to Dr Maarsten about my concerns and essentially all I got was, 'She's not your responsibility.' So whose is she? Apparently not his, and she's sure not responsible for herself at the moment.

I was seeing Dr Maarsten at his consulting rooms at Fernview once a week. His sessions lasted an hour, an excruciating hour during which, if he didn't have statistics to quote, new drugs to initiate or existing dosages to change, he truly seemed at a loss as to what to do.

I think he too may have initially interpreted my chatty, purposeful and up-beat demeanour as an emergence out of depression. After all, he'd only ever seen me straight off the back of a course of ECT and already medicated, so his point of reference for the 'normal' me would have been somewhat skewed.

It was the obvious changes in my appearance that seemed to begin to make Maarsten uneasy: the brighter sparkly nail polishes, the younger-style clothing, my new-found love of jewellery. He decided to ask me about it.

'I notice you've sort of changed your image of late. Any reason for that?'

'That's great coming from you,' I hurled back at him, 'always looking like you just stepped out of Legoland or somewhere.' I thought I was hilarious. Maarsten remained deadpan.

'And I can't help noticing,' he continued, 'is that . . . an engagement ring?'

'U-huh,' I said, flaunting it at him proudly. 'December ninth.'

'Oh.'

'God. You don't seem real happy for me.'

'I suppose I don't understand the urgency.'

'Well, for one thing I want to have another baby, and I want to do it right this time.'

'Rebekah, this is something we need to discuss. I can think of a multitude of reasons why you should refrain from becoming pregnant at the moment. Not the least of them being your medication.'

'What about the medication?' I began to worry, thinking of what I'd been up to of late.

'The *Epilim*'s probably the one of most concern. It can cause serious birth defects, particularly on the kind of dosages you're taking.'

'Like what kind of birth defects?'

'There's a big risk of spina bifida. Rebekah,' he read my expression, 'are you pregnant already?'

'I don't know. It's possible.'

'With Nigel?'

'Of course with Nigel!' I snapped.

'When did the two of you decide you would try for another baby?'

'We didn't. I've kinda . . . been tampering with the security.' I giggled.

Maarsten exhaled heavily and massaged his forehead with his thumb and forefinger.

'You can't honestly believe having a baby right now would be a responsible thing to do, can you?'

'Why not? I can do what I like.'

'Rebekah, I want to try you on some lithium.'

'Lithium?' I said, remembering how Amelia had told me it made her feel numb. I didn't want any numbing right then. I'll just pretend to take it; he won't know the difference, I thought.

'You'll need regular blood testing on this.' He tore the new prescription from the printer and handed it to me. 'There's a risk of toxicity with lithium so we have to check periodically that the levels in your blood are within therapeutic range.'

Well, that would dash my plan.

'Before you use that prescription, do a pregnancy test, would you? If it turns out positive, give me a call.'

Two days later I was menstruating. I began the new drug as ordered.

Anyone meeting me then for the first time would probably have thought me outgoing, gregarious, perhaps a little intense, but nothing more. Although my behaviour was easier to accept for those close to me than it had been, it was evident that something was amiss. I could go from happy to snappy in a split second and had no qualms about speaking my mind directly to anyone I deemed deserving. Though my moods weren't swinging, they were in a constantly heightened state.

Although Maarsten had not said it outright, his prescription of the lithium indicated he suspected I was hypomanic. I was displaying classic symptoms. Hypomania is a mood disturbance with similar characteristics to mania, but it is not as severe as full mania. Someone suffering from hypomania might have a decreased need for sleep, be over-talkative, become irritable, be suddenly extremely goal-focused and driven to perform at work or school. They can be easily distracted, agitated and begin over-indulging in pleasurable experiences such as spending sprees or sexual activity. What differentiates hypomania from mania is that it isn't severe enough to cause impairment in the person's day-to-day functioning or to require hospitalisation. Whereas mania has the propensity to trip the sufferer into psychosis, hypomania does not.[1]

A patient who has recurrent depressive episodes interspersed with mania is likely to receive a diagnosis of bipolar I mood disorder, formerly called manic depression.[2] A patient with recurrent depressive episodes interspersed with hypomania is likely to be diagnosed with bipolar II mood disorder.[3]

11 September 2000

Medications:
Prozac, 20 milligrams
Epilim, 1400 milligrams
Clonazepam, 1 milligram 4 x day
Lithium, 500 milligrams

Bek now on lithium. I've had a good look at what lithium is prescribed for: mood disorders and 'some types' of depression. I wonder if he's suspecting a mood disorder. I suppose it would make some sort of sense. I'm going to have to try to speak to him again, but it's like bleeding a stone. Such a strange man. He won't even make eye contact with me. Bek tells me she's tried to get him to talk to her about certain things and all he seems to say is, 'Yes, I realise we will have to get to that at some point.'

The other day he told her that if she felt she needed psychotherapy he knew someone he could refer her to, to be seen in conjunction with him. Unbelievable. Why can't he do it? Don't psychiatrists offer psychotherapy?

27 September 2000

Went to Bek's today about 11 am. Rang the bell three times before she answered. Said she was sleeping. Jemima was in her cot, awake, with a dirty nappy. Told Bek I'd take her somewhere for a coffee. Said she felt unwell and really just wanted a day at home. She looked very unkempt. She urged me to take Jemima somewhere with me for the day, but something about her enthusiasm to be alone troubled me. I stayed with the baby until Nigel got home. Bek spent most of the day in bed.

1 October 2000

Nige called about 8 pm. Said to meet him at hospital emergency then hung up abruptly. Bek's overdosed on *Xanax* pills, and cut her arm with broken glass after drinking alcohol. Taken by ambulance to casualty. Stayed with her a while, then took Jemima back to their place and put her to bed. I went home when Nigel arrived at about 10.30. He was called out again at about 1 am. I had to pack the baby up and get back over to the hospital to bring Bek home.

2 October 2000

Spoke with Bek by phone before work this morning. Still sounding no good. Drove the hour to work ridden with disturbing thoughts about the way she'd sounded. I was about to call Nigel before class started, urge him to call Maarsten about Bek. As I was walking to the office, an announcement came over the PA system. Nigel was on the phone for me. He told me Bek had taken a 'whole heap of shit' again, must have been not long after I had spoken to her. I told him to hang up and call an ambulance and to ring Maarsten immediately. I called back after a few minutes. Bek was on her way to hospital emergency again. Nige sounded despondent, fed up. I had to walk out of work again. Drove to the hospital. Bek in a serious condition. She took 32 *Mellaril*, 40 *Clonazepam*, some *Xanax* and maybe *Prozac* or *Valium*, or both! The *Mellaril* has affected her heart. She's hooked up to an ECG and intravenous tubes. They truly don't know if she'll be all right. She was fading in and out of consciousness, slurring her speech, charcoal spread all over her face. I urged Nigel not to let Jemima see her mother like this but to let me take her back to our place for a while, but he wouldn't listen. I know she's only a baby but this could leave a lasting impression. I felt angry towards him.

pm

Went home for dinner, then back to hospital till about 10 pm. The nurse detected sugar in Bek's urine tonight while I was there, then drew blood. Test to be done to determine if she might have diabetes.

3 October 2000

Returned to hospital this morning. Bek out of trauma room and in main emergency area. More alert and no longer on drip. Her mental state very confused – says she's bored! I asked the doctor on duty three times over the course of the day if the blood test results were back re diabetes, but nothing.

pm

Got word Bek's being discharged from casualty and Nige is taking her into Fernview. Got the all clear with her heart. I went and picked Jemima up from child care. Nige to pick her up on his way home tonight. Still no word re Bek's blood test for diabetes.

The nurse in Fernview HDU offered to get me some sandwiches from the kitchen as I'd arrived there after 5 pm and missed dinner. I declined, handing my bag over to him to conduct his own search for 'sharps' as I crawled into the bed, pulled the quilt up over my head and fell asleep.

Some hours later I heard my door pushed open and footsteps beside my bed. I assumed initially it was a nurse doing the hourly bed check until I realised there was no torchlight. I opened my eyes and in the semi-light spilling from the nurses' station made out a crouched figure in the corner of my room.

'Trouble sleeping?' he asked in a loud whisper. 'Me too.'

Like a duck, he waddled towards me, crouching only inches from my bed. I gasped when I noticed his face, hatched all over with semi-healed cuts. He held his pyjama top in his hands, twisted around like a big thick rope.

'We could take 'em you know,' he said, jerking his head at the nurses' station.

'Six of us, three of them.' He wrapped his top around his own neck and tugged on both ends, simulating strangulation. 'It'd be too easy. Think about it. Too easy.'

I had to gulp hard in order to free my throat to speak. 'I just need to go to the toilet. Can I think about it for a sec?'

'Okay, be quick,' he said, allowing me to slide past him into the bathroom next door. I shut myself in, cursing as I rediscovered the doors had no locks.

'Rebekah, are you in there?' A nurse was at my door now that quite a few minutes had passed.

'In here,' I called. 'Just finishing up.'

'Okay, be sure to hop straight back into bed when you're done.'

'I will, I will.'

Did no mention of a sighting of my night-caller mean he'd skulked out before the nurse had started the rounds? Or was he hiding under my bed, or in my cupboard? To ask the nurse from the bathroom if he could see anyone else in my room would have sounded nuts if no one was there. I stayed put, leaning hard against the door until I heard the nurses' station door click shut and it seemed safe to assume all other patients had been found in their own rooms. Exiting the bathroom, I flicked on my main bedroom light and kept it that way for the rest of the night.

The following morning, as the patients gathered around the common area collecting their orders from the breakfast trolley, I was relieved to see my visitor from the night before in his room, appearing to pack his bags, overseen by a nurse. Was he being shipped off to the public psych ward? Had he been seen leaving my room? Had he been caught doing something else beyond the manageability of the Fernview HDU team? I didn't much care. I just knew I'd be feeling a lot safer from there on in. But I was in for yet another shock. I sat down at the dining table next to a middle-aged female patient and began to eat my cereal. It wasn't until she politely asked me to pass her the sugar that I realised who she was: Nathan's mother.

She was obviously heavily medicated and I was relieved that when our eyes met I detected no flicker of recognition in hers. I didn't want to have to be explaining to her how I'd wound up in these circumstances. Then I forgot my self-consciousness for a minute: what had happened with her that she'd ended up in the locked ward of a major psychiatric hospital? I was hurrying my breakfast so I could scurry away to my room when the nurse approached and began handing out breakfast medications to all the patients as we sat around the table.

'There you go, Robert,' he said, placing a pill-filled medicine cup in front of the young guy opposite me, 'and Sylvia,' he gave Nathan's mother hers. 'For you, Jennifer. They're cute PJs you're wearing. Miranda . . . and last but certainly not least . . .' *'Don't say it, don't say it'*, I willed in vain, '...there you go, Rebekah,' he finished off cheerily.

Nathan's mother sat with her water glass poised and looked from the nurse to me.

'Rebekah?'

I cringed, realising there was no escape. I didn't have the energy to feign ignorance.

'Sylvia. My gosh. Wow, what a surprise.'

'Yes, it is,' she replied and we both sat there, resisting the reflex to follow with, 'So how are you?' or 'What brings you here?' Regular niceties could be so inappropriate in a place like that.

I began to put my dishes away on the food trolley.

'I'll pop by your door later and say hello,' Sylvia said, adding, 'Only if that's okay?' when I took a moment to answer.

'Sure,' I said. What else could I do? Avoiding anyone in such tiny quarters would be impossible. At least I'd have some time to think up some things to say.

She knocked on my door about an hour after breakfast, waking me up. I'd gone back to my room with the intention of getting ready for a shower and had fallen asleep on my bed – the lithium was making me so lethargic.

'I'm sorry,' she said. 'I'll come back.'

'No, that's okay. Come in.' I hoped she'd feel guilty for disturbing me and not stay long.

'How's your little baby?'

'She's not so much of a baby any more. She's almost a year and a half. She's good.'

'And Nigel?'

'Still putting up with me.'

'So things obviously haven't been going too well.'

'No, not exactly.' I wasn't keen to elaborate, though it was clear she wanted me to. 'The doctors are having a hard time trying to get my treatment right. And how's Nathan?' I hadn't the slightest desire to speak about him but was intent on deflecting her interest in me.

'Oh, he's all r— Well, no, actually . . .' She stunned me by starting to cry.

'What's happened? Is he okay?'

'He's fine. It's everyone else's life he's ruining. He's partly the reason I'm in here. Our family just can't take it any more. It's so horrible to say, but each time we get a call from the police we sort of hope it's to tell us he's dead. He's just bleeding us dry, in every possible way. We've been told to change the door locks and stop answering his calls, but I can't bring myself to do it.'

That sounded a bit harsh. 'Well, can't he move out? He must have plenty of money from his modelling.'

'Modelling?' She shook her head. 'Is that what he's told you? Darling, he's never modelled a day in his life. Nathan's a drug addict and petty thief. The only legitimate money he gets is from Centrelink (DHSS). When he's spent all that on whatever drugs he can get his hands on, he has to resort to more unsavoury methods for income.'

'Oh, God,' I said, feeling suddenly ill. 'Of course, I knew about the heroin use, but I had no idea . . .'

'He rarely gets heroin. It's way too expensive for him. Mostly he uses alcohol and prescription drugs. His favourite is injecting sleeping tablets. His father's even caught him drinking aftershave. He's been through every rehab programme in Australia. We've also sent him to a clinic in New Zealand. His habit's nearly bankrupted us and we've just got no more to give.'

'But what about Hugo Boss and Calvin Klein? What about Europe and America? What about his agent ... what's her name ... Lucinda? He speaks to her all the time on his mobile phone. I've seen him.'

'He uses the phone for his drug deals. There's no Lucinda. And if he told you he was travelling overseas it was probably when he'd gone into rehab somewhere.'

'What?' I said, stunned by disbelief. It was all so difficult to digest, I wondered if her medications weren't perhaps making her a tad delusional.

She pressed her hand on mine. 'You're not the first one to have been deceived by him, sweetheart.'

'He even told me he'd gone out with Natalie Imbruglia. How embarrassing, I've been so gullible.'

'He's very manipulative and he uses his good looks to his advantage extremely well. I'm really very sorry, but you need to know. He's no good. Please, for your sake, don't have any more to do with him.'

I certainly had no intention of doing so and I'd be changing our home phone number at the first chance I got. I just couldn't believe I'd had him around my baby. What a fool I'd been!

5 October 2000

They've let Bek out of hospital so she can see a GP and organise to see an endocrinologist. Test for diabetes was positive. Jemima staying with me. She's very clingy and sad. Crying a lot and saying she wants 'Mamma'.

◆◆◆◆◆◆

Maarsten described my diabetes as 'bad luck' but was mainly concerned by the fact that my requirement to take insulin was going to be like 'keeping a loaded gun in the house' as far as my suicidal behaviour was concerned. He would be contacting Nigel, he said, to ensure that it was treated as such. Poor Nige was about to have to coordinate yet another supervisory responsibility, this time of securing my supply of insulin, of having my required dosages measured out and of having me watched while injecting them. The procedure would be necessary four times daily.

Mum refused to accept that a diagnosis of a serious physical illness amidst everything else that was going on was mere coincidence. She began researching possible links between any of the medications I was taking, or had been taking, and diabetes. Her suspicions were aroused when she came across a journal article from *The Annals of*

Pharmacotherapy entitled 'Olanzapine-induced glucose deregulation'. The article discussed six published reports implicating olanzapine (*Zyprexa*) in causing glucose dysregulation. The conclusion it drew was that, although more investigation was required at that stage, olanzapine 'may produce exacerbation or new emergence of diabetes mellitus'.[4] Mum immediately recalled the *Zyprexa* Max Braydle had prescribed.

There are two types of diabetes: type I diabetes, also known as insulin-dependent diabetes or early-onset diabetes; and type II diabetes, also known as non-insulin-dependent or late-onset diabetes. Type I diabetes is the kind that usually begins in childhood or adolescence. It requires treatment with insulin injections usually three to four times a day. It is thought that in this kind of diabetes insulin-making cells in the pancreas have been destroyed, resulting in an inability to metabolise glucose. Although type I diabetes can strike at any age, the chances of it occurring beyond the early twenties are drastically decreased. There is, as yet, no prevention or cure for this kind of diabetes.

Type II diabetes is more common in people over the age of forty, who are overweight and have a family history of diabetes. Type II diabetes is caused either by inadequate levels of insulin, or by insulin that doesn't work effectively in the body. It is usually managed with a modified diet, exercise and oral medication. Sometimes insulin injections are required. Type II diabetes accounts for around 90 per cent of all diabetes cases.

I had been diagnosed with the insulin-dependent type, the kind that usually begins in childhood. There is a chance that I was simply 'unlucky' to have inexplicably developed insulin-dependent diabetes at the age of twenty-eight. There is also another possible explanation. *Zyprexa* (olanzapine) is one of the atypical antipsychotic class of drugs that includes *Clozaril* (clozapine), *Risperdal* (risperidone), and *Seroquel* (quetiapine), among others. This class of drugs debuted on the market at a similar time to the SSRIs. They are approved for the treatment of schizophrenic psychosis, and some are approved for acute manic episodes associated with bipolar mood disorder. However, doctors are permitted to prescribe them 'off label' for any condition they deem appropriate.

As thousands of people worldwide were prescribed these drugs, the evidence that they were linked to diabetes and other, sometimes fatal, pancreatic conditions became impossible to ignore. In 2002 both the British and Japanese government authorities ordered that *Zyprexa* be issued with product-labelling information regarding diabetes risks.[5] In 2004 the US FDA ordered all manufacturers of atypical antipsychotics to change their labelling to the same effect.[6] By 2007 Eli Lilly & Co., the makers of the drug, had agreed to pay US$1.2 billion to settle 28,500 lawsuits from people who contended that they developed diabetes or other diseases after taking the drug. At least 1,200 more lawsuits are pending.[7] In addition, Lilly are currently under investigation by the US FDA after company information, revealed during one of these suits, showed it trained its sales force to downplay the risks posed by *Zyprexa*. The February 2000 documentation states that clinical trial participants taking *Zyprexa* developed high blood sugar at diabetes levels at more than triple the rate of those taking the inactive placebo. This information was not submitted to the FDA. Rather, Lilly went on to issue this advice to its sales staff: 'We believe it is essential to weaken this link to neutralize the diabetes/hyperglycemia issue. Neutralizing any concern from our customers will be essential to the future growth of *Zyprexa* in the marketplace.

'... We will NOT proactively address the diabetes concern,' the staff were further told. 'The competition wins if we are distracted into talking about diabetes.'[8]

Zyprexa became the company's top-selling drug, bringing in US$4.76 billion in 2007 – about a quarter of Lilly's revenue.[9]

In October 2007, Lilly strengthened existing warnings saying that *Zyprexa* was more associated with high blood sugar levels, a risk factor for diabetes, than similar medications.[10]

3 December 2000

Medications:
Prozac, 20 milligrams

Epilim, 1400 milligrams
Clonazepam, 1 milligram 4 x day
Lithium, increased since Mellaril OD

Bek asked me today if I'd bought an outfit for the wedding. I hadn't even realised I was invited. The way she'd put it to me before, I thought I was the baby-sitter. Now all of a sudden I'm the mother of the bride. She doesn't know, of course, that I also have to attend a formal presentation night on the same date! She seems very down and unmotivated. I wonder if she's regretting having organised everything so soon. I suggested that she could always postpone, that people would understand, but she said it was all done now and anyway, what message would that send to Nige?

I think if they were to be truthful with each other she'd find he was probably feeling the same way. They have put the honeymoon on indefinite hold. They were arranging to go to Tasmania but Bek said it would be a complete waste, that they'd rearrange it when she was feeling more up to it.

I've read about 'emotional blunting' with depression and that's exactly how Bek seems at the moment – blunted. Her eyes are expressionless, her face lifeless. She doesn't seem to care much about anything. She still hasn't arranged to see the diabetes educator or dietician, as the endocrinologist said she must do. I don't know that she's taking her insulin the way she's meant to either. She's still complaining of headaches and exhaustion.

On the morning of our wedding day Nigel went sailing with his mates. I had chosen my new friend Dee as my bridesmaid. I'd met Dee at Fernview while she was visiting a fellow patient in the mother–baby unit. She had a little boy, Jamie, the same age as Jemima. The two of them had taken an instant liking to one another, and had been inseparable whenever Dee came to visit her friend. The minute he left Jemima would be asking when he was coming back. When I was discharged Dee had invited me over so the kids could play in an environment other than a hospital. The two of us began to get along as well as our children did, and over time we developed a solid bond. Dee was studying a Master's in psychology, which added a unique dimension to our friendship: more than just a trusted companion, she was often my counsellor as well.

I spent the hours before the 3 pm civil ceremony at Dee's place getting pampered, spruced and . . . drunk. Over the previous few weeks, the appeal of being a bride had eroded away and with the ceremony imminent I found myself requiring any means at hand to assist me through the day and get it over with.

'Come on,' said Dee, knocking on the bathroom door, 'the car's here and the photographer wants to get a quick picture of us in it before we leave.'

I stood before the mirror in my make-up, gown and pearls, trying mightily to invoke the energy my tracksuit-yearning body would need to carry off being glamorous and the centre of attention. Dee thrust a bunch of pink and cream roses in my hand when I finally opened the door.

'Do you think that's wise?' she said, watching me detour to the kitchen to once again refill my champagne glass.

'I'm not going to let any Moët go to waste!' I said, concentrating hard to conceal the slight wobble in my step as, glass in hand, I walked out of the front door. Dee was a generous, warm-hearted soul. She probably would have been my first choice of bridesmaid even if I'd still had all my close friends around me. But the reality was I didn't. Many of my friends had pulled away from me. My instability and unpredictability were proving too disturbing for them. The majority of guests at the wedding were our families, friends of family, Nigel's mates, and other couples who were mutual friends of Nigel's and mine.

It proved a lovely day. I looked elegant in my dusky rose dress, Nigel strikingly distinguished in his midnight-blue suit. We stunned the guests awaiting our arrival as we stepped from our wedding car – a classic Jaguar – looking like a couple of movie stars. Jemima, in her white frock with piping to match my dress, was delightful, playing up to the crowd like the born entertainer she is, convinced the gathering was in her honour.

A delicate breeze swept the scent of summer through the beach-front rotunda where, during a simple yet captivating service, Nigel and I tearfully pledged our lives to one another before an applauding crowd. Or so I've been told. My memory of the day is so sketchy and substance-obscured that I've needed to study the photos at length to establish some kind of cohesive recollection.

9 December 2000

What a day! No one would ever have guessed that this was anything other than a perfectly planned and executed wedding. A mild, warm afternoon. A gentle breeze and a backdrop of sunlight sparkling on crystal blue water. The magnificent burgundy-coloured vintage Jag and the young couple looking like they'd just stepped from the pages of a magazine. Jemima was in a real party mood, her mamma and dadda all dressed up, cameras clicking, music playing and people. She loves people!

When I gave Nigel a hug and welcomed him as my son-in-law I saw the tears well up and one escaped, rolling down his cheek before he had the chance to hide it from me. I wonder what was going through his head today, really.

We were very late arriving at the presentation night tonight. They had held up the formal proceedings waiting for us. Their facial expressions were priceless when we offered our excuses for being so late – Bek got married this afternoon.

TEN

Since starting on the lithium my world had turned black and white. I felt little more than a scooped-out husk of myself. I couldn't feel joy. I couldn't feel compassion. I couldn't feel remorse . . . or love, or sadness, or enthusiasm, or disappointment, or anything. I simply couldn't feel. Our honeymoon was never rescheduled. What was the point of a holiday – the transportation of my depleted self from one location to another? Come to think of it, what was the point of anything? I dragged myself to yet another compulsory, pointless visit with Maarsten.

'So, Rebekah. How are things?'

'I've been offered a place on one of the courses I applied for a while back,' I said flatly. 'The letter arrived today.'

'Really. Which one? I know you applied for a few.'

'Professional writing and editing.'

'Writing and editing? I didn't know you'd thrown that one in too. Well, that's terrific. I think it will be really healthy for you to involve yourself in something like that.'

'I wasn't going to accept.'

'Why?'

'What have I got that's worth writing about? I've got no idea why I even applied for it. I write a few piddling poems while I'm at Elm Court and Ashgrove and all of a sudden I think I'm Hemingway.'

'I still think you should accept. You might regret it later if you don't.'

'Just what is the meaning of it all?'

'What? Study?'

'Everything. Life. I mean, what's our purpose?'

'That sounds like a very existentialist question.'

'What is it that keeps everyone going? We spend most of our lives at work earning barely enough to support our family, dedicating the majority of our time to maximising profits for self-interested, amoral multinational corporations who, in return, make life as difficult and meaningless for the individual as possible. And then to think we go and have children and inflict a lifetime of it on them as well.

'Life really ain't that great – why are we all so intent on procreating and forcing the heartache and stress on another, helpless generation? All these new-age, idealistic books that have sprung up of late: "You can change your destiny, just believe in what you want and you will get it, your angels will guide you." Let's face it, we're all just fools going from one stop to another on God's little rail system. The only thing that differentiates us from one another is that some of us get to ride in first class and others in economy; some have a window seat and others don't.'

'Perhaps *defeatist* would be a more apt description,' muttered Maarsten to himself. 'Are you wishing your *train* would hurry up and reach the end of the line?'

'I wouldn't be too disappointed if it did. Put it that way.'

Maarsten swapped my *Prozac* for *Faverin*, another SSRI. Drug reference material for professionals warns specifically about the potential for lithium to increase the effects of *Faverin* if they are co-prescribed.

I reluctantly heeded Maarsten's advice about going ahead and accepting the offer of a place on the Diploma of Arts (Professional Writing and Editing) course. And by the time the first day of class came around, I was bloody glad that I had! I bought myself a new outfit and went and got my hair done, just for the occasion. Fearful that my mousy brown, shoulder-length hair was going to give a lousy first impression of me to a group of new people, I decided a change was definitely in order. Something that would give my appearance a bit of a lift. I opted for some highlights, in a lovely bright purple.

28 March 2001

Medications:
Faverin, 200 milligrams
Lithium, 1250 milligrams
Epilim, 1400 milligrams
Catapres (clonidine – antihypertensive, used also for anxiety),
not sure of dosage
Valium, 5 milligrams 3 x day
Ambien (sleeping pill), 10 milligrams

Maarsten wants Bek back in hospital, but she's refusing to go.
Shades of previous times: no regard for privacy or modesty, making
tasteless comments to people, etc, etc. She asked me over there
yesterday. When I arrived she had locked herself and Jemima out
of the house. Used my mobile to arrange for Nige's mate Shaun to
come. He rode over on his bicycle. Bek quite 'out of touch': repeatedly asking the same questions, not remembering what day it was,
confusing yesterday with days prior. Went to toilet in the vegie patch
in full view, with Jemima trying to emulate. Distracted Mima as best
I could. All this while Shaun was up on the roof trying to break into
the house.

1 April 2001

Took Jemima to an Easter egg hunt. Bek came and took her home
at about 4.30 pm. Nigel phoned at around 9 pm to say that Bek
'had fallen in a heap' and was hysterical. He's taking her back to
hospital.

4 April 2001

Bek discharged and sent home. Spoke to her by phone. Said she was
tired, clumsy, disoriented.

Dying for a Cure

5 April 2001

I phoned Nigel from work this morning. He sounded peeved. Bek had cut herself again last night. He said he was going to take her back to hospital later. Then he called me at work in the early afternoon, already at Fernview. Said Bek had done 'a whole heap of shit again'. Drinking alcohol, cutting up. Maarsten's told Bek he wants her to 'veg out' in her room and avoid stimuli. Only immediate family to visit.

Called in to Fernview on my way home from work. Hardly recognised Bek. She had her face plastered in make-up and was wearing a jewel-studded collar around her neck that she'd borrowed from one of the other patients. Throwing her arms around everybody and kissing them, calling them 'darling' and 'gorgeous'. Spoke quite calmly about what she'd done to herself yesterday as if relating something from a TV soap. She'd used a razor, broken mirror and a knife. Said she wanted to die in a way that Jemima wouldn't realise was suicide.

✦✦✦✦✦✦

Unable to ignore the public outcry regarding the ever-emerging evidence of SSRI suicidal behaviour and the lack of government action about the issue, in 2004 the US FDA convened meetings of its advisers to investigate. Two public meetings were held, which people travelled from one side of the country to the other to attend and tell their stories to the panel.

Glen Macintosh, father of suicide victim Caitlyn, was one of those attending. He describes Caitlyn's childhood as 'typical' with 'no real major problems . . . [but] then sixth grade came along. The older kids picked on her . . . she didn't quite fit in. At the same time, she was having trouble sleeping.' A school counsellor suggested she see a doctor. The doctor said she was depressed and prescribed *Seroxat*.

'After a week it was obvious it wasn't working,' says Macintosh. 'Her mood deteriorated, she was despondent, just like a zombie.'

Caitlyn was then referred to a psychiatrist, who prescribed *Lustral* instead. Things dramatically worsened.

'She became suicidal,' says Macintosh, 'thinking of throwing herself out of two-storey windows. She'd doze off in class and wake from a dream where she was lying in a pool of blood. They said she was majorly depressed with psychotic features.'

She was then prescribed a combination of anti-anxiety medication and antipsychotic drugs. Soon after, at school one day, Caitlyn hanged herself from the back of a toilet door with her own shoelaces.

The FDA heard many of these kinds of testimonies, from grieving family members of those who had become suicidal after SSRI treatment, and also from some victims themselves who had survived thwarted attempts:

'He told me, "I cannot stand the way this drug makes me feel." Two days later he committed suicide.'

'She stabbed herself twice in the chest with a large chef's knife.'

'How do you erase the picture of your child trying to run in front of a moving car?'

'She became extremely violent towards us. She would run to the silverware drawer, get a knife and attempt to stab herself.'

'Six weeks after I'd been put on the drug . . . I swallowed a cup full of poisonous bathroom cleaner.'

'He pulled his car into a factory garage, started his engine, and waited until he died of carbon monoxide poisoning.'

'I put a .38 Special Smith and Wesson revolver under my chin and pulled the trigger.'[1]

After hearing many of these kinds of testimonies, in March 2004 the FDA began issuing its SSRI suicide warnings.[2]

SSRIs have come to be one of the most commonly prescribed medications in the world. Since their debut in the mid 1980s they've been marketed as a safe and effective treatment for depression and an expanding list of other conditions, such as social anxiety and obsessive compulsive disorder. Concerns about their safety began as far back as the 1990s, when the first reports describing a possible association with suicide and suicidal behaviour (discussed in chapter eight) surfaced. However, for nearly every bit of evidence showing the potential of SSRIs to cause what they're supposed to cure, proponents of SSRIs have attempted to counter it with often widely publicised claims to the contrary.

In an attempt to clear the confusion, at around the same time the FDA was doing its analysis of SSRI studies, a team of eminent independent researchers decided to do their own systematic review of every SSRI randomised controlled clinical trial ever to be published. Their findings, published in the February 2005 issue of the *British Medical Journal*, were intriguing. When looking at the overall figures, there appeared to be no significant difference in rates of suicide between the groups of people given SSRIs and those given placebo. At first glance this might seem to dispel the claims that SSRIs cause people to suicide. However, on closer inspection it was revealed that while suicides had decreased in the population with major depression, for those with milder depression and other conditions there was as much as an *eightfold increase* in the rates of suicide. The results for the major depression group when combined with the results for the others gave a misleading overall null effect.[3] These findings are consistent with those of Teicher and his colleagues, discussed in chapter eight, that antidepressants might attenuate suicidal risk in some people, but exacerbate it in others.

Other than its publication in the *British Medical Journal*, one of the world's most reputable medical journals, this study didn't seem to get much attention. Unlike studies talking up the benefits of antidepressants and attempting to counter any news of their negative effects, studies like this one rarely circulate in mainstream media. Hence, a lack of awareness among the public of their existence.

Just months before the FDA announced the findings of its most recent SSRI review, GlaxoSmithKline, makers of the SSRI *Seroxat*, made an astonishing admission in May 2006: on closer inspection, existing clinical trials of their drug did reveal a significantly higher[4] incidence of suicidal acts among adult subjects taking the drug compared with those who were taking placebo (sugar pills).[5] Following the announcement a spokesperson for the company said: 'At some point, the FDA is going to say what their analysis shows across the [SSRI] category . . . We felt like this was information we wanted to share with physicians.'[6] One can only imagine how much suffering might have been prevented were they able to 'share' this information a bit sooner.

6 April 2001

Called in to Fernview at lunchtime. Bek had been out and got her nose pierced and was wearing a blonde wig. Says she's been hallucinating, told Maarsten she was seeing the floor rising up, ants crawling across her bedspread, and hearing people talking to her from the bedroom when she goes into the bathroom, but there's no one there.

I took Jemima back in to have dinner with her mamma. That was a bit of a disaster. Bek began a food fight in the dining room with another patient. I had to get up and leave.

But there is better news. Maarsten's finally made his diagnosis: bipolar I mood disorder. Perhaps now he'll get the treatment right.

How relieved I was when Maarsten finally awarded me a diagnosis. Like an impatient child eagerly awaiting the end of a long journey, I'd been hounding him every couple of weeks to tell me if he'd arrived at his decision yet. I'd been so upset with him when he'd been reluctant to embrace Max Braydle's opinion that I had borderline personality disorder and had left me dangling in limbo. Now that I could be categorised, he could tailor my treatment, target my illness and make me better. But, just as importantly, I could feel like I belonged somewhere. I could join a support group, receive monthly newsletters with advice from professionals and letters from fellow sufferers. I could contribute to online forums. The only thing more isolating than having a mental illness was having a mental illness 'not specified'.

Nigel, on the other hand, could not have been more crushed; crushed by the monumental betrayal of his mantra and all the words of well-wishers that had helped with its conception. *Transient*: the word now jeered at him, as he realised all the sacrifices he'd made based on its promise, all the decisions; he was *married* to me now. *Transient* – it sure didn't apply to bipolar mood disorder.

ELEVEN

The *DSM IV* is a reference text used by psychiatrists worldwide for the diagnosis of mental disorders. By checking off my symptoms against *DSM IV* criteria for bipolar I mood disorder, Maarsten had given me an accurate diagnosis. As the manual states, I'd had: 'A distinct period of abnormally and persistently elevated, expansive or irritable mood, lasting at least one week.' During the 'mood disturbance' I also had had, as required, three or more of the following 'persistent', 'significant' symptoms:

- Inflated self-esteem or grandiosity (tick)
- Decreased need for sleep (tick)
- More talkative than usual or pressure to keep talking (tick)
- Flight of ideas or subjective experience that thoughts are racing (tick)
- Distractibility (tick)
- Increase in goal-directed activity (tick)
- Excessive involvement in pleasurable activities that have a high potential for painful consequences (tick).

There is even a special classification for 'post partum onset' of the disorder.[1]

Finally, the past year and a half was making sense: the depressive moods, then the elevated mood, the periods when I seemed to be experiencing both concurrently (known as a 'mixed state' and also classically symptomatic of bipolar mood disorder).

Maarsten appeared awfully pleased with himself as he broke the news to Nigel and me, stating confidently: 'Mania is 16 per cent more likely to emerge following the birth of a child.'

He appeared extremely relieved that the puzzling pieces of my behaviour during the past eighteen months seemed to be beginning to fit. It had been a long hard road, but he'd finally cracked it. Or had he?

He seemed to have overlooked this brief, but crucial notation in the DSM IV:

> Note: Manic-like episodes, that are clearly caused by somatic antidepressant treatment (e.g., medication, electroconvulsive therapy, light therapy) should not count toward a diagnosis of bipolar I disorder.[2]

Equivalent stipulations are made in relation to hypomanic-like episodes and bipolar II.[3]

Several clinical investigations conducted over the past ten to fifteen years have revealed quite an astonishing rate of serious mood disturbances following SSRI treatment, particularly where *Faverin* (fluvoxamine) was the drug under investigation. In 1992, Peyre and colleagues reviewed the histories of 189 patients treated with fluvoxamine and found a rate of 2.5 per cent for 'manic switches'; that is, the development of mania during treatment for major depression.[4] According to official guidelines, a rate of 1 per cent for an adverse drug reaction is defined as 'common'. One per cent doesn't sound like a lot, but in relation to a reaction caused by a medication that is prescribed to millions, a 1 per cent rate translates to a huge amount of individuals being potentially affected.

In 1996, Howland from the University of Pittsburgh School of Medicine found eleven cases of SSRI-induced mania among approximately 184 patients treated at a university hospital. Eight of these patients became psychotic and four were so agitated they had to be put in seclusion.[5] The following year, in 1997, Ebert and six other researchers attempted to develop a rate for severe mental aberrations caused by fluvoxamine. They carried out a prospective study of 200 inpatients taking the drug over a total of 8200 days. Fourteen of these patients developed hypomania and a further three 'developed a reversible change of mental status with insomnia, agitation, confusion and incoherent thoughts'. Seventeen reactions out of 200 patients comes to an incredible rate of 8.5 per cent.[6]

Numerous other individual case reports have been documented in medical literature concerning the capacity of SSRIs to cause mania, a number of them referring specifically to fluvoxamine as the offending agent.[7]

In addition to its alerts regarding suicidal behaviour, the FDA has also warned about other symptoms associated with these 'new generation' antidepressants, including insomnia, panic attacks, anxiety, irritability, hypomania and mania. Rather than acknowledge that newly emergent mania or hypomania while on antidepressants is likely to be a drug-induced side effect, some clinicians prefer to see it as evidence that the patient had a latent mood disorder that the SSRI has 'unmasked'. This makes it sound as though instead of inflicting serious harm on the patient, the marvellous little drug has helped to elucidate the full extent of the patient's condition to their doctor. In the apparent absence of common sense, the mania-inducing agent is not stopped. Rather, treatment with it continues, with the addition of a mood-stabilising or antipsychotic agent. Psychiatrist and author Grace Jackson expresses her dismay at those of her colleagues who insist on using this illogical rationale:

Biopsychiatry has grown disturbingly fond of blaming the patient rather than the cure as demonstrated by the now standard invocation that psychotropic drugs have merely 'unmasked' a latent bipolar condition whenever treatment coincides with the onset of manic or hypomanic symptoms. One can only wonder how long this behavior would be tolerated in another specialty of medicine. If an antacid caused a patient's heart to stop, the medical profession would consider it an abomination for gastroenterologists to claim that treatment has merely unmasked a latent dysrhythmia.[8]

Many prescription drugs have the propensity to cause symptoms similar to those of mania and hypomania as a side effect. For example, antihistamines and steroids are known to induce aggression, excitement, irritability, hallucinations or euphoria.[9] As the medication withdraws from the patient's system, so do its effects and the patient is not considered to have a mental disorder.

In *The Antidepressant Fact Book*, Peter Breggin explains that SSRIs can cause exactly the same stimulation effects – including increased energy, loss of appetite, insomnia and anxiety – as amphetamines, ecstasy and cocaine. SSRIs increase serotonin; some of the other latest antidepressants (such as *Efexor* and *Zispin*) increase serotonin and noradrenalin. The aforementioned illicit drugs boost these two brain chemicals too, with the addition of a third, dopamine. 'The stimulating effects of SSRIs,' Breggin writes, 'are demonstrated by what happens when people . . . have . . . exaggerated reactions to the drugs. Mania . . . is the most extreme manifestation of SSRI stimulation.'

Mania is often accompanied by feelings of God-like power, invulnerability and violence.[10] The manic person often feels driven to carry out elaborate plans, however bizarre, destructive or doomed they may be.[11] The DSM IV notes that 'antisocial behaviours may accompany the manic episode . . . Ethical concerns may be disregarded even by those who are typically very conscientious.'[12]

'In my practice and as a medical expert,' continues Breggin, 'I've evaluated people . . . whose lives have been ruined as a result of SSRI-caused mania. They have broken with loved ones, wasted their savings, robbed banks or committed violence. Their actions have been . . . totally incompatible with their character and conduct prior to ever taking an SSRI.'[13]

◆◆◆◆◆◆

16 April 2001

I'm on leave for a few days and Maarsten's allowing Bek home on the

proviso she attends the day programme at the clinic twice a week. I
spoke with him and tried to appeal to him about how difficult it was
going to make everything for the rest of us if she were to come out of
hospital. I explained how hard it was to have to try and keep tabs on her
all the time as well as take care of the baby. Told him how distressing
it was the last time she was home and I had to have her with me while
Nigel worked. One afternoon while I had the baby outside in the push-
chair Bek went into my bathroom and took a blade from my razor. She
emerged through the screen door covered in blood, in front of the baby.
All he could say was, just as he's said before, 'She's not your responsibility.' I couldn't get him to understand that I would be the one having to
deal with the situation if it arises again. I can't be that detached. She's
not my patient, she's my daughter. I'm dreading this.

17 April 2001

Jemima in child care today. Nigel was to drop her there then bring Bek
over, but Bek drove herself here instead, despite Maarsten telling her
no driving. She bluntly asked me for money. I said I didn't have any.
She said she needed it to do a floristry course and that she would pay
me back in instalments. Suggested she didn't start any more courses
at the moment. Told me to get off her back. Stormed out and sped off
in the car when I said, 'Is that all you came here for, money?'
   Phoned Bek at about 6.30 pm. Nigel answered, exasperated. Said
Bek had been drinking again. He had found champagne bottles and beer
cans in the car. Said she'd been hitting him and pushing him around.
Told me he was planning to call Maarsten. Heard Bek whack him and
demand to know who he was talking to, so I let him go. Five minutes
later Bek phoned here, yelled at me that she was sick and tired of Nigel
and me being in 'cahoots', then slammed down the phone.

18 April 2001

Bek to see Maarsten today. Waited anxiously all day – didn't hear from
anyone.

pm

Just got off the phone from Bek, who was very evasive about appoint-ment. Said she'd gone to the hairdresser this afternoon but couldn't remember how she got there! Supposed that she'd driven the car. No driving, no alcohol, Maarsten said. Nige's sister has now taken the car and Nige has thrown out all the grog.

19 April 2001

Spoke to Nige around 7 pm. He whispered to me that Bek had been up till the early hours of this morning cleaning out the fridge, sorting through photographs and wiping down all the window ledges. She'd been aggressive with him tonight when she discovered he'd got rid of the alcohol: punched him in the mouth, threw his mobile phone and all his work papers in the sink full of water. Bek got on the phone. Told me that she's 'shit scared' of being with Jemima. Admitted she'd been searching the house for grog. Told her it was better to be a chocoholic than an alcoholic and told her to walk to the shop after she'd hung up. Nige is going with her to see Maarsten tomorrow. I'll call him too.

I had never seen Nigel so devastated as when I slogged him in the mouth. His hand went immediately to his lip and he just stared at his blood-covered fingertips for a few moments. When he looked up at me it was with a mixture of fear and utter incomprehension.

'You're out of control,' he moderated his contempt-laden voice. He whisked sleeping Jemima from her bed and threw a day's worth of clothes into a bag for the two of them. With nothing but a furious screech of tyres, they drove off into the night.

Shit. Now he was going to be brooding around for God knows how long. What could I do to make him get over it? By the time he arrived home the next day, I had organised the ultimate peace offering. Exalted by my own genius, I popped out to get myself a suitable celebratory outfit.

Nigel wasn't letting me near Jemima alone. As he bathed her and dressed her for bed I spruced up my appearance in preparation for the arrival of our secret guest. Surprised by very little of late where my actions were concerned, Nige took no notice of me freshening my hair and make-up, and carried on with reading Jemima her bedtime story and settling her down to sleep. I went and slipped into my cheeky new attire. I admired myself before the mirror for a few moments – unperturbed by my lithium-induced weight gain, which had me spilling out the sides and over the top of it – then hid what I perceived as my undeniably gorgeous self in a dressing gown until the time was right.

'Who the hell's this going to be?' said Nige when the doorbell rang at 9.30 – the first words he'd spoken to me since the night before.

'Right on time,' I said, glancing at the clock. 'I think you'll find it's for you.'

Nige wedged the television remote into the side of his lounge chair and reluctantly went to answer the door, confused. I ran past him to the bedroom, pinching him on the bottom and giggling at how mismatched his expectations were to the reality waiting on the porch.

'Boy, are you going to think I'm the best wife!'

He opened the door very tentatively.

'Nigel?'

'Yes?' Nigel stood slack-jawed, trying to figure out who the heavily-painted, fur-coat-and-stiletto-wearing young woman was on the doorstep, and dreading his assumptions might be correct. She turned and nodded to a man standing a few metres behind.

''Bout an hour, maybe one and a half,' she told him, and he left to sit in a car parked in the street.

'Your wife was obviously keeping this a sexy little secret, huh?' She brushed past Nigel into the hall, shaking free of her coat to reveal a scanty nurse's costume. I bounded from the bedroom to greet her. Nigel stayed pressed against the wall, in shock.

'Hi.' I stretched out my hand and shook hers. Is that what you did when you greeted one of these people?

'Brandi,' she said. 'Good to meet you both. Okay, so where's it going to be happening?' She turned to Nigel. 'I s'pose I should be asking you. It's your show after all.' She flirtatiously ran her finger along my belly while looking seductively into Nigel's eyes. 'I'll just need payment first, though,' she said, snapping back to business mode.

'My . . . what? Show?' Nige had found his voice and dealt it through gritted teeth. 'Bek, what have you done now?'

'It's okay,' offered Brandi. 'You're not gonna do it. You're just watching.'

'Yes, it's all for you, hon,' I said, truly nonplussed by his response.

'We've got a baby just in there. What the hell is wrong with you?'

Brandi began looking edgy.

'What the hell's wrong with *you*?' I said, switching to fury. 'Most guys would be thrilled. I suppose I shouldn't have been surprised. I am, after all, married to the most uptight, boring piece of tumbleweed on the face of the earth.'

'I'm sorry, Brandi, but we won't be going through with this.' Nige leant into the doorway of the bedroom and grabbed his wallet from the bedside table. 'I imagine we must owe you something for your trouble.'

'Well, the rate's for an hour or part thereof, so, minus the fifty dollar phone deposit, one fifty.'

'You must be kidding.'

'Don't worry.' I said. 'I've got the cash.'

Brandi swapped the money for a business card, which she slipped in Nigel's top pocket. Then she re-robed and left the two of us in our entrance hall, in a whirl of hairspray and perfume.

'You are such a friggin' weirdo,' I said.

'And you're . . .' Once again, Nige was lost for words.

26 April 2001

Group of us from school supposed to go away today for a long weekend. Everyone very disappointed when I said I couldn't go, tried to pressure me to change my mind – just couldn't understand when I said I had to go to Bek's. I know everyone's sick of it, but they need to understand Bek cannot be left alone with Jemima at the moment.

Bek's place a complete pigsty. She'd been up since 3 am so I tried to convince her to have a sleep while I cleaned up. She went for a run instead.

Fernview called around midday to say they had a bed for her. Told Nige and then drove Bek to hospital. On the way in the car she was absolutely atrocious to poor Jemima: pinching and poking her, antagonising her and making her cry. I looked in the rear-vision mirror and caught her tugging on her little earlobes and screamed at her to stop. Jemima slapped her in the face and I thought, 'Good on you.' Bek called her a 'miserable little brat', then went all morose. I couldn't wait to get her out of the car.

Maarsten wants Bek to stay three to four weeks. He's got her a bed with the adolescent patients at the moment, until something comes up in the adult ward. He's stressed to Bek that she's 'very ill'. Nige is going to have to take Jemima with him to the office on the days she's not already in care. For the rest it'll be a team effort between Nige's dad and me. Maarsten's written a letter to the college so Bek can defer her writing course. That plan was doomed from the start anyway.

I'm having trouble sleeping – thinking of Bek, haunted by her image. Where's all this going to end?

I was no longer just a danger to myself. I was getting continually ambushed by feelings of acute rage and was devoid of the impulse control to refrain from acting on them. I'd physically abused Nigel several times, I'd punched walls and smashed a number of household items. It was frightening everybody, particularly where the vulnerability of Jemima was concerned.

Courts around the world all too regularly bear witness to the catastrophic manifestations of SSRI-induced violence. In 1999, after suffering bouts of depression and anxiety, Australian hobby farmer David Hawkins was prescribed *Lustral* by a locum GP. Two days later he killed his wife. Hawkins had gone to bed that night after a cosy evening of playing cards and watching television, but woke in the early hours of the morning full of panic. His wife went to make him a cup of tea; Hawkins took some *Lustral* pills and went to get wood to rekindle the open fire.

'She passed me in the doorway,' says Hawkins, 'and said, "I'll make you a cup of tea."' Those were her last words. There was no argument, no warning: Hawkins, with a reputation for being a passive, loving gentleman, strangled his wife to death.

'My head seemed to be bursting,' he says. 'I couldn't see my wife's face. [It was] almost as though I was watching myself doing what I was doing.'

David Healy, who wrote a critical report for the defence, said that the case was very, very clear-cut: 'I can say to you that, absolutely, she would be alive today if her husband hadn't been put on this drug.'

Hawkins pleaded guilty to manslaughter on the basis of substantial impairment.

In sentencing Hawkins, the judge stated, 'I am satisfied that but for the *Lustral* he had taken, he would not have strangled his wife.'[14]

The maker of the drug, Pfizer, stressed that it was important for people to understand that this was 'one, single, very unusual, isolated episode'. But, sadly, several more cases seem to indicate otherwise. In 2003, Australian woman Merrilee Bentley tried to kill herself and her two young daughters by feeding exhaust fumes into the family car via a piece of hose. The judge ruled that her medication had significantly impaired her capacity for rational thought and handed down a four-year suspended sentence. Merrilee had been taking *Seroxat* for an extended period of time before being switched to *Efexor* five months before the terrible event. She had been having daily thoughts of suicide for eighteen months. Merrilee has now stopped the treatment and her father says, 'Since ceasing these drugs I've observed a marked improvement in my daughter's health and coping abilities.'[15]

Soon after starting on *Seroxat*, American man Donald Schell shot and killed his wife, daughter and granddaughter before turning the gun on himself. Schell's family brought a case against GlaxoSmithKline, the maker of the drug, and were awarded US$8 million in damages.

Also in the US, while at work Joseph Wesbecker shot and killed eight people, injured twelve, then shot himself. He had been prescribed *Prozac* a month before the killings. His relatives sued *Prozac* manufacturer Lilly, alleging that *Prozac* caused him to commit the crimes.[16] The company won, but it was later revealed that Lilly had secretly settled the case during the trial. As part of the settlement the plaintiffs offered the jury a watered-down case, enabling Lilly's victory. The presiding judge later found out about this deal, and changed the verdict to reflect the fact that Lilly had settled the case with prejudice. The Kentucky Supreme Court found that Lilly might have committed 'fraud' and that it had 'manipulated' the court system.[17] This is but one of several hundred lawsuits *Prozac* maker Lilly has faced in the US since 1994.[18]

If these drugs have the potential to be so dangerous then how is it that they are prescribed with such enthusiasm? How is it that they are even approved for use in the first place? Decisions made by the US Food and Drug Administration (FDA) influence the actions of drug regulators and health-care watchdogs around the world. In evaluating experimental compounds for approval the FDA looks for 'two similar and well-monitored phase III trials* . . . [that have shown] a statistically significant therapeutic effect in the absence of unacceptable toxicities.' However, there is no limit on the number of studies that a drug company may submit in pursuit of this goal.[19] Moreover, there is much manipulation and adjustment of a trial that can, and does, take place in order to ensure a drug the highest chance of FDA approval, and which can obscure the reliability of results.[20]

One strategy is to include in the study only a narrowly defined group of subjects who are expected to respond well to the test drug.[21] Another trick is non-comparable dosing.[22] This involves the use of non-equivalent doses of the newer drug seeking approval compared with an older drug. A moderate dose of the new drug is administered to one group of trial subjects, while the subjects receiving the older drug get 'super-doses', much more likely to cause side effects. In one study submitted to the FDA for the antipsychotic *Zyprexa*, subjects on an older antipsychotic, haloperidol, received between four and twenty times the dosage relative to the *Zyprexa* group.[23] Needless to say, the *Zyprexa* came out appearing to cause fewer adverse effects than the older drug haloperidol.

---

*Clinical trials comprise five phases: pre-clinical, where the substance is tested on non-human subjects; phase I, where the substance is tested on human healthy volunteers; phase II, where it is tested on human subjects suffering with the condition the substance is supposed to treat; phase III, the last trial required before approval, which is a randomised controlled trial (RCT) where the substance is tested for efficacy and safety against placebo and/or other treatments (usually 4–6 weeks in duration); and phase IV, post-marketing trial.

In other trials, there has been a failure to report or disclose all findings. Keeping in mind that drug companies can run as many trials as they wish in an attempt to achieve the quota of two 'showing significant therapeutic effect', researchers may find that their funding simply dries up midway through a study when it is proving to reveal undesirable results. Such was the case in a panic disorder study comparing the efficacy of tranquilliser *Xanax* against a variety of non-pharmaceutical treatments.[24] When it became clear that the most effective treatment was a combination of exposure therapy* and relaxation techniques, 'Monitoring and support stopped abruptly . . .'[25]

It's recently been discovered that some events observed in clinical trials were recorded using terms that made them sound less serious than they actually were. When the FDA conducted an analysis of a trial of *Seroxat*, they noticed that there were substantially more events of 'emotional lability' on the drug than on placebo. On closer inspection it was revealed that 'emotional lability' actually meant suicidal behaviours.[26]

David Healy, a prescriber of SSRIs himself, because they can be 'an awfully useful group of drugs', calls for reforms to the drug-approval process so doctors and patients get a more complete assessment of a medication's potential benefits and risks.[27] In a recent *Health Day News* article he said:

> Although data submitted to the FDA show an excess of suicides with every antidepressant licensed since 1987 compared with placebo, this simple but crucial finding continues to be obscured. Companies actually manipulated the data and did it in such a way that [health authorities] were aware of it and didn't correct it.[28]

Even if a researcher develops concerns about a drug's safety in the course of testing, he or she can be gagged by way of a 'non-disclosure'

---

*A technique used to treat phobias, post-traumatic stress and other anxiety disorders, whereby the anxious person is exposed intensely to the anxiety-inducing situation until the anxiety disappears.

agreement from disclosing these concerns. And as the data from clinical trials are considered proprietary information belonging to the company who funded the trial, many negative findings are never publicly disclosed.[29]

Research published in the *New England Journal of Medicine* in 2008, revealed that of 74 antidepressant studies registered with the FDA, all but one that had shown the drugs in a positive light had been published in medical literature. Conversely, studies viewed by the FDA as having negative or questionable results were, with three exceptions, either not published or published in a way that, in the opinion of the researchers, nevertheless conveyed a positive outcome.[30]

Compounding matters yet further is the issue of conflicts of interest among those clinicians responsible for advising the rest of the medical profession on how to prescribe certain drugs and treat certain illnesses. Almost 90 per cent of authors of clinical practice guidelines have ties to the pharmaceutical industry.[31] In the words of Grace Jackson: 'It would be hard to overstate the ethical crisis which has emerged in the field of psychiatry due to conflicts of interest and the intentional manipulation of trial designs.'[32]

Everyone breathed a big sigh of relief when Maarsten ordered me back to hospital. Right then, hospital was the place I wanted to be too. Many of the patients on the adult ward were those who kept bouncing home for a few weeks or months and then back into hospital again. There were lots of familiar faces and lots of socialising to do. Max had once mockingly referred to the clinic as Hotel Fernview, and currently that was precisely the atmosphere my bent perception was lending it. I was completely unfazed by the plastic-covered couches, or the tiresome psychiatric-pink décor (pink is considered to be the most calm-inducing colour). I didn't bat an eyelid when I accidentally caught a young female and middle-aged male patient having sex in the stairwell. I was totally accepting of all the things I'd previously considered loathesome, including the 4.30 pm dinnertime, the woman who practically monopolised one of the only two televisions by growling and snarling like a dog at anyone who dared to change the channel from DIY gardening shows or the international news broadcast. I didn't even care when one patient allowed his grotty, menacing bikie mates to camp on the floor of his room each night, with the staff either too afraid or too indifferent to challenge him on it. Nothing could dampen my exultation. Nothing, that was, bar someone trying to hinder something I was intent on doing.

Although programmes such as group therapy, yoga and relaxation were held both morning and afternoon at Fernview, attendance was optional. I preferred to spend my days catching public transport into the local shopping precinct with whomever was willing to join me. I spent so much money with Nigel's and my joint Visa and ATM cards that all direct debits for our household bills began to bounce. In the presence of Nigel and Maarsten I was forced to cut the cards up.

But if they thought that was going to stop me . . . A quick check of the *Yellow Pages* told me there was a branch of our bank easily accessible by train from the hospital. The very next day I paid it a visit and reported my cards stolen. The nice lady ordered me new ones – she even organised for them to be mailed to the hospital's address. Within a few days I was back enjoying my spending sprees.

It wasn't long before Nigel cottoned on: one look at our bank statements demonstrated an all-too-clear picture. At home a stack of hounding final notice statements was rapidly building. Ironically, the most relentless of the hounders was the credit department at Fernview.

When Nigel told Maarsten what I'd done he revoked my leave privileges and confined me to the ward. He also added *Zyprexa* back to my mix of medications.

TWELVE

'Shit!' I cursed under my breath when I overheard one nurse say to the other, 'Hey, Nick, someone's bag's in the lift.'

'Who's packed their bag and put it in the lift?' he called to any patients within earshot. I didn't own up but a quick check of the contents soon revealed that it was mine. Naturally Maarsten was informed that I was trying to abscond. He immediately attempted to get me into the HDU, but there wouldn't be a bed there for at least a couple of days. So, in addition to the prohibition on any leave from the hospital building, my bags were locked away in the nurses' station and I had to report to my allocated nurse every hour. I was to leave the ward only to attend the dining room at mealtimes.

How silly, I thought, that I'd even bothered to pack my things in the first place – after all, it's only stuff. Within an hour of the new laws being laid I simply walked from my room with nothing but the clothes I was wearing and my credit card, and slipped into the lift while no nurses were about.

The first whirl of fresh air as I burst through the front doors of the clinic embraced me like a welcoming friend. I pulled it deep into my lungs, fuelling my exhilaration; the blissful promise of freedom surged through my body. A taxi promptly responded to my signal to stop. I wrenched open the door.

'You take Visa?'

'Sure do.'

I named my destination and bounded into the back seat. 'The scenic route, if that's okay, along the beach.'

'No worries, love.'

'Oh, and if we could go through a McDonald's drive-through on the way.'

It took about forty-five minutes for the staff at Fernview to realise I was gone. Maarsten and Nigel were alerted immediately and the police were put on stand-by. Under normal circumstances police might not respond to a missing persons report for twenty-four or forty-eight hours, but when it's a psychiatric fugitive their reflexes are a bit quicker. Nigel requested that they did not become officially involved unless my whereabouts remained elusive after all the obvious places had been checked.

No one expected locating me to be quite as simple as it was. Nigel walked in the front door at home to find me reclined in an armchair sipping a glass of red wine. I resisted him with great fervour when he told me he'd have to take me back. That was until he shared with me his advice from the hospital that if I didn't go of my own accord it would be arranged that either the CAT (Crisis Assessment Team) or the police would forcibly take me to the nearest public psychiatric ward.

I was genuinely surprised to see Maarsten waiting for me when I arrived back at Fernview. I'd been relocated to a room right next to the nurses' station.

'They called you, did they?'

'Of course they called me. I was the first person they called. Did you actually think they wouldn't notify me? Rebekah, I really don't want to have to make you an involuntary patient, but if you don't start to comply with what you're being told, you will leave me no choice. I will have to arrange for you to be taken somewhere else. Do you understand?'

'Why are you so intent on strangling my soul? Why are you smothering my spirit? You won't be happy, will you, until you've beaten me into the mould that fits all your other boring, conservative, middle-class, worried-well patients. They're the only type you can handle.'

'You'll need to stay in your room until there's a bed in HDU,' he continued. 'You'll be escorted to the dining room for meals.'

I threw a shoe at the door as he closed it after him. The following morning I used my mobile phone to call anyone and everyone I could think of to beg them to help. First I tried the Chief Psychiatrist's office at the Department of Human Services. I appealed to them that I was being held against my will, even though I was a voluntary patient, and could they intervene to get me out. They told me to speak to my psychiatrist about it. I called each and every member of my extended family. Surely someone would step in and bat for me?

'Just keep taking your medication, do what your doctor says, and stay focused on getting better,' was the general consensus.

Desperate and exasperated, I tried to make a run for it to the lift, only metres from my room. But they were ready for me this time and, quick as a flash, two nurses – one male, one female – formed a human barricade between me and the doors. I tried to dodge them but they were very well rehearsed in a neat little blocking manoeuvre and moved beautifully in unison to buffer me away. I lunged at them in a futile attempt to ram straight through the middle. The male nurse tripped me off balance, scooped me up and deposited me, kicking and screaming, back in my room.

A bed was *made* available for me in HDU that morning.

2 May 2001

> Medications:
> Zyprexa, 10 milligrams
> Faverin, 200 milligrams
> Epilim, 1400 milligrams
> Lithium, 1250 milligrams
> Catapres, dosage unsure
> Valium, 5 milligrams 3 x day
> Ambien

I cannot believe Maarsten has her back on *Zyprexa*! Surely he knows about the diabetes link. Bek's blood-sugar levels were so high the other night her endocrinologist had to make a special trip into Fernview to see her. All he did, though, was increase her insulin dosage – no mention of the *Zyprexa*. Will give Bek one of the *Zyprexa*/diabetes articles I found last year on the internet to show Maarsten. I will write to her endocrinologist as well.

11 May 2001

Bek home from hospital for her birthday. Mum came up to see her. I took
a cake to the house. Bek's friend Dee came over, as well as her neighbour, Jenny. Bek was awfully quiet. Kept saying how tired she was and
leapt at the chance when I said she should go and lie down. I suggested
we go out for dinner but she said she wasn't up to it, just wanted to
get back to the hospital. I can't get over how much weight she's gained
since she's started the *Zyprexa*. I reckon she's put on at least seven or
eight kilos in the past two weeks.

With the *Zyprexa* failing to stamp out my mania, Maarsten had shortly
after added the old-style antipsychotic and major tranquilliser *Largactil*
(chlorpromazine). *Largactil* on its own has a very high propensity to
cause severe akathisia. With the other akathisia culprits, *Zyprexa* and
Faverin, already in my system, a vortex of akathisia despair began to
devour me after only a few doses of the new drug. The *Faverin* was
increasing my serotonin, the *Zyprexa* and lithium were fighting to suppress it. The *Largactil* was subduing my dopamine activity as was the
Zyprexa. The lithium also reduced noradrenalin action and caused a
general dampening of nerve activity, while the *Epilim* and the *Valium*
were increasing another chemical messenger known as GABA. My
brain was a biochemical battle zone.

The akathisia and the mania took turns in driving my actions. At times
they were present concurrently, manifesting themselves in true reality-
relinquishing insanity. The akathisia spun like a dynamo throughout
my body, whipping up a frenzy of friction and angry nerves, screaming
and clawing to break out of me. Incessant pacing was the only way to
expend some of its vicious force.

As I'd sit before Maarsten, rocking back and forth with my arms
wrapped around my torso, trying to hold myself in, I'd plead with him
to do something more about the anxiety. He'd ponder, 'Hmm, it's not
just the kind of anxiety we're all familiar with, is it, related to job stress
or public speaking?'

Peter Breggin describes the danger of akathisia as insidious. He explains how doctors often mistake akathisia as their patient's own anxiety or agitation and mistakenly increase their medication, worsening the condition. Since medication-impaired patients often have little or no idea what is happening to them, he writes, they cannot point to their drugs as the culprit:

> The experience of akathisia is so distressing and strange that patients often sound irrational when trying to describe it. They say things like, 'I have electricity going through my veins,' or 'It's like someone is scraping my nerves with a knife-edge.' Unfortunately, many doctors don't recognise these statements as typical descriptions of akathisia . . . and may even misdiagnose the patient as suffering from delusions or hallucinations.[1]

Maarsten never mentioned akathisia. He continued to overlook it, even though its symptoms were staring him square in the face. He simply kept aiding and abetting the main offender, *Largactil*, upping the quantity and frequency of the dosage; literally dousing the fire with fuel.

A pattern had developed where I'd be sent home for a trial few days after one or two weeks at Fernview, only to rebound straight back in again. On some occasions I would have caused harm to myself; on others I'd just be begging desperately to be taken back because the akathisia was so intolerable.

Maarsten's diagnosis of bipolar disorder had initially held so much promise – a specific diagnosis would mean specific answers, I'd imagined, specific treatment, identification of a specific brain chemical to be rebalanced. But months had passed and my condition was as volatile as ever. Maarsten's bag of tricks was almost empty and it was becoming apparent that he was as flummoxed as everyone else.

'He is, after all, a specialist in family psychiatry, not mood disorders,' observed Nigel.

Nigel made sure he was present during one of my brief visits from Maarsten while I was an inpatient at Fernview. He asked that Maarsten refer me on to an expert in bipolar disorder.

'We understand it's not really your main focus, and we really think it's time we got an expert involved,' said Nige.

'You're right,' responded Maarsten, 'it's not my area of expertise. But I'm not prepared to let Rebekah go.'

We were both dumbfounded. *Let me go. What?* I needed his *permission* to see a different psychiatrist? What he did agree to allow was for me to be seen by a professor of psychiatry the next time he was visiting his regular patients at the hospital. I had heard plenty about this professor. His expertise was often consulted by other psychiatrists at Fernview when they were struggling with appropriate treatment for their patients. I felt a surge of hope when Maarsten suggested this option. I had been speaking to a patient just the other day who had been seen by this professor. He had diagnosed the patient with a condition other doctors had seemingly missed. He initiated a new medication and the patient said he hadn't felt so good in years. A fresh set of experienced eyes was going to be the answer. I just knew it.

Unsettled by Maarsten's exertion of self-importance, Nigel and I decided that whatever the professor had to say, we would find me a different psychiatrist anyway. Maarsten's attitude had been ridiculous. And not only that; he'd admitted that his next plan of attack for me was more ECT. When Nigel had baulked at that suggestion, Maarsten said he would hold off initiating it until the professor had given his opinion.

Nigel rang all the other psychiatrists consulting at Fernview over the next couple of days and then several in practice outside the hospital. It rapidly became dauntingly clear that Maarsten's permission would indeed be required before anyone else would accept me as a patient. After explaining my situation, almost every doctor that Nigel called said that their 'books were full' and they weren't taking on new patients. The remaining few more bluntly explained that they wouldn't consider me unless I had 'reached an agreement' with my current doctor.

So it was official: I belonged to Maarsten.

The eccentric professor came to see me at around 6 pm one evening. He listened attentively as I explained my situation. He asked plenty of questions and wrote plenty of notes. He concluded that ECT was inappropriate and that the antidepressants might be counterproductive while I was experiencing mood fluctuation. He would suggest to Maarsten, he said, that he consider stopping the *Faverin* at some stage. Other than that, he told me, I would just have to learn to 'manage my illness' and he would recommend that I be discharged from hospital.

He might just as well have told me I had to manage being burnt alive.

I'd all but beaten a path through our house from my perpetual traipsing of the lounge room and hallway. I'd tried circuiting the block, but had felt so deranged, so unsafe. The akathisia gave the chaotic sensation of everything, internal and external, spinning out of control; as if the earth would catapult me off. A filthy, foreboding cloud of impending doom shadowed my every move.

'You've got to call the hospital, tell them you're bringing me back in.' I bounced from foot to foot. Nigel lay underneath our jacked-up car, inspecting an oil leak. His muffled response was inaudible.

'Nigel, please!'

He wriggled out and jumped to his feet. 'I said I'm busy. We're not all going to revolve around you. Whatever it is, deal with it.' He turned back to the car. Since my visit with the professor, Nigel was struggling to resist the notion that I was exaggerating matters, that I simply wasn't exerting enough self-control.

'I hate you!' I shrieked and kicked the garage door. Jemima, who'd been watching from her swing set, came running to my aid.

'Mamma, cwoss. Dadda, bad.' She clung on to my thigh. My head felt like it was about to explode. My surroundings – trees, ground, sky – seemed to rush at me. I pounded at my temples with the heels of my palms. Nigel swept Jemima away.

I dashed in the back door, snatched some money from the kitchen table and tore out into the street. I didn't expect Nigel to come after me, but I threw him off my scent anyway by turning to the right out the driveway then ducking down a pathway and changing direction. My thoughts

eddied with dizzying speed – *hopeless, helpless, hopeless* . . . I ran bare-
foot for a couple of kilometres to a small supermarket and purchased a
packet of old-style razor blades. Around the corner was a seldom-used,
poorly maintained children's playground. Feeling satisfied this was a safe
spot where no one would intervene, I crouched behind a bush, tore the
packet of blades apart with my teeth and lined one of them up against
my wrist. The discovery of an anonymous, blood-soaked suicide victim
slumped in a neighbourhood park would be a heinous thing to inflict on
a passer-by, particularly a child, but nothing of the sort crossed my mind.
I had to end the double-edged despair of the suffering I was enduring,
compounded by the inability of anyone to understand it.

I closed my eyes, bit my lip and swiped at my left wrist. I significantly scored the skin, but the veins remained intact beneath a delicate
membrane. I fought hard to ignore my rising nausea as I inspected my
vulnerable vessels, quietly pumping, dependably supporting the life I
so desperately wanted to end. I whispered an apology as once again,
eyes clamped tight, I plunged the razor down with a mighty blow.

Thick, warm pulsating blood cascaded from my arm in big con-
tinuous waves. I'd been utterly unprepared for the sheer volume of it,
drenching the front of my clothing and pooling on the ground. Panic
switched me to self-preservation. Adam had been right all that time ago
back at Ashgrove – don't give yourself time to chicken out. I flexed my
wrist, pinching together the gaping edges of skin with my good hand,
but it was useless: the steady blood stream hammered at the makeshift
mend, breaking its banks.

Home was too far away, so I staggered through the side streets to
the nearby home of a friend I'd met through our local council mothers'
group meetings. She'd had postnatal depression, she'd understand.

Justine's initial reaction when I rapped on her sunroom window was
of pleasant surprise. It soon turned to horror when she opened the door
to me and registered my state.

'I've cut my wrist,' I said matter-of-factly.

'Okay,' she said, guiding me in the door and over to her sofa, 'come
in, take a seat. Michael!' She called to her husband, trying hard to temper her quavering voice, 'We've got Rebekah here in a bit of trouble.

Can you just keep Thomas occupied in the rumpus room? I'm going to call for help.'

Meanwhile, Nigel was checking the nearby railway tracks.

Justine rode with me in the ambulance to the same emergency department I'd now been treated at several times for psychiatric emergencies. My file, which had been non-existent prior to SSRI treatment, was now very thick indeed.

Diagnostic testing showed I had severed 90 per cent of my median nerve, the nerve responsible for movement and sensation in the thumb, first two fingers and a large section of the palm. Ninety per cent of a major ligament had also been sliced through. Absolute overkill.

I was admitted and referred for emergency reconstructive surgery. The doctor explained the prognosis.

'We will be hoping to at least get you some function back into your fingers. But I'm afraid there really are no guarantees. Other people with this kind of injury have ended up permanently like this.' He made a pistol shape with his hand. 'You may or may not regain some sensation. You'll need intensive occupational therapy post-operatively. You really did a number on yourself, didn't you?'

I should have been devastated by this news but the mania was on the rise again, converting everything to ecstasy.

'You really should be lying down, or at least sitting on the bed,' the doctor advised. 'You must keep that arm elevated.'

I went to hoist my bottom onto the bed, thoughtlessly using my arms.

'No!' he shouted, but too late. I'd ripped apart the wound again and the pressure bandage rapidly turned red. He rang the buzzer for assistance and unwrapped the tourniquet. As he did, my arm ejected big sprays of blood across the bed. He inspected me, very disconcerted as I laughed at the display.

While still in emergency, awaiting admission to a ward, I was given another psychiatric assessment. I later got a copy of my medical records from this hospital. These are the interpretations of what I'd had to say:

Twenty-nine-year-old mother of a two-year-old lacerated her left wrist after feeling rejected by husband in context of borderline personality structure and bipolar disorder diagnosis. Not formally diagnosed until 'postnatal depression' two years ago.

The psychiatrist had noted I had been a 'good student' with 'good friendships', had had 'not many sexual relationships' and a 'good employment record'. One of her colleagues during a later assessment wrote that I 'got along well with peers' and 'relationships – stable, break-ups – amicable'. But, despite this, she still documented several times that I had a borderline personality structure.

The American Psychiatric Association (authors of the *DSM IV*) point out:

The essential feature of borderline personality disorder is a pervasive pattern of instability of interpersonal relationships, affects [how a person behaves or presents themselves], and self-image, as well as marked impulsivity that begins by early adulthood . . . . These characteristics are severe and persistent enough to result in clinically significant impairment in social, occupational, or other important areas of functioning.

The relationships of individuals with borderline personality disorder tend to be unstable, intense, and stormy. . . . These individuals often have notable difficulty with occupational, academic, or role functioning. Difficulties in relationships . . . are also common.

The clinician should . . . ascertain that the personality traits are of early onset, pervasive, and enduring; they should not be transient or present in only one situation or in response to only one specific trigger.

The psychiatrist chose to focus on my 'marked impulsivity' and 'self-mutilation and recurrent suicidal behaviours, and gestures', which, in a person with a borderline personality, are often precipitated by 'perceived or actual rejection'.[2] Hence her conclusion, I guess, that I had deeply lacerated my wrist after feeling rejected by my husband. She made multiple notations that my psychiatric symptoms, including a sense of 'hopelessness' and 'inability to contain my anxiety', were in the 'context of a two-year illness'.

It was now just over two years since Jemima's birth and twenty-two months since I first took an SSRI.

1 July 2001

Went to see Bek around 11 this morning. Surgery's been postponed again – first it was put back to 2 today, now not happening till tomorrow. Nigel and Dee were just leaving when I arrived. When we were alone I tried to get Bek to explain what she'd been thinking when she did this to herself – was it a true attempt, or a cry for help? Said she thought it would be simpler to create a 'clean slate' for everyone, especially Jemima, who she said would be too young to remember her anyway. All we would have to do is organise a funeral, then go on with our lives!! This was said with a sort of calm confidence – as though she had some higher knowledge that this would really be best for us all.

Around 11.30 Justine arrived. Bek was completely detached from what she'd put Justine through only yesterday. Sat up in bed chatting away about 'piercings' and asking Justine's opinion about her nose ring – did Justine think it made her look immature? Justine's eyes betrayed her perplexity and hurt as Bek continued to natter on with small talk, so blasé and nonchalant in the aftermath of such a horrendous ordeal. Here was Justine, quite outwardly traumatised by yesterday's events – to whose quick thinking and practical assistance Bekie owes her life – and there was Bek flitting from one trivial subject to another. Justine's unease was obvious and soon she said her goodbyes and left. I wonder, will she ever speak to Bek again? This detached indifference, this lack of realisation Bek has of the enormity of her actions and their impact on everyone else is so chilling, almost psychopathic.

2 July 2001

Nigel dropped Jemima here at 7.30 this morning. She's to stay for a couple of days. Told Nigel about the disturbing things Bek had said yesterday. Said he'd call Maarsten.

Bek went to surgery today around 11.30 am. Back in ward around 4 pm. Spoke with her briefly by phone. Sounded very dopey – probably morphine. Nige stopped here for dinner on his way home from work. Asked if he'd been to see Bek. No. Asked if he planned to. No. Has spoken with Maarsten. Said he was not forthcoming with any advice. Nige suggested to him that Bek stay on at the public hospital, transfer to psych ward there, but Maarsten said that would not be advisable.

Jemima very upset when Nigel had to leave. He put her to bed, but she cried and cried after he left. I cradled her in my arms and sang her lullabies – just as I had done so many times for Bek. She's well past lullabies now, though. What has happened to her? How has she become what she is today? She is truly losing her mind. In spite of all the medication she's taking she just continues to get worse. How do we go about finding her the right help? Maarsten is getting nowhere with her.

The hospital rescheduled my operation three times before they finally proceeded. Each morning I'd fast – except for a small sip of water to wash down my regular medication – and prepare for the procedure, only to be told by a member of the surgical team a short time before I was expecting to be wheeled to theatre that I'd been once again pushed to the back of the queue. Self-abusers are given a very low priority when there are other patients requiring care. For two days my median nerve remained severed and dying.

'Ah, no worries,' I'd respond in my euphoric mood to advice of each delay. I even suggested they shift me down to the psych ward – though I knew of its reputation for being one of the worst around – so I could free up the bed for someone else.

It was a ward nurse who finally stood up for me upon hearing the news of the third postponement.

'She's diabetic, for heaven's sake,' she said to the surgeon. 'You can't keep making her fast like this!'

A couple of days after surgery I was sent back to Fernview with my arm in a rigid plastic cast that went from my elbow to my hand, where it wrapped around like a fingerless glove. I was told to attend an out-patient clinic affiliated with the general hospital for adjustments to the cast and occupational therapy twice a week – a new challenge for Nigel and Mum: the clinic was about thirty kilometres from Fernview.

The cast drew me lots of attention back at Fernview. To all those who asked what I'd done, I gave the explicit version of the truth. Some cringed at the detail, but others thought it was pretty cool.

THIRTEEN

4 July 2001

>Faverin, 200 milligrams
>Lithium, 1500 milligrams
>Zyprexa, 10 milligrams
>Clonazepam, 1 milligram 2 x day
>Ambien
>Codeine
>Naprosyn
>Antibiotic

Bek lithium-toxic due to *Naprosyn* that was prescribed as a painkiller
for her wrist. *Naprosyn* increases lithium levels and the two should
not be co-prescribed. It was first given to her after surgery and then
Maarsten wrote a repeat for her back at Fernview. It was a pharmacist
who noticed the error and corrected it. Bit late though, Bek's been really
ill – poisoned by the lithium – due to Maarsten's stuff-up. Does he have
any idea what he's doing? Want some answers from him on this one.

12 July 2001

Apparently drug-sheet ordering *Naprosyn* has been removed from
Bek's drug file at Fernview.

13 July 2001

Nige picked Bek up from Fernview and took her to her follow-up appointment with the plastic surgeon today. They were kept waiting for hours. They called in here on the way home, around 5.30. The news from the surgeon wasn't good. He said she may as well have severed her thumb. He removed the stitches; she had a new cast made.

Bek and Nige had meeting with Maarsten this morning. According to Bek he more or less admitted to an error in writing up the *Naprosyn*, but strongly disagreed that he had put her in a potentially life-threatening situation!

I was awake from 2.50 am. Too scared to close my eyes, keep having horrid dreams about Bek.

Maarsten announced he would be cutting out the *Faverin*. I was on 200 milligrams and the plan was to stop it completely, with incremental reductions over two weeks. Those who have a sound understanding of the gravity and danger of psychiatric medication's withdrawal effects recommend a very slow and gradual weaning process, known as the '10 per cent method'. This involves a 10 per cent reduction in dosage approximately every ten days, if the medication use has not exceeded a year. If the individual has been on the drug for longer than a year, then a reduction every few weeks is likely to be more appropriate. For example, weaning from a 200 milligram dosage would go as follows: first, reduce from 200 milligrams to 180 milligrams and take the latter dose for the appropriate period of time based on how long you have been on the drug. Second, reduce from 180 milligrams to 160 milligrams, again staying on this dose for a prolonged period of time. You should continue like this until you are down to 0 milligrams. However, the very last dose might be the most difficult to stop and it might be necessary to reduce this one even more gradually. For example, you could progress with 25 per cent reductions of the final amount over a few weeks. So, with 20 milligrams remaining, you'd go to 15 milligrams, 10 milligrams, 5 milligrams, then 0 milligrams.[1]

I should have been weaned off the *Faverin* over three to four months. Instead, it was halted eight times as fast.

Maarsten increased the *Largactil* once again, and prescribed it in syrup form rather than tablets, for more rapid absorption. He exhaled a deep sigh of relief as the *Faverin* vacated and took with it the mania.

As I became rapidly wizened and crippled by the full wrath of *Largactil–Zyprexa* tyranny and SSRI withdrawal, he noted that 'depression' was the least of our worries – 'mania is so much harder to manage'. The akathisia ripped through me yet again, extracting my power to speak and shadowing my every move with its menacing presence. I needed encapsulation in the smallest, most confined space possible and was riddled with fear if I was anywhere but cocooned and rocking in my bed.

Daytime bed rest was forbidden at Fernview so I would pace the remotest possible sections of the hallways, shrivelled and spooked. I'd spend my sleepless nights in the outdoor smoking courtyard, ignoring the nurses' prompts to go to bed. Cigarettes at fifteen-minute intervals would pull me through to dawn.

As Amelia had casually observed all those months ago, it is a rarity to find a psychiatric patient who doesn't smoke. It's even more rare to find a psychiatric patient who isn't medicated. A psych patient's fervour for smoking goes beyond a simple nicotine addiction or the fact that it is one of the few ways to while away hospital boredom. Smoking in fact reduces the levels of antipsychotic medications, such as *Zyprexa*, in the body, and stimulates the same brain chemical (dopamine) that the drug works at suppressing.[2] So psychiatric patients' compulsive smoking can be a desperate yet unconscious attempt to quell antipsychotic side effects such as akathisia.[3]

I took my further mental corrosion as proof that I needed antidepressants; just look at what was left when they were gone. I pleaded with Maarsten to put me back on them. This was insufferable. But he flatly refused to reinstate the *Faverin*, or any other antidepressant. All hope seemed spent. What was there left to do but proceed with the one thing guaranteed to terminate this agony once and for all?

I stopped declaring to Maarsten how I felt. Each time he dropped by my room to check on my progress I'd play the best I could at showing him I was improving.

'I think I'm ready to go home now. I think I'll manage.' I sat on my bed, the quilt over my lower body concealing how I had to hold my legs with my hands to keep them from jittering. I forced my twitching mouth into a smile.

He bought it and arranged my discharge for the following day.

Dee, my bridesmaid, came to visit me that afternoon. She was shaken by my appearance and demeanour. She took me out to a café, where I sat hunched and voiceless, chain-smoking between cups of coffee. She was incensed when she heard I was being sent home from hospital and demanded Maarsten's phone number. Now almost qualified with her Master's degree in psychology, Dee wanted to try to approach him with professional as well as personal concerns. But I refused to supply her the details and begged her not to make contact.

When we returned to Fernview, Dee spotted Maarsten in the hallway. Ignoring my requests not to, she bailed him up and asked for a word in private.

'As a concerned friend,' she said to him, 'I urge you please not to send her home. I have never seen her so badly affected. I fear she won't survive it if you do.'

Maarsten only seemed irritated by this attempted influence by a 'rookie' and paid no mind to her appeal (nor Mum's, nor Nigel's) to keep me in hospital. To my relief.

31 July 2001

Picked Bek up from Fernview. She should not have been discharged! She'll be staying with me for a couple of days until adequate supervision can be organised at her place. She's been sent home with an enormous bag of lethal drugs again. No card or chart to explain dosages – have to read labels on packets and bottles.

1 August 2001

Having trouble finding someone to look after Bek. Nige rang Maarsten
to ask for her to be readmitted. Maarsten said no – he wants Bek
to stick it out at home for a couple of days. He suggested she keep
taking *Largactil* in incremental doses until she either feels it doing
some good or her hands begin to shake! When I asked Bek if she was
thinking about doing anything to herself I was met with silence.

Mum barely let me out of her sight on those first couple of days home
from hospital. But on the afternoon of the second day she was faced
with a dilemma surrounding a hospital appointment of her own that
she was unable to miss. She could either take me with her and risk me
running off while she was in having her procedure, or she could leave
me locked in at her place, but alone. She decided on the second option.
Loading the car up with my medication and all other easily accessible, potentially harmful contraband, she nervously left me confined for
what she estimated would be a few hours. She'd pretty much ensured
I couldn't easily seek out death; what she hadn't considered was how
easily I might arrange for death to be hand-delivered.

The minute she left, I set to acting out the plan I'd been fixated on
since Maarsten had confirmed my discharge. It was a simple one, but
involved reinstating a connection I'd worked hard at breaking.

After learning the truth from Nathan's mum about his seedy lifestyle, I'd done all that I could to stay well under his radar, including
having our phone number changed and unlisted. To my surprise he
hadn't tried quite as hard to pursue me as I'd feared he might. There
was just once – that I was aware of, anyway – that he'd shown up on
the doorstep, ringing the bell, knocking on the windows, then pleading with me when he worked out I was sitting in the lounge room
ignoring him. That had been months ago; happily I'd not heard from
him since.

But now there was nothing more urgent to me than to get him on the
phone. The fact that it would void all my efforts to rid him from my
life fazed me not the least – all things going to plan, my drawbridge to

Nathan and everyone else in the mortal world would soon be permanently raised anyway.

I dialled Nathan's parents' number, hoping dearly for two things: one, that Sylvia had not found the strength to kick Nathan out of the family home; two, that he answered the phone.

'Yeah?' was how Nathan answered. He didn't know who I was for a minute, but when the penny finally dropped he was really happy to be talking to me. I pretended I'd been thinking about him and was wondering how he was doing. Then I pretended I was doing fine and I asked if he'd like to get together again soon, just like old times. Then I pretended I wanted some drugs to take to a party to share with some friends. I told him if he could get me a deal of heroin, I'd shout him one of his own.

He didn't buy it at all. Even he could tell immediately that I wasn't 'fine'.

'What do you really want it for, Bek?'

'Like I told you, I'm going to a big dance party. Everyone uses drugs at those things, right?'

'Not usually heroin, Bek. You sound bad, real bad. I'm not getting you something like heroin when you're like this.'

Why did everybody have to think my life was so goddamn important!

'No, no, you've got it all wrong, really.'

'Well, it wouldn't matter anyway. It's dry out there at the moment. There's hardly anything around, certainly nothing my contacts are able to get their hands on, anyway.'

Crying out in despair, I slammed down the phone. I didn't believe a word Nathan had said at the time, but he'd been telling the truth. Around mid to late 2001, the supply of heroin to Australia was down to a trickle. Addicts were having to turn to other synthetic drugs for a fix, such as methamphetamine and ecstasy. I remember hearing on a news report that when the heroin trade peaked again many, many months later, overdoses soared because users hadn't had access to anything quite so pure in a very long time.

An overdose: it could have been so perfect – peaceful, merciful, absolute. But without Nathan's help, it would be impossible. I only had splinters of memory from that night that we'd used it, and none involved where or how we'd got hold of the stuff. Damn Nathan! Why, under all those layers of his addiction and its related antisocial behaviour, did he have to have principles all of a sudden? I sat contemplating simply smashing a window and running out in front of a car – it could work. Mum did live on a very busy main road. But it was out of the question. Though still substantially impeded, since stopping the antidepressant my conscience had slowly begun to re-engage, at least to the extent that it wanted Jemima spared the possibility of having to live with the knowledge my death had been violent and bloody.

When I left Mum's to go home, Nigel's dad was there to look after Jemima and me during the day. Although he'd been well versed by Nigel in all the protocols for keeping me out of harm's way, I felt hopeful he'd let something slip. He did.

Delivered to me like a divine gift was the opportunity to hoard an entire vial of my insulin – three weeks' worth. Nigel had measured my lunchtime dose in a single syringe and locked the rest away. But as I went to administer it, I intentionally dropped it on the floor, bending the needle, rendering it useless. My father-in-law was forced to unlock the supply to allow me to get some more. He watched me as I measured out the insulin in a new syringe and returned the remainder to the locked cupboard. What he hadn't noticed was that I'd managed to sneak another completely full vial into my bra, then later slip the spent lunchtime syringe into my pocket. I willed the entire afternoon that his surveillance of me would falter just enough for me to be able to finish the job. But it didn't – he took his responsibility as guardian very seriously and watched me like a hawk.

He stayed and ate dinner with Nigel and Jemima, then Nigel walked him to his car. My opportunity! I retrieved the vial, syringe and my suicide note – penned right under my father-in-law's nose while I'd pretended to write in a journal – from under the mattress where I'd stashed them. I drew a full syringe of insulin and shot it into my belly. And then another and another. How completely perfect. Having insulin around *was* like having a loaded gun in the house, Maarsten had said it himself. Only it was a lot cleaner – I'd just fall into a coma and not wake up. Nige would think I was asleep until it was too late. My note instructed him to tell Jemima I had died from a diabetes-related condition. How it hurt that I couldn't tell her goodbye and how much I loved her, but if I did she'd know my death wasn't an accident.

On my fourth plunge Nigel burst into the bedroom. On his way back up the driveway he'd seen me in action through a break in the curtain. The vial and syringe, which I hadn't had the chance to conceal, confirmed his suspicions and he went to the phone to dial for an ambulance. I jumped on him, tugging at his arm and begging him no. He shook me off into a heap on the floor. I grabbed at his leg but he kicked me aside. Another regrettable display witnessed by Jemima.

With my arm still in the splint from my last visit, I was back at emergency on a dextrose drip. Fernview was full, and so was this hospital's psych ward. Once the dextrose stabilised my blood-sugar levels I spent nearly two full days being shifted from cubicle to cubicle, watching as numerous patients were admitted upstairs to a ward, and a proper bed, ahead of me. Occasionally a nurse would look in on me, but for most of the time I was left alone to rue the failure of my suicide attempt.

'When do you think there might be a bed for me?' I asked a female registrar when she came to check my drip.

'We've got teems of people needing treatment for injuries that weren't self-inflicted. You'll get your bed in due course.'

After about thirty-six hours a young male nurse took pity on me.

'Have you managed to get any sleep yet?' I shook my head. 'I'll try and get you moved to one of the walled-in cubicles, it might be a bit quieter. What about a shower? Have you had one?' Another head shake. He clicked his tongue in disgust at his colleagues' neglect.

'I'll go get a tub and a sponge – we can at least get you freshened up.'

I was quizzed again by a psychiatrist, whose notes say I 'was well until PND (postnatal depression) diagnosis after birth of first daughter for which antidepressants were prescribed. Details of present illness: described sudden onset of fear, impending danger . . . only feels safe in bed . . . Suicidal intent in the context of depressive mood as part of bipolar mood disorder', which he also recorded had only been evident since the prescription of antidepressants.

As part of these admission records someone had filled in a 'suspected adverse drug reaction' form and submitted it to the drug regulatory agency. Had someone finally realised that the reason I had been 'well' until 'PND diagnosis for which antidepressants were prescribed' was because it was the antidepressants that had made me ill in the first place? Had they made the connection between the onset of mania and the initiation of antidepressant treatment? Had they realised that the intense 'butterflies in the stomach', 'onset of fear' and 'impending danger' were akathisia? Perhaps then they'd also seen the link between *Zyprexa* and my diabetes. If so, the report would include *Lustral*, *Dutonin*, *Prozac*, *Faverin*, *Zyprexa* and *Largactil*. Had someone, at long last, realised everything had been a big, very tragic, drug-induced mistake?

No. The drug under suspicion was my insulin. The adverse reaction: low blood sugars.

4 August 2001

Bek awaiting transfer back to Fernview. Nigel tried getting her admitted to the Jordan Street psychiatric clinic instead, but they're not interested. They told him that it was best for her to stay where she was known. I still ask myself the question, how would she be without any of the current medication? Surely she wouldn't, couldn't, be any worse. I told her today to care for herself the way she'd care for someone else in her predicament, but it's hard to know how much she takes in and what's really going on behind those vacant eyes. She's just gone down yet another flight of stairs. How long till she reaches the basement?

5 August 2001

Jemima's back staying with me again. She's been very distressed. Saw the paramedics putting an oxygen mask over her mum's face

and lifting her into the back of the ambulance. Took her to the zoo
as a bit of a diversion from all the trauma. She was gorgeous. She
absolutely loved the 'efents' and the monkeys, especially the tiny ones
in the cage. She had 'chippies' for lunch and strolled around the kiosk
following the seagulls. Said she wanted to take an 'efent' home to her
'pace' and she was going to keep it in the cupboard. We bought her a
little soft elephant to take home.

7 August 2001

Bek transferred back to Fernview today. Called in to see her around
5 pm. She was lying in a darkened room, very despondent. Not up to
talking. She said Maarsten thought her depression was triggered by
going home and the anxiety associated with that. She told him she
thought she was best when just taking lithium and *Faverin*. She said
he agreed but instead of reducing any of the current medication he
reintroduced clonazepam to the current list!

Bek was upset that Nigel had been terrible to her on the phone
– refused to bring her cigarettes. I tried to explain that he wasn't very
well and how much pressure he is under with all the running around he
has to do right now. Nige told me he'd asked Bek if she was still feeling
unsafe. She'd said, 'No, not while I'm in here. There's nothing to hurt
myself with.' Implying that if there were something she'd use it?

It seemed an absurd ambiguity, but in the absence of the *Faverin*, the
tranquillising drugs such as *Zyprexa* and *Largactil* seemed able to inflict their full sedating strength on my external movements while still
whipping my nerves into a frenzy on the inside. Through all the chaos I
had still been plugging away whenever possible with exercise: jogging
or swimming. But I was now barely able to lift my legs off the ground;
I would go under in the pool. My akathisic pacing had become a shuffle: known as the 'drug shuffle' due to the sheer number of psychiatric
patients who develop it. I'd pass plenty of others on their laps around
the ward.

10 August 2001

Saw Bek again this afternoon. She's been transferred out of HDU back to the regular adult ward. Thought she might have been a little better at first, but she broke down when speaking of her depression and her inability to cope without antidepressants. I told her what I had read about antidepressants not being good in bipolar disorder because they can trigger manic episodes and rapid-cycling. She said Maarsten had said he thought she'd lost faith in him – he reiterated that he believed he had managed her case appropriately. He seems to be quite self-congratulatory with regard to his diagnosis and treatment, which has been to add more and more medication.

11 August 2001

Between Fernview and the general hospital admissions, Bek's had eighty-two days in hospital in the last four months.

12 August 2001

Bek allowed home on day leave. Phoned on her way on the mobile to ask if I could come and sit with her for a few hours while Nige went sailing. Went down about 12.30. Mima was very surprised to see us. She met us in the driveway and said, 'Come into my shome.' Bek in almost zombie state – very slow and heavy in her movements, head bowed most of the time. Made her a cup of tea, she nearly fell asleep while drinking it. We took her and Jemima to the park down on the foreshore. Jemima loved having her mummy there. As we got back in the car to return to the house she said, 'No take Mummy in a tubble (hospital).' She was worried that we were going back to Fernview.

FOURTEEN

Maarsten, though far from admitting defeat, swallowed a little bit of pride and decided to seek the opinion of a psychiatrist who specialised in mood disorders – not a complete review, he just wanted help determining whether or not I should be put back on an antidepressant. He seemed frozen to the spot with his decision-making in the light of the way everything had been panning out.

Nigel collected me from Fernview to take me to the appointment with the specialist, and had prepared himself to do most of the talking – I was still virtually muted by the akathisia. I'd written out a page of notes that I could just hand to the doctor should Nigel not be allowed to stay with me the whole time. Turned out, though, little talking was required. The specialist drew his conclusions fairly rapidly, and made a number of recommendations. I rummaged through his words, tossing them aside until I struck the ones I was after: 'You should go back on the *Faverin*.'

If I'd been able, I might have sprung from where I sat in my fractured state – knees clung to my chest, eyes furtively glancing, voice but a whimper deep in my throat – hugged the man and thanked him. He continued further with his conclusions, but my attention now wafted off into a void – I heard but snippets of the rest. He advised that I have ECT, then retracted the suggestion when Nigel told him I'd already had it. He showed surprise. Clearly he couldn't have seen a full history of my treatment. His other stipulation was that I cease taking the *Largactil*, though he didn't elaborate on why. I can't help but think it was because he knew it had me stricken with akathisia. But whatever his rationale, Maarsten was either ignorant or dismissive of it – my records show he continued to prescribe *Largactil*. The specialist also wanted me to continue with the lithium, and particularly the *Epilim*. I would need that, he said, to counter any mania-inducing effects of the *Faverin*.

Nigel and I made another attempt to get me away from Maarsten and Fernview by asking this doctor if he'd be prepared to take me as a patient. But he declined, stressing that his role was only to give a second opinion. He added that he thought most of my issues were parenting-related anyway, and therefore I'd be best off staying with Maarsten.

I was able to take a dose of *Faverin* that night back at Fernview. Soon I'd be planted firmly back in the Land of No Consequences.

'Rebekah, can you hear me?' A hand slapped my cheek. What? The word sounded in my head but wouldn't pass through my lips – I couldn't make them move, nor my head, nor arms, nor any part of me. I had only partial, blurred vision through drooped, disabled eyelids. A small crowd of smudged, faceless figures bustled about my bedside.

'Jeez, she's foaming again. Can someone get me a face washer?'

'You've checked her pulse?'

'Yeah, it's pretty weak. We're going to have to get her into recovery position; she's going to gag on all this saliva otherwise. Can you help me lift?'

1 September 2001

Medications:
Zyprexa, 10 milligrams
Faverin, 200 milligrams
Epilim, 1400 milligrams
Lithium, 1500 milligrams
Catapres, dosage unsure

Dying for a Cure

Clonazepam, 1 milligram 4 x day
Mogadon (for sleep)

Went to visit Bek in hospital yesterday and just knew there was something very wrong. Her thoughts and speech were all over the place,
and there was something really strange about her eyes, as if she was
having trouble focusing. I asked her if she'd done or taken anything
she shouldn't, which she denied. I went and found a nurse and asked
him to come and have a look at her. He took us both into a small room
and asked Bek if she felt okay. She responded 'yes' to him, of course.
'But just look at her,' I said. By this time she was slurring her words.
Bek gave the excuse that she'd missed one of her lunchtime medications and the nurse replied, 'There you go then. That's it,' and took her
to the medication window and gave her what was possibly her second
lot of lunchtime meds.

I've just come back from the emergency department at the public
hospital near Fernview, where Bek is once again strung up to heart
monitors. When I'd seen her yesterday and tried to alert the nurse, she'd
taken twenty-five *Phenergan* tablets, which she'd bought at a pharmacy
while out for a walk, then taken back at the hospital. By last night she
was paralysed in her bed and rushed to casualty by ambulance. *Phenergan* is apparently a similar substance to the *Largactil* she's on and an
overdose of that sort is very, very dangerous. She seemed to be improving just before I left her a bit earlier and they were talking of discharging
her back to Fernview. That was until she asked me who'd left the ballet
slippers on the shelf beside her bed. Then, a bit later, she admired
the beach scene painted on the overhead light and was laughing at a
supposed apple balancing on her belly. She became really aggressive
with me when I said I couldn't see them. I told the doctor. He said they'd
order a CT [computed tomography] scan of her head.

pm

Just home from driving Bek back to Fernview. Somewhere between
the treating doctors' change of shifts the authority for the CAT scan

was cancelled. She spoke to me about what she'd done. Adamant it was not a suicide attempt, that she was just trying to get some sleep. She was quite perplexed at the results of taking so much *Phenergan*. Seemed to have no grasp of concept that twenty-five times the specified dosage was going to harm her. Unbelievably, she's managed to dodge another bullet.

5 October 2001

As I write this tonight my heart and my head are at such odds. Only two days until we leave for the holiday of a lifetime. I should be bursting with anticipation and excitement – nearly two years since deciding and no one could have predicted what these two years would bring. I've come this far – planned, saved and organised. Physically, I'm exhausted; emotionally, I'm in turmoil; mentally, I'm consumed – devoured by my own doubt as to whether I should go. With all that's happened in the past couple of weeks I've wondered – are these omens of foreboding, warning me not to go?

September 11 looms large in everyone's minds, but on 'our' night of September 11 Nigel's phone call alerted us to Bek storming out of home. She turned up here some hours later, drunk and drugged on her so-called medication. Shortly after Susan from next door showed up, distressed and crying – her dog had run away, could we help her look for it? Bek took the opportunity of this distraction to disappear into the night. We searched for her (Bek that is), found her wandering aimlessly and escorted her home. We then returned home to TV footage of the second plane flying into the twin towers in New York! With the spectre of worldwide terrorism looming large people ask, 'You're not still going away are you?' I think if 'it is written' somewhere that I should perish in a terrorist attack on a plane or in the London underground in the year 2001 then so be it!

This week I was told my long-service leave could be cancelled because they can't find a suitable replacement for me. Bek has developed complications with her diabetes and I've come down with positional vertigo. I can't move my head without throwing up, let alone fly.

Bek told me this morning she's feeling very 'unstable emotionally'. How do I get over my guilt at having to leave Nigel to care for Bek and Jemima solo? It's been so difficult, even with me around. Tuesdays the baby's been in child care. Wednesdays and Thursdays Nigel's taken her to work with him, then I, using my class preparation time, have picked her up and brought her back here. Mondays and Fridays Nigel's just been grabbing whomever happens to be about – his dad, his aunty, Bek's friend Dee – to spend the day with them both. If none of them can offer any more time, I suppose Nigel's going to have to take sick leave – if he's got any left.

If I do go, what will I come back to? Will we get as far as Singapore and have to return? Will we be flying off into a war zone? Indeed, will we get home at all? If I don't go . . . I'm afraid I might just disintegrate, crumble away and disappear. No, tomorrow I'm putting the cats in the cattery and finishing the packing. No backing out now. Sunday's the day.

✦✦✦✦✦✦

After only a few days back at home from Fernview following the *Phenergan* overdose I hightailed it to the hairdresser to quench an impulse for a make-over. I had my hair dyed jet-black and cut into a three-inch crop. The hairdresser reacted with reservation when I said that I'd decided my hair was detracting from my features and I wanted to shed it to reveal my beauty, just like Halle Berry. He did it anyway, leaving me looking even more spherical than the *Zyprexa* already had. Since commencing it I'd gained around twenty kilos.

A couple of days later I was at Fernview's day programme. A few other patients and I were outside on a break having a cigarette when one of them, Anna, a Russian lady, said, 'Rebekah, what you do to yourself? Look now at your hair. I used to think you look so pretty.'

Later on that afternoon, while attending Maarsten's session, I related with a chuckle what Anna had said.

'Her English really isn't the best. I'm sure she didn't mean it to come out that way. You should have seen everyone else's faces. About three people spoke at once, all desperate to change the subject.'

Maarsten reclined in his chair, clasped his hands in his lap and rhythmically bounced one foot effeminately crossed over the other. With eyebrows peaked he scanned me from my feet upwards. Meeting my eyes he slowly blinked and said, 'No. I think she probably did mean it that way.'

My light-hearted reaction was turned on its head.

At the session's end I went straight to the toilets and inspected myself before the mirror, back and front. For the first time it struck me just how fat I had become.

10 October 2001

Visited Windsor Castle today. Lit a candle for Bek in St George's Chapel and wrote in the petition book for prayers to be said for her at next Sunday's service.

11 October

Took the tube to Waterloo for the London Eye this morning. Sky overcast, drizzly rain . . . just like home really! After passing through heavy security finally got aboard. Fortunately there was only one other couple in our 'gondola' – George and Evelyn. We struck up conversation. Incredibly, not only had they visited Australia a few times, they had twice stayed with friends only a few miles from home! By the time the gondola had completed its round trip we had exchanged names and numbers and had an invite to stay with them in Cambridge when we pass through!

13 October

Lit a candle in Bath Abbey. Said prayers for Bek.

Dying for a Cure

16 October

Lit a candle in Chester Abbey this morning, before sitting and watching the frolicking squirrels on the lawns outside.

18 October

York Minster today. Lit another candle.

19 October

Departed York early this morning and made our way south through Robin Hood country. Hoped to make it to Cambridge by lunchtime but were delayed in traffic. Arrived at George and Evelyn's in time for afternoon tea. We were warmly welcomed to their beautiful home. Evelyn is a costume designer and has a magnificent collection of period costumes and matching accessories. Such a clever lady. We dined out at a cosy local restaurant and the night seemed to fly by as we found we had so much in common. They have a son, twenty-eight years old, who has suffered a mental illness after a bout of depression while at uni. They have been through a similar kind of hell these past couple of years, watching his life disintegrate.

20 October

Said our goodbyes to George and Evelyn this morning after breakfast. Wish we could've stayed a little longer but we had to get back to London to return the hire car. We've promised to stay in touch. It was so easy to speak to Evelyn about Bek – she is the first person I have been able to talk to who knows exactly what it has been like. I shall miss them.

✦✦✦✦✦✦

The comment about my appearance slung at me by Maarsten would not be washed clean, no matter how I tried. It ravaged my confidence and plucky outlook like a drenching of acid. I stopped looking in the mirror, now nauseated by the vile, pathetic blob who stared back at me. I embarked on a diet of nothing but three 200 ml Tetra Paks of liquid meal replacement per day – a grand total of about 600 calories – which should have had the weight falling off. After two and a half weeks my weight had stabilised, but I hadn't lost an ounce. I wasn't surprised. And I knew damn well that if I kept this up I'd probably die from malnutrition before I lost any significant amount of weight. It was more than just calories responsible for my expansion.

◆◆◆◆◆◆

23 October 2001

Paris. Set off on foot this morning to find a 'poste'. Called home and spoke to Bek. She's not doing so well. She sounded dreadful. The minute I hung up I wished I hadn't called. The thoughts began to swim around in my head again.

Caught a bus to the Louvre, but it was still closed due to an industrial dispute. Decided to walk along the banks of the Seine and made our way to Notre Dame. Sat in the square out front and chatted with a nice young English couple over for the day to celebrate her twenty-second birthday.

I was not at all prepared for what came next. On entering the cathedral I was overcome with the most powerful surge of emotion. I was overwhelmed by a sense of timeless spirituality, enveloped by a sense of awe that seemed tangible. It penetrated to the very core of my being. I wanted to pray. I wanted to cry. I felt as though I could lay myself prostrate upon the floor the way the nuns and the monks do, submitting themselves to the power, the wisdom and the mercy of their God.

I lit a candle for Bek and the words 'Out of the depths I cry to you, oh Lord. Lord hear my voice' sprang from some distant corner of my mind, obviously written indelibly during my years in Catholic schools. I quietly wept as I explored every niche and alcove, every altar, every woodcarving, memorial plaque, stained glass window and statue, before I could leave.

I left Notre Dame with an undeniable feeling that something was about to change.

On my next day at Fernview I asked the nurse who ran the day programme if I could have a look through the pharmaceutical reference guide they kept there. She had a few copies so she said I could borrow one and take it home. I wanted to see for myself which of the drugs I was taking caused weight gain. I already knew about the *Zyprexa* – everyone at the clinic who was on it (and that was a heck of a lot of people) expanded before your eyes like they'd been inflated with a bicycle pump; real ugly weight too, all stacked on round the middle like a big blubbery tyre – but what about the other drugs? I searched through the listings: *Zyprexa*, weight gain; *Epilim*, weight gain; *Largactil*, weight gain; lithium, weight gain. Bloody hell!

I flipped to the page for my treasured *Faverin* – the only drug I cared about taking – and ran my finger down the list of adverse reactions, praying weight gain was not one of them. Clear. I brought the book to my face and kissed the page.

I decided then and there that the *Zyprexa* had to go. So did the *Largactil*. I'd be able to manage to feign taking those two without Maarsten's knowledge. As for the lithium and *Epilim*, I was blood-tested every few weeks for therapeutic levels of those, so it looked like I'd be stuck on them. Ah well, losing two out of the four was bound to help me get some weight off.

I'd have to be very, very careful about it, though. The first whiff that anybody – Maarsten, the nurses, Mum, Nigel, anybody – got of me stopping medication I'd be severed from Fernview and committed to a public psych hospital to have the medication forced into me via injection. I knew that for sure. Maarsten had spelt it out to me, on more than one occasion – bipolar disorder required medication for life.

Nigel measured out that night's doses and I threw them into my mouth with a slug of water. Mimicking Fernview's protocol he watched and waited till he was satisfied I had swallowed, before easing his guard. This was the usual bedtime routine, with one small but significant twist. I'd become quite skilful at opening my throat for all eight tablets to go down at once, but that night I faked a struggle. I sought out the largest of them with my tongue, the *Zyprexa*, and pushed it into the side of my cheek, before gulping down the others. In a wish granted, Nigel hadn't asked for an inspection of the inside of my mouth as he sometimes randomly did. Once back in my room I spat the purple pill into a tissue, wrapped it tightly and placed it inside my underpants. When Nigel had left for work in the morning it would be thrown into the storm-water drain at the front of the house.

I continued this for about a week. Then I began to plan how to do the same with the *Largactil*. There were a couple of reasons this was going to be trickier than the *Zyprexa*. For a start I took this one in liquid form, and three times a day, not just once. A strategy to overcome this hurdle occurred to me. I recalled another patient warning me to make sure I rinsed my mouth thoroughly with water after each dose of the syrup because it had the propensity to erode the enamel on your teeth. I complained to Maarsten that I'd seen evidence of it happening to me and requested he switch me back to tablets. He agreed.

The *Largactil* tablets were among the tiniest of all my pills and I took two of them in each dose. It demanded a little more tongue agility to sort them from the rest, along with the *Zyprexa*, at night, but my determination saw me through.

Within a week or so of this drug reduction a number of remarkable things began to happen. My diabetes had been surfing dangerously out of control, with my blood sugar often reaching levels of thirty or more (safe range for a diabetic is between four and eight). I'd been chastised on a regular basis by the nursing staff at Fernview for 'not taking my condition seriously'. In the absence of *Zyprexa* my blood-sugar levels slid back under control and my insulin requirements reduced dramatically. I lost five kilos, effortlessly.

But by far the most significant change was the dramatic dissipation of my agitation and anxiety. My ability to sleep returned, as did some of my focus and self-control. I could sit still; I could read a magazine; I could hold a steady conversation. Upon acknowledging and congratulating me on my obvious improvement Maarsten advised that I could now probably afford to begin weaning from the *Zyprexa*. But he did hasten to add this was on the condition I attend the day programme twice a week instead of once, so I could be more strictly observed.

It was at one of the first of these outpatient days that another effect of stopping these antipsychotics presented itself. At a morning tea-break I sat among the smokers and habitually lit up a cigarette. The smoke hit my tongue with such potent acridity I reflexively tried to spit it from my mouth. Thinking that particular cigarette must have somehow spoilt, I lit another. But it had the same effect. Determined to make sense of this I asked another patient if I might try one of theirs. It was equally repugnant; I was unable to tolerate even one further drag. I stubbed it out and sat back, completely perplexed. It would be several years until I would understand that as the antipsychotics evacuated my system, so did the subliminal need to flood it with nicotine in an attempt to minimise the torment they were inflicting.

To Maarsten my ability to achieve something as positive as giving up smoking was more evidence that he was successfully helping me turn the corner. Six weeks later, and with no hospitalisations, he suggested I also begin reducing the *Epilim*. It never once dawned on me that either the *Zyprexa* or *Largactil* could actually have been causing me any mental damage. They were both sedating drugs, after all. I only became vehemently averse to them on discovering I could blame them for making me so huge. Certainly, no one else pointed any fingers at medication either. I continued to display plenty of less acute symptoms akin to those of psychological illness, so in our naïvety, Nigel, Mum and I believed the last six or seven months had simply been a random exacerbation of my illness – to be expected, apparently. Just as a chronic condition like asthma can become a dire threat to life under certain circumstances, so could a mood disorder. What was important now was to work at identifying what those circumstances were so we could formulate strategies to handle them better.

Maarsten instructed me to keep a record of all my daily thoughts and behaviours in a 'mood diary' – a commonly recommended exercise for bipolar patients. He'd first told me of the need to do this much earlier in the year, just after his diagnosis, but needless to say I became completely incapable of it. Mum had printed a month's worth of pro forma mood diary sheets off the internet, covered and bound them for me, but they remained untouched somewhere in my dresser drawer.

Maarsten stressed how imperative it was going to be to have a consistent record of my reactions to things, particularly as we'd agreed I could resume my professional writing course when college restarted in February, a couple of months away.

I dug out the diary again and began rating my mood, as specified by the instructions, as 'severe', 'high moderate', 'low moderate' or 'mild' under the category of either 'manic' or 'depressed'. Mum, by way of her regular evening phone call, would always check with me that it had been done.

There was plenty going on worthy of entries, such as the night I attended my sister-in-law's house-warming party and swallowed so much of my anti-anxiety medication I fell asleep after half an hour and was unable to be roused before ten o'clock the following morning. I also mindlessly reversed my car straight through the barricade of a split-level car park, leaving it teetering on its chassis until help arrived. By the time I was rescued quite a crowd of very entertained onlookers had gathered.

Exemplifying my still tempestuous mood was the incident, weeks later, when I told a senior lecturer in the middle of a tutorial at college to 'cut the bullshit' when I became irritated with his digressions. And I staged a walk-out against another teacher when she annoyed me one day by chastising a student while the class looked on.

'We don't have to stand for this,' I declared to the rest of the students, standing abruptly and knocking my chair back against the wall. With a 'let's go' motion of my hand, I got the entire class filing behind me out the door, swayed by my medication-fuelled charisma.

But interspersed with an array of behavioural blemishes was something distinctly resembling adjustment. I was cohesively and consistently remembering appointment times, providing care for Jemima, doing bits of the housework and, albeit with difficulty, fulfilling the basic requirements of my writing course.

When Jemima had turned two and a half, I suddenly realised that amidst all the drama and chaos she had missed being baptised. On the one hand I was sad that she hadn't received this sacrament as a newborn, which I'd always assumed any child of mine would. But on the other I was pleased that in my mental absence no one had been tempted to step in and arrange it for me. My baby had already been deprived of so much of her mummy's dedication and I'd been deprived of the joy of providing it. Arranging her baptism could go some way to amending this injustice. Filled with a long-forgotten sense of pride, I booked the church, invited the guests and selected the sweetest outfit for Jemima. And six weeks later, when the day of the event came around, I still had the presence of mind to host the celebration.

Jemima's beaming face in each and every photo of that day speaks volumes of her delight at having her mummy within reach again.

Almost midway into 2002, Maarsten reduced my required attendance at his rooms and the day programme to once weekly. I'd now also been weaned from the *Epilim*, leaving me on regular doses of *Faverin* and lithium only, with *Valium* on standby if I felt I needed it. To Maarsten, my apparently fairly tenuous grip on lucidity, combined with my turbulence of mood, was proof that lithium would always be required. If an acute manic episode struck again – which was what he said 'we' had survived during the past year – he emphasised he would not hesitate to hit hard again with the *Zyprexa*, *Largactil* and *Epilim*.

The nurse who ran the day programme began remarking on how good I was looking.

'The blunting has lifted from your eyes,' she said. She praised and commended me for the tremendous effort I was contributing to my recovery. She referred to a photograph she had copied and given to all the patients enrolled in the programme. It was a picture of a forest with ferns, shrubbery and thick ground cover growing all around – except in one section, which had been permanently flattened from walkers using it as a thoroughfare. She used the picture as a visual analogy for the kind of concerted effort, commitment and dedication that was required to change our dysfunctional behaviour and thought processes.

'See,' she said to me, holding the photo before me, 'you've made up your mind and you're beating that path to health. I'm so proud of you for putting in the hard work.'

Little did she know I was having to do no such thing. Although sublimely relieved by this hiatus of middle-of-the-night phone calls, trips to casualty and juggling the care of Jemima, Nigel and Mum were still on tenterhooks, waiting for the first sign of another launch into mania. Indeed, so was I.

It had been months since I'd started the mood diary and I simply couldn't ignore that I hadn't had a single occasion to rate my mood any higher than a 'low moderate' for either mania or depression. I seriously began questioning whether I actually had bipolar I disorder. I had a bit of a look around on the internet and discovered some articles describing the less severe version of the condition, bipolar II. At my next, now fortnightly, visit to Maarsten, I asked what he thought.

'You do not have bipolar II, you have bipolar I.'

'But is it still bipolar disorder if there's only been one distinct period of the illness that then subsides for ages?'

'Of course. That's the mood stabilisers doing their job.'

'Even if the mood swings disappear altogether?'

'Yes.'

'Even if the patient's not on medication any more?'

His voice took on a cautionary tone.

'Rebekah, we've discussed this before. You will always need, at a minimum, a therapeutic dose of lithium in your system. You have an illness that needs medicating. Don't lose sight of how destructive you can be at your worst.'

Knowing full well that a bipolar patient stopping medication of their own volition because they 'felt they didn't need it' was considered a reliable sign that mania was imminent, I didn't mention it again. He did suggest, however, that I try a reduction in *Faverin*.

With memories of the hideous experience the last time he'd done this to me still very fresh, I was extremely reluctant.

'Not like last time,' he said. 'We won't cut it out completely, just a reduction. Down, say, 50 milligrams to 150 milligrams. And if that works, we'll step you down again to 100. But if we can see from the first reduction it's not working, we'll go straight back up again.' I agreed but only on that final proviso.

Shortly after this reduction, I began crying frequently with no worthy trigger and was very easily angered at the slightest irritation. I was also dizzy and nauseous. I directly attributed these emotional symptoms to a resurfacing of my depression.

I'd tried twice now, unsuccessfully, to reduce antidepressants and this simply made it unequivocally evident to me that I needed them and that was that. The other more physical symptoms completely escaped me as having anything to do with a reduction of the drug – I put them down to an unfortunately timed virus.

When I told Maarsten of my symptoms he conceded I was probably right in my opinion that I wouldn't be able to do without at least some amount of antidepressant. He immediately reverted me to the original dose.

At breakfast a few days later Nigel handed me an application form: Centrelink (DHSS) – payments for people with disabilities, illnesses or injuries.

'Your mum and I have been talking about it. As long as you're unable to work . . .' his voice was heavy with sympathy, 'well, Bek, I'm afraid we're going to have to do something. You've got an appointment at the Southern Region office for one o'clock. Your mum said she'd go along with you.'

He placed an envelope bearing Fernview's logo on the bench in front of me.

'Dr Maarsten's written a letter of support. You'd better take it along.'

As he shut the door behind him on his way to work, I flipped the form face down on the kitchen bench so the concepts of 'Centrelink payment' and 'disability' might cease to inflict their degradation. I wanted to laugh at the very notion that I needed welfare, but knew I didn't really have that luxury. Reality was what it was, and I was still a long way from being well enough to hold down a job. Nigel's modest salary was simply not withstanding my medical costs, now exceeding around US$75,000, many of them not covered by health insurance. Unless something changed we might have to consider selling our house.

But I needn't have feared my dignity was to take another battering. The Centrelink clerk read my application no further than the part about Nigel's income. It was too high and I didn't qualify for a cent. Privately a little bit relieved, I calmly accepted the rejection and stood to leave the interview room. Mum grabbed my arm and pulled me back down, retorting on my behalf, 'You've got to be kidding! They're barely able to keep up with basic living expenses. They've got a child to support. What do you expect them to do? Sell their house?'

'Other than perhaps approval for some extra subsidised child care, I'm afraid...'

'But you can see it all there – we've written it all out – their expenses exceed their income.'

'As I said, apart from perhaps some extra child care...'

'And that's the best you can do?'

'I'm afraid so, ma'am.'

'For God's sake, these are not extravagant lifestyle choices they're making; they're medical expenses. What? You don't believe she's ill?'

'It's not that at all...'

'Just because she's not hobbling about or writhing in pain . . .? Oh, what's the use!' Mum quashed temptation to appeal to his conscience any further, realising it was bureaucratically invalidated.

FIFTEEN

One weekend, about two-thirds into 2002, I forgot to collect a prescription, forcing me to endure two days without *Faverin*. Emotional volatility began to gather speed again and so did nausea and dizziness. I was at the chemist door by opening time on Monday morning to get the pills and halt my spiralling depression. While I was waiting for the pharmacist to fulfil my prescription I asked the assistant for some over-the-counter nausea medication.

She knew me, and that I had diabetes. She selected a box of pills from the shelf and called to the pharmacist, 'Are these okay for a diabetic?'

The pharmacist came down to the counter with my box of *Faverin*.

'How long have you been feeling nauseous?'

'Only a day or so.'

'Have you missed any of these?' She indicated the *Faverin*.

'Two doses. I forgot to put in my prescription on Saturday.'

'Well, that's it then.' She went and got me a cup of water, broke open two blisters of *Faverin* and popped them in my hand. 'Take them right now. Your nausea will be from the withdrawal.'

Withdrawal! What withdrawal? What was she talking about?

I typed 'SSRI+withdrawal' into my web search engine when I got home. I was stunned when up cropped links to several discussion boards. I read in mouth-gaping amazement story after story of people unable to stop taking SSRIs. There was complaint after complaint of irritability, anger, tearfulness, depression, nausea, dizziness, even hypersensitivity to light and sound: all the things I'd experienced both times I'd tried to reduce the *Faverin*. My God.

One website with patient information about withdrawing from SS-RIs even gave this collection of symptoms a name (albeit a euphemistic one): SSRI discontinuation syndrome.

I was so angered. Why had no one told me? I'd asked pointblank about addiction to these bloody drugs!

It was the first thing I mentioned to Maarsten at my next visit. But he maintained there was no such thing as a 'discontinuation syndrome'. My trust in him, already under considerable strain, now buckled with the cumulative recollection of all his errors to date. There was the co-prescription of lithium and *Naprosyn* leading to lithium toxicity, and the failure to acknowledge any possibility of a link between the *Zyprexa* and my diabetes. Then there was the knowledge I'd gained a few weeks back while looking through the pharmaceutical reference text that the drug combination of *Prozac* and *Mellaril*, which Maarsten had pre-scribed in the early months of treatment, is strictly advised against be-cause it increases the risk of sudden heart failure.[1] And he apparently hadn't provided all my notes to the mood disorders specialist he'd sent me to for a second opinion. And now this!

How could I be sure that anything he had to say was accurate? How could I possibly accept his diagnosis of the lifelong stigmatising illness of bipolar disorder with any confidence?

There was only one way to test if I really did have it. I'd need to see if the symptoms were apparent while I was off the mood-controlling medication. I just had to find someone completely independent of Maarsten to assess my state of mind. But how? Dear God, how?

A couple of weeks later, I'd just slung the strap of my handbag over my shoulder and was rising from my chair in preparation to leave Maarsten's office when he asked me to wait, saying he had something significant to discuss with me. My first reaction was to wonder why he couldn't have discussed whatever it was sometime during the fifty-five near-silent preceding minutes, and my closely followed second reac-tion was to try and contain my rush of panic – what's he going to do to me now? But when he continued, his words were so unexpected, so thrilling, that I had to ask him to repeat them just to make sure it wasn't wishful thinking that had me hear him say, 'I'll be moving practices at the end of this month, starting up on my own quite a long way from here. I won't have admitting rights to any hospitals any more. I'm sorry I have to do this to you, but it really is unavoidable.'

Oh, wow! I couldn't have dreamt up anything more perfect than this. His new practice was more than an hour's drive all the way across the other side of town from my place; Maarsten was going to have to refer me on to someone else. Fate can be so amazing: just as you begin to succumb to a seemingly undefeatable onslaught of impossibility, it can drop a solution right into your lap.

'I know it will be difficult for you,' Maarsten continued, 'and it's going to take quite a bit of adjusting.' I nodded, solemn-faced, in agreement, while rejoicing on the inside. 'But nothing has to change before the end of the month, so you've got a few weeks to get used to the idea.'

I was so elated by this promise of reprieve that it took me a number of days before I began to wonder to whom Maarsten would pass me. Would it be someone from Fernview I already knew? Or would it be someone completely new, hired from elsewhere to take over Maarsten's role? Of course, ideally, it would be someone of my choosing, far away from Fernview, but I knew that wasn't going to happen. Oh well, beggars couldn't be choosers and, Lord knew, my prayers had been riddled with begging for something just like this to happen.

By the time my next meeting with Maarsten came round, out of curiosity I thought I'd ask if he'd decided yet who it might be. He looked at me, puzzled. 'What do you mea – Oh, I'm sorry, I mustn't have been very clear.' His next words hit me like a slap. 'When I move I expect you to come with me.'

I fired straight back, 'But what about the distance? You'll be miles from my place. It'll be a half-day round trip to come to your sessions.' I wasn't giving in without a fight.

'Yes, I realise that. That's why I said it would take some adjusting on your part. Many of my patients are in the same boat. Those who live on the north side of town and have had to travel a great distance to see me at Fernview are now very happy. But others, like you, understandably are less thrilled about the idea.'

'And what about hospital, if I need it? You said you wouldn't have admitting rights.' There had to be a loophole, something he didn't have an answer for.

'Correct, but if needed I can arrange for a colleague to look after you while you're in hospital. I can see you're not too pleased. We can reduce the frequency of your sessions. I think you might be ready to try going down to maybe three-weekly. That will lighten the burden at least a bit.'

'Yeah,' I said weakly, yielding inevitably to his omnipotence.

If only, if only, I had someone to talk to freely. Someone to absorb the overflow of my misery, on whom I could rest my anguish. Someone who wouldn't feel the need to medicate, hospitalise, tell my psychiatrist. Someone I could trust. I needed someone I could trust. But anyone who used to go by that description had turned informant in the name of my supposed welfare. There was no one. No one to whom every word out of my mouth did not pull with it a string of negative baggage from the past couple of years. No one. Except, wait . . . no one that I knew, perhaps, but what about people I didn't know and who didn't know me? There were hundreds if not thousands of them out there on the internet! Of course there were – I'd seen them all posting back and forth to each other on the discussion boards I'd been looking at for information on antidepressant withdrawal. Could there be a more perfect way to talk anonymously to an empathic ear?

Jemima was pottering about the garden while Nigel tinkered away at his car out in the garage. It was still an hour or more before lunch, so I seized the opportunity to log on to the Web. My search of depression +discussion+board delivered me over fifteen million results. I eagerly selected one that sounded legitimate, but was deflated to discover I had to register before being able to post a message. I would need to submit all my details required by the website's administrator. Then, if my registration was accepted, it said, confirmation of this along with my login details would be sent to my email address within twenty-four hours. That long? I tried a different board. It had the same registration requirements, though it didn't specify how long I would need to wait to get the email giving me the go-ahead. But I'd still have to wait.

It didn't matter how many others I tried – it was the same story. So I registered with two and accepted I wouldn't be talking to anyone just yet. I was happy to discover, though, that although I couldn't actually contribute anything, on some of the boards I could read other people's messages. Reading down the list of topics – 'another attempt, very lonely, how do I deal with this anxiety?' – I clicked on one that stood out from the others:

Toxic Psychiatry – you gotta read this book! Has anyone read this book by Peter Breggin? He's a psychiatrist and he writes about things like how ECT can damage your brain and that the modern psych medications are just as dangerous as the ones from the fifties. He talks a lot about chemical imbalance theories and that there's no evidence for any of it. He also says that there's no proof about genetic links to things like manic depression. You can bet your therapist probably isn't telling you about the stuff in this book. None of mine ever has. Anyone with a mental illness diagnosis should read this. It just totally blew me away. Signed by screen name: moody45.

Though the message was days old, it hadn't received a single reply from other members of the board. How I wished I had my login details. I wanted to ask moody45 some questions. What was this book? And who was Peter Breggin? It sounded astonishing, not to mention intriguing that he was labelling his own profession 'toxic'. I typed Peter Breggin into Google and found he had his own website – breggin.com. I went straight to it. The homepage was headed:

PSYCHIATRIC DRUG FACTS
What your doctor may not know about:
How psychiatric drugs really work

Adverse drug effects on the brain and mind
The role of the FDA
Drug company practices
Recent medical and legal developments
Electroshock and psychosurgery

Then a bio of Peter Breggin, including this:

Peter R Breggin began in the full time private practice of
psychiatry in 1968. Dr Breggin has been informing the professions, media and the public about the potential dangers of drugs,
electroshock, psychosurgery, involuntary treatment, and the biological theories of psychiatry for over three decades . . . In 1972 he
founded The International Center for the Study of Psychiatry and
Psychology . . . concerned with the impact of mental health theory
and practices upon individual well-being, personal freedom, and
family and community values . . . For thirty years Dr Breggin has
served as a medical expert in many civil and criminal suits including individual malpractice cases and product liability suits against
the manufacturers of psychiatric drugs. His work provided the
scientific basis for the original combined *Prozac* suits . . .

What potential dangers of drugs and electroshock? Combined
Prozac suits? What the hell . . . ? There'd been litigation over *Prozac*?
Why? What was there about these treatments I hadn't been told? I felt
my cheeks flush with heat, the air around me thicken. What did he mean
by concerns with the impact of mental health theory and practices upon
individual well-being and personal freedom? Was he talking about a
situation like mine?

Where was this Breggin located? Could I get a referral to him?
Would it be too far-fetched to hope that he might be an Australian? Yes,
it would be. His postal address was listed halfway down the page: New
York. Of course, America.

I explored the site a little further and came across a list of Breggin's publications, both scientific articles and books. I spotted the one

mentioned by moody45, *Toxic Psychiatry*, and jotted down the publishing details along with two others: *Brain-disabling Treatments in Psychiatry*, published 1997, and *The Antidepressant Fact Book*, published in 2001.

Until this moment I'd been dreading the arrival of the following day, Monday, because with it came my appointment with Maarsten, but now I couldn't wait for it to come round so I could start ringing some bookshops. There would be great comfort in knowing for certain that I could get hold of one of Breggin's books. It felt as if finally there might be someone on my side. Being cloaked in the security of that notion would make sitting in the chill of Maarsten's judgement that bit easier to endure.

I'd just hung up from my third call to local bookstores. No one had heard of Peter Breggin or any of his books.

'You could try Borders,' the last shop assistant advised. 'They're American-owned and stock some US publications that are otherwise unavailable in Australia. Your other option is Amazon, of course.' Expressing my gratitude for her suggestions I hung up the phone and went straight to look up the number for Borders – the quickest option, it seemed.

The man at Borders said that *Brain-disabling Treatments in Psychiatry* and *The Antidepressant Fact Book* would need to be ordered in. As for *Toxic Psychiatry*, he wasn't sure – it was a much older book, published 1993, and he couldn't be sure that it would still be in print.

'Actually, you wouldn't believe it,' he then said, 'but the computer shows we've got one in stock. Have you got a minute? I'll just go and check that it's actually on the shelf.'

I said that I did have a minute, although I was lying because I was going to be late for Maarsten and I knew he would make something of my tardiness.

The man returned to the phone to confirm they did have the copy but it was in pretty bad shape from customers flicking through it. I said I'd be there later that afternoon to collect it.

I wanted to be alone and completely uninterrupted when I started reading *Toxic Psychiatry*. Not only because I intended to savour every detail, but also because it was a really thick book, obviously containing quite a bit of technical information, and my brain was not the swift decipherer and calculator it used to be; it was going to take large amounts of effort not only to concentrate on the text but to retain what it contained.

It was close to midnight when I finally had the solitude I required. Jemima had stopped calling out for a glass of water, for her quilt to be tucked in or for her teddy bear to be picked up off the floor. I rolled away from a sleeping, snoring Nigel and went to the bed in the spare room. I lay on my back, *Toxic Psychiatry* propped on my chest, rising high and falling heavy with my breath. I read the same line printed on the cover, an extract from a review of the book, that I'd read over and over since getting it home: 'An all-out attack against the deception, half-truths and downright lies of psychiatry'. I opened it and hoped that I could handle what I was about to read.

The book was divided into five sections that appeared to be independent of each other. The table of contents listed topics such as depression and bipolar disorder, ECT, lithium and antipsychotic drugs. Because the book was published in 1993, when atypical antipsychotic drugs such as *Zyprexa* and SSRI antidepressants like *Prozac* had only been around for a few years, there was very little information on these. But the section on antipsychotics covered those from the older neuroleptic class, of which I'd been on two – *Mellaril* and *Largactil*. I decided that would be as good a place as any to start.

Maarsten had told me little about any of the drugs he'd prescribed me. When he'd given me these two I was told they were sedatives, nothing more. At one stage when he'd really ramped up the dosage of *Largactil* he'd given me a second pill, an antidote by the name of benztropine, with the message to take it if I started to get trembling in my hands. That was it.

Now I read with increasing sadness how these drugs had been impeding the function of my nerve pathways from my deeper brain to the frontal lobes – the same pathways that are cut in a surgical lobotomy. I read how a staggeringly high number of people on these drugs end up with hideous adverse effects, some of them irreversible. I read the list, feeling incredibly fortunate I'd escaped suffering them. Then I reeled as I read one unfamiliar word with an all-too-familiar description: akathisia.

'A bizarre form of hyperactivity with an inner irritability that drives the person to move about . . . Sometimes it can reach extreme proportions of anxiety and anguish. [It's] typically found in up to half of the patients taking neuroleptics (antipsychotics).'

I held the book closer to the inadequate throw of light from the bedside lamp and read the words over; they seemed to stand from the page alone. Maarsten did that to me? I had to fight an urge to vomit.

Sleep was out of the question that night as I lay there blinking into the blackness, stuck in a loop of thought about the multitude of times the evidence of akathisia had been so blatantly obvious to Maarsten and to the nursing staff at Fernview. And what did Maarsten do when I expressed my textbook symptoms to him? Gave me more of the drugs that were causing them. He'd induced the suffering that I'd seen no solution for but death, then sat back and labelled me mad for my reactions. Lying curled on my side, I pulled the quilt higher and clutched it tight around me – pointless, though, for it wasn't the cold from which I quivered.

Attempts at planning an escape from Maarsten consumed me over the next few days, to a point where there was little room for anything else. I could barely sleep or face eating. Both Nigel and Jemima would repeat themselves three or four times before I'd notice they were speaking to me. But I did not stumble upon any solution with practical merit that had not already been explored to the point of exhaustion many times over. Yet to hell with practicality. This was my *life*.

In my desperation more daring concepts began to look feasible. Perhaps I could register with a new GP somewhere far away – say I'd just moved into the area, and get a referral to someone there. I'd manage the travel. I could tell Maarsten that Nigel might be getting an interstate transfer with work and we could be moving. Then I could just cancel any future appointments and change our home phone number. Maarsten might assume we'd moved and just let me go. Oh, who was I trying to kid? No, he wouldn't. One phone call to Nigel's office would blow the whole charade. If anything was going to fast-track me back to hospital with a skinful of drugs it'd be getting caught out scheming to 'emancipate' myself like that.

No, stupid, stupid. Even if I was to move legitimately it'd be with nothing short of a full handover of my clinical history to a psychiatrist of Maarsten's choosing.

What if I was to run away? Take Jemima with me. Would Maarsten send the police? Even if he didn't, Nigel would be sure to.

Nigel had long ago stopped asking me how I was feeling, even in passing, simply because I think he'd become terrified of the answer. But my stress must have been so apparent now that he made a point of asking, 'Whatever's going on? You'll talk to Maarsten about it when you see him next, won't you?' To which I burst into tears, probably ensuring Nigel would never make that mistake again.

Why didn't I just go and get *Toxic Psychiatry* and show Nigel what I'd read? Just tell him outright what I now knew about the treatments I'd been given. Because Nigel and I rarely shared a conversation about anything these days, let alone one about a topic of that magnitude. And because my diagnoses and past behaviours pretty much negated the validity of anything of substance that came out of my mouth. As far as Nigel was concerned, the nine-year-old writings of one unfamiliar psychiatrist from America would do nothing to counter his distrust of me or an opinion I voiced.

What a futile existence. I had no life, only a life sentence. With the dawn of each day I sank further into myself, the only place I felt safe. At least for the time being. It was inevitable, I supposed, that sooner or later that self-injurious drive would resurface, and then where the hell would I flee?

Dying for a Cure

A couple of weeks earlier, Mum had received a parcel from her friends in Britain. It contained a video tape and an accompanying message dated 17 October 2002:

> Thought you might find this programme of interest. Not sure whether you'll get it there in Australia or not. It was on BBC TV here the other night. It's about some remarkable newly discovered effects of the newest kinds of antidepressant pills. Saw it and immediately thought of all the heartbreaking stuff you were telling us about Bek when you were visiting last year. Don't know if it relates to her particular situation, but thought you might find it of some use. Pray it offers some hope. Trust you're both keeping well. Sending lots of love from damp old England. Evelyn and George P.S. Hope the tape's compatible with your system there. I've been assured it should be.

How considerate of them, Mum had thought, turning the tape to look at its labelled spine: *The Secrets of Seroxat*.[2]

Seroxat, Seroxat. Not a drug she'd ever heard of. Perhaps it's brand new, she'd pondered. No doubt it was being touted as the latest panacea. Her scepticism dampened Evelyn's optimism and Mum had put the tape aside, intending to watch it at some stage but not giving it terribly high priority. But seeing me now, disturbed and upset and therefore apparently on the crest of what she anticipated to be a descent into the depressive cycle of my mood disorder, she wondered if it might be worthwhile learning what this drug might have to offer. She could barely believe she was possibly about to encourage me to try yet another, but if it had the slightest chance of hindering a recurrence of the nightmarish events of my last plummet, and if Evelyn had faith in it . . .

It was with a good deal of hesitation she presented the tape to me. She knew too well from plenty of past experience that I was likely to dismiss any input from her regarding my treatment as ignorant interference.

'But I thought we could watch it together,' she pressed, when I'd given her the negative response she'd predicted. 'Don't you want to at least see what it's all about? It's a new drug – it might mean a new possibility.'

'It's not a new drug, Mum.' My irritation was obvious. With all I'd been learning of late, the last thing I needed was Mum suggesting I try more medication. '*Seroxat's* just another name for one of the SSRIs. *Aropax*, I think it is. And I'm sure I know what it's going to be all about: how for some lucky people it's been the secret to saving their lives, or some such crap. I just don't really need that right now, Mum. Thanks anyway.'

The issue was dropped immediately and, once she'd left, so was the tape – in the bin.

But a couple of days later, I read an email from Mum, forwarded from her English friend, and I was scrambling through household waste to find the tape. It was this bit that had turned me scavenger:

The show's caused the most startling reaction over here. Apparently the BBC received hundreds upon hundreds of emails after it aired. Many of them were from people who had unwittingly suffered ill-effects of the drugs – like the ones discussed in the show – while thinking they were just experiencing a worsening of their mental state . . . it appears many doctors are not even aware . . .

Mum had added: 'Have you watched it yet? Sounds like it's not what either of us assumed it to be.'

In my haste to view it now, I misaligned the tape against the slot several times before it was finally swallowed by the player. I sat back, hugged my knees into my chest and pressed 'play'. A moment's footage of the show's introduction flashed on, followed rapidly by a screen full of squiggly horizontal lines and a ghastly squealing sound from the VCR. We hadn't used the thing in ages and it was on its last legs. I leapt from the chair, thumped on 'stop', 'eject', and reached in to salvage the cassette. Trailing after it as I gently pulled it from the slot was some of the tape, dragged from its casing by the faulty player. After smoothing out the tangles and winding everything back on the spool, I sat back in my chair and, fingers crossed, tried to play it again.

It now appeared to be okay. I turned up the volume:

[Narrator]: The chances are you, or someone you know, is taking *Seroxat*. It's almost taken over *Prozac* as Britain's most popular antidepressant. But for some, the 'happy pills' have a darker side . . .

A darker side? Oh, Christ. What was I going to learn now?

[Narrator] Ed started to suffer from anxiety. His mother took him to see a doctor. The doctor prescribed *Seroxat* . . . after going on the drug, the son she knew began to change.
[Ed's mum]: . . . he said . . . he didn't feel real sometimes . . . he just became much more introverted and liable just to go off into a mood for nothing at all . . .
[Narrator]: And things were to get worse, much worse Within a fortnight Ed started mutilating himself . . .

The twenty-something rock-band member pulled away his clothing to reveal self-inflicted cigarette lighter burns and razor blade cuts.

[Shelley Joffre, interviewer]: Had you ever done anything like that before?
[Ed]: Never. Never, no . . . I went back to the doctor just a month after I first started to take *Seroxat*, and that's sort of a little while after the burning and what-have-you had started. They said continue taking *Seroxat* . . .
[Joffre]: So there was no suggestion it was the drug causing it?
[Ed]: No, not at all.

Like an unforseen punch, this information left me winded.

[David Healy, Director, North Wales Department of Psychological Medicine]: . . .

Ah. I'd seen this guy's name on the Web.

. . . We'd run a trial where we'd given a group of healthy volunteers an SSRI. These included GPs, consultant psychiatrists, senior nurses . . . What we'd seen was when people went on the wrong drug for them, that they went through a state of mental turmoil . . . a state where people are having thoughts and impulses that they've never had before, thoughts of harming themselves or others . . . Within a few days of being on the drug they begin to have thoughts like this.

No way. No *way*.

I hit the rewind button on the remote so I could hear 'Ed' again. But when I pressed 'play', the player squealed its garble again for a second, then silence. The screen displayed a blank, deathly blue. There was no repairing the film this time, it'd been snapped clean in two. I cursed the machine, but only half-heartedly – I'd heard for the moment about as much as I wanted to. Momentarily numbed by what I'd watched, I sat back in the chair and ran my fingers over the scarred ridges in my forearm. I hadn't been on *Seroxat* but I knew from my recent reading that all the SSRIs were so similar in action that to just about all intents and purposes they could be grouped together. Had an SSRI played some part in my mental demise? No, I'd been self-harming well before I'd taken anything, hadn't I? Wasn't that why I first sought treatment?

'Oh, God,' I said out loud, squinting through the mental fog of the last three years. What drug was I first put on?

I strained hard, but in vain. Though I was loath to admit it, all the drugs and especially the ECT had dimmed my cognition and memory. Random chunks of the past (both before and after the treatments) were now blanks. I'd frequently lose my train of thought – sometimes mid sentence – and I'd struggle quite often even to recall familiar words, like names of common objects: footpath, fork, clothes line . . . How was

I going to remember details from a couple of years ago?

I picked up the phone and called Mum.

'How are you?' she asked.

'Stunned. Stunned. I just watched the video.'

'So, what was it all about? Any value in it?'

'Like nothing you could imagine. It was about side effects – side effects I never knew existed . . . The people on the tape, they didn't know they existed either . . .'

'Evelyn said that, but what sort of –'

In my eagerness to share my new knowledge and get to the question I so urgently wanted answered, I kept talking as if Mum hadn't, my words gathering pace.

'There was a professor – Healy. He said he'd done a trial, a trial on healthy people, and they began to act like they were mentally ill after they were put on an antidepressant.'

'Right . . . just backtrack a minute –'

'Hang on, I've got to tell you. There was this guy, a young guy, given an antidepressant 'cause he was anxious, or something. Get this – he started to harm himself – never done it before – started to harm himself after taking the drug.'

At the sound of me so wound up, Mum began to regret she hadn't watched the video first, or at the least insisted she watch it with me. She hoped to goodness it hadn't triggered a swing in my mood, as it was well documented certain stimuli could.

'Did you get that?' I added with irritation at her lack of response to what I'd just said. 'He began to harm himself *after* he went on the antidepressant. Never done it before.'

'So, what were they getting at? That the antidepressant had caused it to happen?'

'Yes, exactly.'

'Wow. Seems like a pretty dramatic claim.'

'As I said, it wasn't just that guy, there was a professor too. He'd conducted his own trial and found these drugs can be really dangerous.'

'Hmm.' Mum knew there had to be another side to all the glowing reports about all these antidepressants that had dominated for so long.

But as for the accuracy of what I was telling her right now, well . . . who knew? She wanted to see the show herself before drawing any conclusions, but of course she couldn't because of the chewed-up tape.

'Mum, what I need to know is when I began to harm myself. I was really hoping you might remember.'

'Oh, gosh. I only became aware of that sort of thing long after it had begun. Both you and Nigel were keen to save me from it, I think.'

Damn it.

'I do know it started very early on,' she added.

'I really need to find out exactly when.'

'Why is it so important?'

'Because it was me doing that which formed the basis for so much of the treatment that followed. What if the really crazy stuff happened after the antidepressant? What if I never needed it – what if the cure was actually the cause? There might be nothing wrong with me.' I was thinking out loud and realised I'd said too much.

'Just steady on a minute. I'd be the first one to accept the antidepressants might have had the propensity to exacerbate your symptoms, but don't go getting carried away. You've been doing so much better since Dr Maarsten's got the lithium right, but don't get lulled into a false sense of security. Perhaps you can reconsider stopping the *Faverin* based on what you've just learnt, but don't make the mistake many people with bipolar disorder do and stop your mood stabiliser because you think you're doing better. Don't throw the baby out with the bath water.'

I got straight on to the BBC's website once I'd hung up from Mum, and was relieved to find a transcript for *The Secrets of Seroxat*. Now I could read the parts of the programme our malfunctioning VCR had caused me to miss, and have proof and a record, if I needed it, of what I'd just seen.

After I'd put Jemima to bed that night I approached Nigel, tentatively. I knew he didn't like to reflect on any of my past crises.

'Nige, had I harmed myself before I'd been given antidepressants?'

'Yeah. You must've. That's why you were given them, wasn't it?'

'Are you absolutely sure about that?'

'Not absolutely.'

'Can you remember the first time I actually did anything?'

'Bek, I've tried hard not to think about it. And I'd prefer not to now, okay.'

'Please, this is important. Can you just remember where I was – home or hospital? What did I use?'

'It's the past,' he snapped. 'Can we just leave it there? Please?' He turned and retreated outside to his workshop.

I was drifting off to sleep that night when I was struck by a recollection. I'd been keeping a diary at Elm Court and Ashgrove all that time ago. It had been part of my therapy to record my thoughts and feelings. I could remember writing poetry in it and showing it to Max. Perhaps it held the answer. But where the hell would it be?

I crept out of bed, taking care not to wake Nige, and started rummaging through drawers and cupboards in the study.

'Bek, what are you doing?' Nigel was standing in the doorway looking highly suspicious.

I'd been so engrossed I hadn't heard him coming. I cringed as I realised the impression my enthusiastic activity in the early hours of the morning would give.

'Did you take your lithium today?' I resisted the urge to tell him where to go.

'U-huh. I'm just trying to find a guided meditation CD,' I said, thinking on the run. 'I thought I could listen to it for a bit with headphones and it might help me to sleep.'

Humility and an even temper were the key if I wanted to be left alone.

'All right.' He turned back towards the bedroom. 'Just don't be up all night.'

My efforts were futile that night, but while searching through some boxes out in my studio the next day, still partially unpacked since we moved in, I struck it lucky. I turned the cover of the A4 lecture pad, with 'Elm Court etc' scribbled across it. A spill of some sort had caused the ink on the first couple of pages to run. I could just make out a few lines of some poetry:

Wind blow me away, rain make me solvent ... with this world
I cannot cope, with myself I cannot cope ... dream or death the
only escape

I was taken aback by the state of my writing: jagged, hassled. The
marked pages crackled as I continued to turn. More poetry and prose.
Then this:

> I'm writing this from inside a psychiatric hospital. A few days
> ago I was sent home on overnight leave from Elm Court and
> I mutilated myself, cut my arm up with a paring knife. Once
> back at the hospital I did it again, couldn't help myself. They
> were getting ready to send me home for good, but now, because
> of what I've done, I'm here. Max had asked me in a couple of
> sessions if I'd ever been into self harm and I answered no. I'd
> actually been disgusted with him just for mentioning it. Now
> I've gone and done this to myself. I'm scared out of my mind.

I dropped back on my haunches, the book flopping to my knees,
and stared into oblivion. The implications of the last couple of months'
discoveries were just too big to swallow.

SIXTEEN

A quick call to the reception desk at Elm Court soon supplied me with the name and phone number of the pharmacy that delivered their prescriptions. I phoned the shop in question and requested a tax invoice listing all my prescribed drugs during the time I was a patient at the mother and baby unit. The computer print-out revealed what I was hoping, and fearing: I'd been taking *Lustral* for something like ten or twelve days when I'd cut my arm. I could remember so vividly being told a multitude of times that SSRIs take weeks to have an effect.

I paid a visit to my local pharmacist and asked her if she could explain the actual action of SSRIs once they'd entered your body. She seemed happy to oblige.

'Which one in particular?'

After I had told her, she flicked her pharmaceutical reference book to the page for *Lustral* and put it on the counter in front of me. 'If there's something you don't understand, just call out to me.'

I learnt that a single dose of *Lustral* reaches peak levels in the system after approximately five to eight hours and begins to clear after about twenty-six.[1] *Faverin* reaches peak levels in three to eight hours and is clearing after about fifteen.[2] Bingo!

Just because there was likely to be no therapeutic effect of *Lustral* before a couple of weeks didn't mean there would be no effect at all.

I decided I really needed to get my own copy of a pharmaceutical reference guide. I knew now that I didn't just have to try to get away from Maarsten; I had to get away from psychiatry. But since so far that was proving unachievable, perhaps my only hope would be to work on getting psychiatry as far as possible away from me.

I had cancelled my last session with Maarsten with the concocted excuse of the flu. But tomorrow's appointment would be unavoidable. I'd go and I would tell him how well I was doing. Not great, just well. Even and tempered. I would focus on achievement rather than feelings: attending class, caring for Jemima, driving the car without crashing it, calmly relinquishing control of family and personal finances to Nigel without giving him a hard time about it. Gradual, logical improvement; even and tempered. There'd be no mention that I'd halved my lithium and reduced my *Faverin* by 25 per cent. And I'd bite my lip hard at the urge to scream that I thought he was a dangerous man who had no right to call himself a therapist.

I think my guardian angel must have come along with me to my appointment that day and influenced Maarsten where I could not. Maarsten compared my most recent blood lithium results (done just before I'd reduced the dosage) against the previous test, and satisfied himself the levels were still satisfactory.

Then he said, 'Well, truly, Rebekah, you're doing so very well now I think we can leave it a few months till we meet again. I'll give you enough prescriptions to tide you over. Just call me if there's a problem.'

I could physically feel him loosen the reins. It wasn't just the reduction in appointment frequency; it was the way he looked at me and spoke to me: like a person, not a case to be managed. He had handed me a tangible gift of empowerment. I almost wept.

I made some headway on my plans before sharing them with Nigel. I waited till it was the weekend, till I was sure his head would be free of work and he could absorb what I was about to say. I served him a piece of freshly baked teacake with a sugary cup of tea and sent Jemima out to play.

I sat next to him at the table.

'As you know, Maarsten's really happy with my progress . . .'

'It's not just Maarsten. It's everyone. You've been doing great, especially the last couple of months. At last you're putting in the effort. Just see what you can do when you put your mind to it.'

'Everybody keeps saying that – "putting in the effort". But the truth is I can't take credit for any effort. I've been really good recently, right, you said it yourself.'

'Yes, you're almost back to being the person I first met.'

'Nige, I've been weaning myself off my medications.'

His fork dropped to the plate.

'Nigel, please, before you get angry, just listen to me. I've never been on so little medication and I've never been more stable.'

I handed him a transcript of *The Secrets of Seroxat* printed from the internet, Peter Breggin's book with all the bits on akathisia highlighted, along with a few more articles from the *British Medical Journal* on the same topic – a few of the vast number of documents I would continue to collect over the ensuing years, elucidating the true cause of my mental collapse.

'I know my integrity is in shreds, but please read this stuff tonight and we'll talk again in the morning.'

He nodded in agreement and I kissed his forehead.

'That's quite unbelievable,' said Nigel to me at breakfast. 'I can't believe it. This akathisia,' he read from one of the *British Medical Journal* articles, 'it says ". . . urge to move, patients often pace with an inability to sit still . . ."[3] You used to pace all the time. I thought it had something to do with your mania. And it says that a terrible sense of dread may be felt in the abdomen. I can remember you saying your stomach constantly felt the way it does when a rollercoaster takes a big drop.'

'And what did you think about the BBC documentary?'

'I was pretty floored by that too.'

I showed him the list of medications and their corresponding dates that I had got from the pharmacy that supplied Elm Court, and the list since sent to me from the pharmacy that supplied Ashgrove.

'I'd been on *Lustral* for roughly ten or twelve days when I cut myself the first time. It was that weekend I'd been sent home for leave from Elm Court – the same one I confronted our bikie neighbour in the driveway, remember?'

'How could I forget.'

'Well, look at this: after that incident Max upped the antidepressants.

It was about then that I became really suicidal. I never got better and he just kept heaping on the drugs. What if it was the drugs that were causing it?'

I could see it was all a bit much for Nigel to digest, but I had to risk pushing my luck. There was more he needed to know.

'This article is by the psychiatrist who wrote *Toxic Psychiatry*. It's about SSRIs and how they can induce mania. He references heaps of studies that have shown mania after taking SSRIs, particularly *Faverin*. What if,' I selected my words carefully, 'what if the antidepressants caused all the serious stuff to happen – the self-harm, the suicidal feelings and then later the mania? What if it appeared to be bipolar mood disorder but in fact it was all caused by the drugs?'

'Bek, I'd really love this to be true, but –'

'The only way we're going to know is if I wean myself off the medication – completely – and I become my normal self. That's what I want to do, but I'm going to need your help.'

'God, Bek, I don't know.'

'Nige, you've never liked that I've been taking medication anyway. All I ask is for you to watch me. I'll decrease the rest of my medication periodically and I'll tell you each time I do it. You need to keep a really close eye on me and tell me if I start acting strange. If that happens I'll just start taking it again.'

'Okay, I guess. I suppose we haven't got much to lose. Things couldn't get much worse than what we've already had to deal with.'

'Thanks, Nige. Thank you.'

The lithium was the first to go. I gradually reduced the remainder of it over a couple of weeks without incident. I'd read about the potential for 'reactive mania' upon cessation of long-term lithium treatment, which had made me quite wary. Even though I'd warned Nigel about the possibility, it could be hard – near impossible – for him to know the difference between a withdrawal response and the real thing. But nothing of the sort occurred.

I did have one reaction to the withdrawal of the lithium, though. One very significant, undeniable reaction, which I embraced with the whole of my heart and soul. Did I say heart? Soul? Embrace? My authentic emotions returned and they flooded my deadened heart and flaccid soul. The essence of life, smothered by the lithium, was once again plump and healthy. The simplest of life's little pleasures were again injected with colour.

The first of them, which will stay impressed in my memory forever, occurred when I was with Jemima at the swimming pool. We were playing in the water, I was dunking her up and down like a teabag and she was squealing with delight. And I felt it too! I looked about me at all the other parents with their children, laughing and splashing and enjoying life, and I felt it too! Life was life again, not just survival.

I decided to try to host an Australia Day barbecue at our house in January 2003 – hopefully to prove to myself that I could. Most of our extended family came along. It was lovely having everyone relate to me with warmth and relaxed acceptance again, rather than guarded caution, bracing themselves whenever I approached for conversation.

Yes, it was wonderful, but also bittersweet. With the ascension of the drug haze came awareness: awareness of right and wrong, propriety and impropriety, and the awareness that I'd behaved abominably around these very same people for the past couple of years. It was like the morning after a party at which I'd been the only one debauchedly drunk, where I had vague and broken memories of making a complete fool of myself, but knew full well that the other guests would remember exactly what I'd done with striking clarity.

Mum pulled me aside to congratulate me on hosting a wonderful day.

'It's incredible. You're just like the old you. What do you think has made the difference?'

'Do you think you could hang around for a while when the others have gone? There's something I need to talk to you about.'

'Sure. Everything okay?' I could tell she thought she might've spoken too soon.

'Everything's fine. I've just got something I need to explain to you.'

We sat down on my bed. I took a deep preparatory breath.

'What is it, Bek? What's on your mind?'

'You remember when I told you about what I saw on that documentary about *Seroxat*?'

'Mm, yeah, I do. Why? What? Have you come off the *Faverin*? That's it, isn't it? That's the difference. I've had a feeling the lithium was all you needed. I'm so pleased.'

'You're partly right. I'm on a little less than half the *Faverin* and I'm not taking any lithium.'

'Oh, Bek, you can't –'

'I haven't been taking anywhere near an effective level for a couple of months,' I hurried on.

'You're kidding? And you've been all right?'

'I'm not kidding, and yes, I haven't felt more normal in years.'

'Nigel knows?'

'We've had a pact. He's been watching me.'

'And everything's been okay?'

'Yes, Mum, it has.'

'Are you going to stay on the *Faverin*?'

'No, that's going too. It's just excruciatingly difficult to stop.'

She put her hand on my knee and gave it a little squeeze. I could see that she was hopeful, but not quite ready to celebrate. That was okay. I had a lot of trust to regain.

She phoned me later that night.

'I've just been looking at some SSRI discussion boards on the internet. There are so many stories like yours. So many cases where they've even *caused* mania.'

'I know.'

'Right from the start I suspected some of that medication was magnifying your symptoms, making you sicker, but I had no idea the full extent of what it was capable of. You know, you got so far down the track of self-destruction that when Maarsten came up with the diagnosis of bipolar, I think I was only too willing to accept it. It seemed to fit, and you did seem to even out on lithium, at first, anyway. Oh my God.

Think back. Dr Roosfeld wanted you off all that stuff. He wanted a clean slate – to see the real you. If only he'd tried a more gradual, gentle approach. Oh, it makes me feel sick.'

'It's okay, Mum. None of us knew.'

'Are you going to tell Maarsten you're off the lithium?'

'And what do you think his reaction's going to be? He's been adamant, defiant even, all along that his diagnosis is right. He's told me that even with one manic episode the bipolar label sticks and that cessation of medication is the first sign of mania, that it means the patient has lost awareness of their own condition. And besides, as if he's going to admit he got it that wrong. Think of the implications.'

'Yes, I know. He had us all convinced about the bipolar and the importance of staying on the lithium for the rest of your life. But it's not only Maarsten here. What about Braydle? If you're right in what you're saying, he's the one who got the ball rolling.'

'I wish I could get hold of my medical records so I could really see the connections between the drug changes and the changes in my condition. See if there's a clear-cut link that Braydle and Maarsten should have picked up on. But I'm only entitled to my public medical records. Braydle's and Maarsten's records are their practices' private property. If they don't want to give them to me they don't have to.'

'You're kidding. Are you sure?'

'One hundred per cent. I checked out the Freedom of Information laws.'*

'Well, I kept a diary.'

'You did?'

'U-huh. I don't have much from Elm Court, but from Ashgrove on I've kept records of your medications, your admissions, what Braydle and Maarsten were saying, your behaviour.'

'Oh, Mum. That's fantastic. Can I see it?'

'I might have to have a look through it myself first. There might be a bit of censoring I need to do. I think some of it will be pretty confrontational.'

---

*This was Freedom of Information applicable to Australian legislation, which could differ from that of the British system.

'Okay, if you must. But don't spare me too much. It's stuff I really need to know.'

Nigel said he would come along to my next appointment with Maarsten. He was urging me to tell him I was no longer on the lithium and explain how well I was doing. It was now February 2003 and I'd been off it completely for about two months, but hadn't had a therapeutic level of it in my system for about three.

Nige said he would sit in the waiting room and if Maarsten tried to come the heavy and force me back on it, or put me in hospital, he'd come in and stick up for me. I was in agreement until I was actually at Maarsten's rooms and was hit with a recollection of the last time Nigel came with me to try and influence Maarsten to refer me on to another psychiatrist. He couldn't have cared less what Nigel thought or had to say. The same would happen this time, I was sure, and I chickened out.

'Rebekah,' Maarsten called me in. He looked me thoroughly up and down. 'You look different.'

'I've lost twenty kilos, that might be it.'

'Yes, I can see. But it's more than that. It's your face, your expression. You look like a completely different person.'

No, Dr Maarsten. This is me. A completely different person is what you and Dr Braydle turned me into.

'Looks like the perseverance finally paid off. It's not unusual for it to take some time to adjust to medication. It's a very individual thing. But we've obviously finally struck the right maintenance combination.'

Allow him his glory – say nothing, say nothing. I'd just finished telling him how unremarkable my life was at present and was desperately trying to conjure up a believable excuse as to why I hadn't found the time in the last three months to get my lithium levels checked when he announced something that hit my ears like the sweetest music.

'Well, I see no reason to continue with regular appointments any more. Your GP can continue to check your lithium levels and write your prescriptions. Just give me a call in six months, or sooner if you need to. Does that sound all right?'

All right? All right? You have no idea.

'Sure,' I said casually. 'I'll call you.' Just as soon as hell freezes.

I walked from his room with the jubilance of a pardoned prisoner.

◆◆◆◆◆◆

I warmly embraced the return of a life lost as all the familiar ways I used to think and feel came flooding back. I increased my contact hours at college and started getting distinctions and high distinctions for my work. I reduced Jemima's day-care hours to cover only the time I had to attend class. She was now also spending a few hours a week at kindergarten, and for the rest I wanted to spend every minute with her. I was struck with sorrow at the realisation of how much of her life, her love and her gorgeous personality I had missed. I knew I'd never be able completely to recover time lost, but boy, was I sure going to try.

My precious, precious girl. She was three years old and only now were we getting to bond.

Trying to stop the antidepressant was a thorn in my side – I'd often make a reduction only to find I couldn't function with what it did to me and had to increase the dose slightly again. It was a real 'two steps forward, one step back' process. The last 25 milligrams were by far the hardest.

One focus of the BBC's *The Secrets of Seroxat* documentary was an investigation into the prevalence of SSRI withdrawal symptoms and the lack of accurate information regarding them. A unique feature of the programme was a nine-month-long video diary of a 22-year-old woman and her plight as she ceased taking *Seroxat*. She missed almost a year of university as the severe withdrawal effects of the drug kept her housebound. She experienced trembling, sweating, hallucinations, headaches and what she described as electric-shock sensations for days following each dosage reduction. She needed to pare down the tablets with a knife in order to make the reductions small enough to minimise these horrible effects. Towards the end, when she could no longer get the tablets small enough, she resorted to taking the medication in liquid form, measured out in a syringe.

These withdrawal problems are not unique to *Seroxat*. They can occur upon dosage reduction of any of the SSRIs. In the UK there have been far more reports of withdrawal problems with SSRIs than with any other medicinal drugs.[4] The symptoms of SSRI withdrawal can be divided into two groups. The first group may be unlike anything you've experienced before, and include the following: dizziness; electric-shock sensations and other strange tingling or painful sensations; nausea, diarrhoea, headaches; muscle spasms or tremor; agitated or other kinds of vivid dreams; and hallucinations.

The other group are the symptoms that might lead you or your physician to think that the features of your original problem are re-emerging. These include: depression and anxiety (probably the most common two symptoms); labile mood (emotions swinging wildly); irritability; confusion; fatigue; insomnia; sweating; feelings of unreality; and change of personality.[5]

David Healy explains that once you know what you're dealing with, it can be quite simple to distinguish between SSRI withdrawal symptoms and the problem the drug was prescribed for in the first place. First, if the problem begins immediately on reducing or halting a dose, or begins within hours, days or perhaps even weeks of so doing, then it is likely to be withdrawal. If the original problem has been treated and you are doing well, then on discontinuing treatment no new problems should show up for several months, or indeed several years. Second, if the feelings disappear when you are put back on the SSRI or the dose is put back up, then it is likely to be withdrawal.[6]

One doctor admits in *The Secrets of Seroxat* that he finds having patients affected by withdrawal quite useful in getting them to remain compliant with his advice: 'I've actually found the withdrawal effect to be quite handy for a few people. It had prompted them to go back on the pills, which is very helpful.'[7]

I wonder how many other doctors share this treatment strategy.

After *The Secrets of Seroxat* aired, the BBC received almost 1500 emails from viewers. Reading through them, I was astounded by the sheer volume of people who, after suffering various combinations of the afore-mentioned symptoms upon cessation of an SSRI, were ordered back on the drug by their doctors, who attributed the symptoms to the re-emergence of their depression. Doctor after doctor was seemingly uninformed of the effects of SSRI withdrawal.

That doctors failed to acknowledge withdrawal symptoms in their patients was probably to be expected, given the results of a UK survey involving fifty psychiatrists and fifty-three GPs. Nearly one-third of psychiatrists and more than two-thirds of GPs were unfamiliar with antidepressant withdrawal effects. Furthermore, only 20 per cent of psychiatrists and 17 per cent of GPs said they always cautioned patients about the possibility of withdrawal events. The dismal results led the poll's authors to concede: 'Education about discontinuation reactions, including the hallmark features, symptoms, and course, is needed for both psychiatrists and family practice physicians.'[8]

Although SSRIs can be extremely difficult to stop, manufacturers seem to get away without informing patients of the potential for addiction by playing semantics with the term. According to the spokesman for the makers of *Seroxat*, GlaxoSmithKline, for a drug to be classified as addictive it must create a need continually to increase the dosage in order to maintain its effect, and cause cravings on dosage reduction.[9] However, the *Collins Dictionary of Medicine* defines addiction as a condition where: 'The use of the drug has led to persistent changes in the way the body functions so that its absence causes physical symptoms – withdrawal symptoms.'

Based on the latter common usage definition of the term, who could deny SSRIs can be addictive?

There is very little information available to patients to inform them how difficult it can be to stop taking an SSRI. Any that does exist tends to indicate that there's only a problem if the drug is stopped abruptly. As demonstrated in the *Seroxat* video diary, and as I was finding out for myself, this is simply not the case.

Over the past two hundred years doctors have unknowingly prescribed an almost uninterrupted succession of addictive drugs, always in the belief they would not cause dependency or that a patient's weak will would be responsible if they did. In the beginning were alcohol and opium, then morphine, heroin and cocaine; alongside were chloral, numerous bromides, barbiturates and related compounds; and then a score of benzodiazepine tranquillisers. In their day, these drugs were prescribed as sedatives for mental distress. Ironically, it was all the bad press surrounding the propensity for benzodiazepines (*Valium*, etc) to leave people hooked that helped open up the market for SSRIs.[10]

Unfortunately for me, *Faverin* didn't come in liquid form like some of the other SSRIs, so I couldn't syringe the last few dosages as the woman on *The Secrets of Seroxat* had done. When I'd last seen Maarsten I'd asked if he could prescribe the *Faverin* in the smallest individual dosages possible – just in case, I'd said to him, I wanted to try a reduction at some stage. He'd written a prescription for 50 milligram tablets; they made nothing smaller. They were scored once down the centre, a provision to take them in 25 milligrams – still way too much. With a pill-cutter I'd bought from the pharmacy I would pare down the pill by 6.25 milligrams each fortnight; a system that at least made the emotional and physical disturbances manageable.

I was trying to put the whole ordeal of the past few years behind me; pretend it never happened; compartmentalise the section of the mind housing the experience – as Nigel seemed to be managing so effectively. But I simply couldn't shake the merciless flashbacks that punctured my daily thoughts, or the themes of helplessness, disempowerment and abuse that pervaded my dreams. I'd be chained in a cage, or confined to a room with a guard constantly on watch. There'd often be a phone that I'd somehow manage to get to, only to realise when I went to dial that some of the buttons were stuck or the wires were disconnected. Sometimes I'd successfully dial but as I'd go to speak, my voice would fail.

Nigel would often wake to the sound of me screaming for help in my sleep, thrashing about coated in sweat. In the mornings my jaw ached from incessantly grinding my teeth, which became so violent that one night I broke a tooth.

Many months earlier I'd told Maarsten how disturbing the dreams were. I'd also told him how petrified I'd become of doctors, any doctors. I hated even going to the GP – I'd avoid it at all costs, unless, of course, it was for Jemima and then I had no choice. My eyes would dart about at the prescription pad, the white-sheeted bed, the latex gloves, the promotional pharmaceutical paraphernalia, and every minute would feel like an eternity until I got out of there. Maarsten had had the audacity to tell me, unapologetically, I was suffering post-traumatic stress.

By June 2003 I was completely free of my psychiatric medication. Withdrawal from the *Faverin* had taken more than seven months. To my family and my few remaining friends – those who'd known me well before psychiatric intervention – the concept that my 'mental illness' had been a direct result of ill-managed medication eventually became easy to grasp.

But what about those who hadn't known me before, during and after? What about the picture my medical records painted of me? There were pages and pages of evidence on file that could very well destroy my chances of doing anything that would require a psychiatric clearance, such as adopting or fostering a child, or entering certain professions. What if I was ever to be wrongly accused of a crime and my character was brought into question?

Mum suggested I go back and see Dr Roosfeld.

'He's the only one who wanted you off the stuff. He probably suspected at the time it was doing you no good.'

'It's a great idea, Mum, but I just don't think I can bring myself to do it. I don't want anything more to do with psychiatrists.'

'He saw you in the midst of it all. If he sees you again now, it's going to be undeniable that you don't have a mental disorder.'

'But, Mum, I told him where to stick his ideas.'

'He's not going to hold that against you. He knew you weren't yourself. Just one visit. Let him see the difference.'

As much as I really didn't want to, I knew that seeing Roosfeld again would be my only chance to have my diagnosis revoked. Even if not for you, do it for Jemima, I told myself. With all the zeal surrounding the notion, albeit in the absence of any sound evidence, that bipolar mood disorder is a hereditary condition, my medical records could possibly affect how Jemima's mental health was perceived one day.

I decided I would go back and see the GP Dan Reubans, the one who'd referred me to Roosfeld in the first place. He'd known me since I was a young child. If anyone was to be able to put the before, during and after into an accurate professional context, it'd be him.

He'd moved practice since I'd last seen him, so I had to track him down. He was working in a large medical centre quite some distance from my home. As he called my name from the appointment book and I stood and walked towards him, he cocked his head in puzzled recognition.

'Hello, Dan.' The moment I spoke his frown softened into a welcoming smile.

'Rebekah. Of course.' He took my hand and shook it warmly. 'Come on through to the room. I'm very sorry about that,' he said, once seated behind his desk and gesturing for me to sit opposite. 'I was thrown for a minute. I certainly didn't expect to see you here. Must be something pretty important if you've travelled all this way.'

I filled him in on everything: the medication combinations, the hospitalisations, my behaviour careering off the rails. He shook his head gravely at each new bit of information.

'And now I have a diagnosis of bipolar mood disorder.'

He halted his note-taking and looked up at me. 'Bipolar mood disorder? Who says you have that?'

'Adrian Maarsten.'

'Ridiculous. You don't have that. Given all you were on I can't see how he could tell anything about you. You know, I reckon you'd better buy yourself a Lotto ticket the moment you leave here. You're clearly one lucky, lucky lady to have survived all this. I'm going to order some tests to see if any permanent damage has been done . . .'

'Well, I've now got diabetes.'

'Oh, no. What a terrible shame. Do you have a specialist seeing to that?'

I nodded.

'Are you insulin dependent or –'

'Insulin dependent.'

'I am so sorry to hear that. I'd really like you to get your liver and kidney function tested as well – make sure that's all okay.' He filled in a pathology slip. 'I can see you're having trouble using your left hand. Is that from something you did to yourself?' I nodded.

'I'll never regain full function. I wasn't well enough to attend the therapy sessions to get it working again. It's too late now.'

'Rebekah, I truly don't know what to say. But one thing's for sure – you can take that diagnosis of bipolar mood disorder and . . .' He screwed up an imaginary piece of paper and tossed it towards the bin.

'Well, that's really why I'm here. I don't think it will be as easy as that. I've got hold of all my public hospital records and it's stamped everywhere. It's going to haunt me for the rest of my life unless I do something to challenge it. I was hoping you might refer me back to see Dr Roosfeld.'

'That would be my pleasure.'

The six-week wait for my appointment with Dr Roosfeld flew by, as time does when you're approaching something you're dreading. What if he ended up being like all the others, unwilling to speak out against their colleagues for fear of landing them a negligence suit? This could backfire and just serve to bolster the diagnoses they'd given me. But he'd certainly shown integrity last time I saw him and called it as he saw it. He didn't come across as being part of the 'club'.

'Oh my,' he said, as I sat down in his office. 'You're a different woman to the one who sat in that very chair . . . when was it?' He checked the folder containing my records. 'Over three years ago. So, what brings you back to me now?'

'After I saw you, things got worse. Much, much worse.' I filled him in on the details, then handed him the computer-generated lists I'd collected from all the pharmacies that had filled my prescriptions between 1999 to when I'd stopped the *Faverin*. 'That's what I ended up being prescribed.'

His eyes boggled as he turned page after page after page.

'I suppose I've come to see you kind of in reverse. After I was put on all those drugs, I was completely out of control. I was diagnosed with a mood disorder, which I simply can't believe I have. It's coming up to a year since I've been off lithium and everything has returned to normal. I've done a lot of research now and it's becoming clearer and clearer to me that the medications themselves could have been responsible for my behaviour. I need to know your opinion of that.'

'Yes, it's quite possible. SSRIs can certainly cause mania, and with everything else you were on, well, who could tell what was going on. But for me to give an official appraisal of your mental health I will need to see you regularly for at least one year, maybe two.'

My heart sank.

'Now, it's completely up to you. I would thoroughly understand if you'd just had enough of psychiatrists altogether. But I cannot be sure of anything unless I see you for an extended period of time. I hope you understand.'

'Yes, I suppose I do. I guess I'll go ahead.'

'All right. Well, you keep up your research and I'll see you in a fortnight.

By late 2004, after twelve months of regular consultations, Dr Roosfeld had made up his mind.

'I see absolutely no evidence of bipolar disorder.'

I swept my hands through my hair, clasping them at the back of my head, and blew a long, slow breath of relief. I apologised for my earlier lack of trust and thanked him for his decision. But otherwise I concealed my exhilaration, still wary of my normal mood fluctuations being misinterpreted. Perhaps I always will be.

'When psychiatrists start giving their patients these mixtures of medications it becomes near impossible to keep track of what's going on,' Roosfeld added. 'It can do patients a lot of harm. In your case it nearly cost you your life. It's quite simple really. If the patient improves on a medication, fantastic. If they start displaying new behaviour since initiation of a medication, you suspect the medication is the cause. You know, one of my old teaching professors once said to me, psychiatry is part science, part gut feeling and part bunkum. Looks like you got caught up in too much of the latter.'

SEVENTEEN

By the time I'd severed ties with psychiatry, I'd been diagnosed by the various doctors involved with the following: postnatal depression; adjustment disorder; narcissistic personality disorder; personality disorder with borderline traits; and bipolar mood disorder. Just about every psychiatrist who assessed me either added a new diagnosis or contradicted the ones prior. When I finally obtained some of my psychiatric records, I was astounded at how littered they were with discrepancies, contradictions and outright fallacies – it was truly hard to believe they'd been written about the same person.

In one set of notes I'm described as having a history of 'stable relationships and personality' then elsewhere of having 'longstanding personality issues'. Determined from one assessment is that I'd had 'none to little' previous drug use, but somehow in another I've had a history of drug abuse. One psychiatrist wrote that I had always been 'friendly, happy-go-lucky' prior to my diagnosis of postnatal depression; another said that I'd been 'depressed all my life'. Falsely documented is that I quit school after Year 10 (I actually completed Year 12), that I have epilepsy (I don't) and that I had an uncle who committed suicide (I don't).Though it's difficult to know how much of this confusion could be attributed to what I'd had to say and how much was due to careless note-taking, one thing is clear: much of what was revealed while I was under the influence of psychoactive medication was completely unreliable. With the exception of postnatal depression, all diagnoses were made only after I was medicated and all were based on symptoms that can be purely medication-induced.

So, how did it all go so wrong? Why was it that the original team of medical professionals – Max and the nurses at Elm Court – hadn't realised that the *Lustral* had caused me to have panic attacks and to self-harm, and taken me off the drug? How did it all spiral so outrageously out of control? How was it that Nigel didn't see a direct correlation between the drugs and my behaviour, or Mum, or I myself, while I still had the lucidity to do so?

The first two hooks were the misunderstanding that SSRIs don't take effect for at least two to three weeks, and belief in the serotonin-imbalance theory of depression. A single dose of an SSRI takes between approximately four and eight hours to reach peak concentration in the system.[1] Therefore it has the potential to affect the body almost right away. Maximum elevation of serotonin (and noradrenalin in the case of drugs like *Efexor* or *Zispin*) occurs after approximately twenty-four to forty-eight hours with most of the new antidepressants (*Prozac* can take longer).[2] Why these drugs often take weeks to deliver any therapeutic effect in those with whom they agree can only be speculated about. After several weeks of drug treatment, at the time when depression may first show signs of being alleviated, serotonin and noradrenalin activity are likely actually to be depressed because of the brain's compensatory mechanism.[3]

Though serotonin has come to be thought of as a brain chemical, over 95 per cent of it is actually produced in the digestive tract. Blood passing through the stomach and intestines picks up serotonin and carries it throughout the body.[4] As John Horgan, author of *The Undiscovered Mind*, puts it:

> Given the ubiquity of a neurotransmitter such as serotonin and the multiplicity of its functions, it is almost as meaningless to implicate it in depression as it is to implicate blood.[5]

The chemical-imbalance theory gave a plausible explanation for why I could make no sense of my behaviour. I had a physical illness due to a situation completely beyond my control; I had no choice but to rely on doctors and drugs.

Trying to find a reason for what was happening would be as futile as searching for a reason for leukaemia or a tumour. So implicit was my trust in the serotonin–depression explanation that when the SSRIs failed to fix me, I didn't question the explanation, I just believed the illness had progressed to something far worse than depression.

I'm quite certain most people would be stunned to discover just how flimsy and dated the evidence is on which the chemical-imbalance theory for depression is based. As discussed earlier on, there were some tentative findings in the 1950s and 1960s that were never replicated by more sensitive studies. Psychiatry seems so keen to have us all believe that psychological problems are physical in origin. Is it because it legitimises psychiatry as a medical profession? Is it because it makes treatment simpler?

So disgusted was the late, internationally renowned, psychiatrist Loren Mosher with psychiatry's misrepresentation of the facts and unhealthy association with pharmaceutical companies, he resigned from his position with the American Psychiatric Association in 1998. His resignation letter includes this about biological theories of mental illness:

> . . . Anything that has an anatomically defined specific brain pathology becomes the province of neurology (syphilis is an excellent example). So, to be consistent with this 'brain disease' view, all the major psychiatric disorders would become the territory of our neurologic colleagues . . . consistency would demand our giving over 'biologic brain diseases' to them. The fact that there is no evidence confirming the brain disease attribution is, at this point, irrelevant. What we are dealing with here is fashion, politics and money. This level of intellectual/scientific dishonesty is just too egregious for me to continue to support by my membership.[6]

Belief in the chemical-imbalance theory of depression and other mental illness can only serve as a prelude to treatment with medication. Peter Breggin writes:

If you want to make people buy a product, you have to convince them that they want or need it. To market psychiatric drugs people have to be convinced they have 'diseases' that can be treated with drugs.[14]

With the exception of those in the US and New Zealand, drug companies are not allowed to market their products direct to consumers. But they are able to use more subtle measures, which are possibly even more persuasive and effective. The Mental Health Council of Australia's campaign to raise awareness of bipolar disorder was launched on Australian television in 2005. It suggests that many sufferers of this condition are only being treated for depression and not getting better. For further information it directs viewers to the website: bipolar.com. au. Once at the site, all mention of the Mental Health Council evaporates; the only evidence of the site's origin is logos and contact details for Eli Lilly, makers of bipolar drug *Zyprexa*. The mauve and purple background colour scheme is that of *Zyprexa*'s Australian packaging. Visitors are invited to fill out a questionnaire that they can take to their doctor to see if they require bipolar treatment. It tells us: 'As bipolar disorder is a biological illness that often has a genetic component, treatment is usually long-term.'[15]

In this sort of practice, no drug name is mentioned, people may be directed elsewhere for further information, and they are advised to consult their doctor. It is known as 'unbranded' advertising and is becoming increasingly common where direct-to-consumer advertising of prescription medications is forbidden. An unbranded public campaign may concurrently be teamed with branded promotion to doctors of a drug suitable for the condition in question. Dutch researchers looked into one campaign in which such an approach was considered to have been used. The campaign, run by Norvatis Pharmaceuticals, was for fungal nail infections. After commencement of the campaign, both consultations for the condition and prescriptions for Novartis' treatment, *Lamisal,* had increased, whereas prescriptions for a competing drug took a dive. Thus an unbranded campaign appeared to have a very brand-specific effect on sales.[16]

In 2004, US$85 million was spent on this sort of advertising through-out Europe.[17]

Another practice exemplified by the Australian campaign is the part-nering of pharmaceutical companies with patient advocacy groups; in this case Eli Lilly with The Mental Health Council of Australia. Many patient groups receive support and funding from drug companies. With-out this funding, says Simon Williams, Policy Director of the UK's Pa-tients Association, some patient groups would simply cease to exist.[18]

Spokespeople for patient groups that receive this kind of drug-com-pany support deny the situation compromises their objectives in any way and seem to see it as a win–win arrangement, advocating that the objec-tive of both parties concerned is simply to see more people treated.[19]

One way that antidepressant manufacturer Bristol-Myers Squibb tried to ensure that more people in Australia were treated for mental illness was by funding the simple tick-a-box screening test for use by family doctors (mentioned in chapter one). It classified 49 per cent of participants as having a mental disorder. The test was later scrutinised by researchers at a leading university and was found to be significantly flawed. According to the researchers, most people diagnosed with a mental illness by way of this test very likely didn't have one at all.[20]

Widening the boundaries of illness in order to increase the market for medications has been termed 'disease-mongering'.[21] One strategy is to take a relatively normal but troublesome condition and make it appear a major health issue which, unless treated with a drug, could seriously affect a per-son's life. Another is to expand the definitions of genuine serious health problems so the boundaries between minor symptoms and debilitating ill-ness become blurred.[22] The practice is 'most explicitly exemplified in many pharmaceutical industry-funded disease awareness campaigns – more of-ten designed to sell drugs than to illuminate or to inform or educate about the prevention of illness or the maintenance of health'.[23]

Concern that the practice is taking control of the global healthcare agenda prompted the 2006 international Inaugural Conference on Dis-ease-Mongering. Healthcare professionals from around the world gath-ered at Australia's University of Newcastle to discuss ways in which this pervasive practice might be combated. Disease-mongering is said to be behind the alarming increase in diagnosis and treatment of depression[24] and mood disorders,[25] and to have shaped public and medical opinion about the need to medicate for osteoporosis, irritable bowel syndrome, menopause, high cholesterol and high blood pressure.[26]

According to world-renowned investigative journalist Ray Moynihan, it's no secret that drug company marketing departments contract advertising agencies with expertise in 'condition branding', whose skills include 'fostering the creation' of new medical disorders and dysfunctions.[27] As a 2003 *Reuters Business Insight* report – designed to be read by pharmaceutical industry leaders – chillingly points out: 'The coming years will bear greater witness to the corporate-sponsored creation of disease.'[28]

I am certain I got caught up in the far-sprawling net of disease-mongering. Had the very definition of 'depression' not been undergoing 'expansion' right around the time I was diagnosed with it, I doubt very much I would have met the criteria. Then all that followed could have been avoided.

So, absolute belief in chemical imbalances and that SSRIs don't do anything for weeks allowed their nasty effects to get a solid hold of me without sufficient suspicion on the part of my family, friends or myself. But what about the medical professionals involved? Surely they wouldn't have overlooked such significant adverse effects?

It comes as a shock to realise that much of what doctors learn about the drugs they prescribe comes in one way or another from the pharmaceutical companies that make them. As previously mentioned, one way that doctors receive their pharmaceutical education is via industry-funded symposia. The information about the latest drugs coming to market is at times presented at these symposia by prominent clinicians on the payroll of the company launching the drug.[29] Another way doctors learn about what to prescribe is from drug company sales representatives. The reps come by the doctors' clinics, delivering information on the latest drugs, along with free samples designed to get patients started on treatment. Even the doctors who prefer not to see drug reps are still likely to be exposed to pharmaceutical company influence. Some rely instead on subscription journals and magazines that summarise the results of clinical trials. But since the appearance of ghost-written articles in medical journals, it has become even harder to separate the spin from the science. Ghost-writing is a practice whereby medical/scientific professionals are paid to lend their names to articles that the drug companies, usually by way of high-calibre PR firms, have produced.[30] According to the deputy editor of the *Journal of the American Medical Association*: 'This practice is well-known, scandalous and outrageous. It is a perfect illustration of deceptive authorship practices for commercial reasons.'[31]

As public funding for research diminishes, researchers are increasingly turning to drug companies for money. Clinical trial data are considered proprietary information, giving drug companies way too much control over how clinical-trial information is disseminated. Not only are drugs painted in the best possible light by way of ghost-written articles, but at times pertinent information pertaining to their safety has been omitted.

A case in point is the paediatric clinical-trial results for *Lustral*, as they appeared in the *Journal of the American Medical Association*. Only one suicidal act on *Lustral* was reported, when in fact there were six in the subject group on which these articles were based. [32]

During the clinical trials of Lilly's antidepressant *Cymbalta* – the medication healthy volunteer Traci Johnson was taking when she committed suicide (see chapter five) – several people took their own lives and yet this information is not freely available, not even to researchers. The reason: it's protected company information.[33]

Drug company influence appears to be everywhere. Even our medicines regulators, including the US FDA, UK MHRA, and Australian TGA, are funded by the pharmaceutical industry.[34, 35, 36] One of the latest conflicts of interest to be exposed relates to the medical experts involved in compiling the *DSM IV – Diagnostic and Statistical Manual of Mental Disorders* – used worldwide for the diagnosis of mental illness. A 2006 study has shown that most of these experts have undisclosed financial ties to the pharmaceutical industry. The importance of the *DSM* to the pharmaceutical industry cannot be overstated: the FDA will not approve a drug to treat a mental illness unless the condition is in the *DSM*. Drug companies then can market approved medications to physicians and, where permitted, consumers. Of particular concern is the study's finding that 100 per cent of the experts on *DSM-IV* panels overseeing mood disorders and schizophrenia/psychotic disorders were financially involved with the drug industry. These are the largest categories of psychiatric drugs in the world – 2004 sales of US$20.3 billion and US$14.4 billion respectively.

'The more lucrative the drug market, the higher the percentage of experts with financial ties – that has to raise serious questions about these panels' objectivity,' says David Rothman, professor of social medicine at Columbia University's College of Physicians and Surgeons.[37]

So, try as they might to make independent, discerning clinical judgements in the best interests of their patients, it must be near impossible for doctors to dodge the ubiquitous presence of the pharmaceutical industry.

'I think all the drug companies are behaving the same way and I think it's because they have to,' says Dr John Abramson, a clinical instructor at Harvard Medical School and author of *Overdosed America: the broken promise of American medicine*. 'It is the industry standard to put forth tainted information to sell the most drugs. Much of the scientific evidence that doctors rely upon to prescribe drugs is more like infomercials than scientific evidence.'[38]

Many people struggle with the concept that a company could be so ruthless as to put profits before people's health and safety. Others firmly believe that the checks and balances put in place by our society would make it impossible for a drug of questionable safety to stay on the market. After all, if people were being harmed by a medication they were led to believe was safe, there'd be a barrage of class-action lawsuits, wouldn't there? Some people believe it proves SSRIs are completely safe because this hasn't happened.

In order to understand why this logic cannot grant us the peace of mind we would hope, it is worth having a look at what happened with the thalidomide disaster of the 1960s. When thousands of malformed babies were born to mothers taking thalidomide it would have been difficult to find anyone who didn't think the drug was to blame. However, no case was ever won against the drug company, Chemie-Grunenthal. The only player in this atrocity ordered to compensate the plaintiffs was the drug's American distributor, for failing properly to monitor distribution of a novel compound. Chemie-Grunenthal managed to evade liability because the plaintiffs could not prove the actual mechanism by which the drug caused the defects. Thus is the case with SS-RIs.[39] Though GlaxoSmithKline admitted in May 2006 that a review of clinical trials showed a significantly higher rate of suicidal behaviour on *Seroxat* compared with a placebo (discussed chapter 10), there has been little concern about litigation. An article in *CNN Money* articulates why: 'Plaintiffs might sue Glaxo as a result of the new information, but the drug-maker would benefit from the fact that causation is unclear . . .'[40]

In the case of thalidomide, Chemie-Grunenthal were able to find experts to testify that the same malformations might have been caused by television rays, botched abortions by the mothers, or a failure of the body to induce the spontaneous abortions that accompany many malformations.[41] Based on this example, it's clear why the catchcry defence of SSRI manufacturers since their drugs became linked to things like mania and suicidal behaviour has become, 'It's not the drug; it's the disease.'

I've concluded that the reason not one of the many medical professionals, except for Roosfeld and Reubans, acknowledged the treatments were causing me grievous harm was because they chose to recognise only drug-company-based information about what they prescribed. Other published medical literature pointing to behaviour such as self-harm and mania on antidepressants existed prior to me being prescribed anything – though it appears neither psychiatrist involved in my primary care throughout this period was adequately influenced by it.

It's difficult to know just how many people are suffering the way that I did because of medication that is supposed to be helping them. But if the dramatic increase in the numbers of mentally ill persons since the introduction of SSRIs and the atypical antipsychotics like *Zyprexa* is any indication, then it's likely to be a fair few. In the US the combined sales of antidepressants and antipsychotics jumped from around US$500 million in 1986 to nearly US$20 billion in 2004, a forty-fold increase. During this period the number of disabled mentally ill in the US increased from 3.31 million people to 5.726 million. That's an increase of 410 people newly disabled by mental illness every day.[42]

Professor Gordon Parker of the School of Psychiatry at the University of New South Wales (a leading Australian university) acknowledges that experiences like mine are 'quite common'. A supporter of the view that some depression might have a biological element, Parker says: 'We see depressed people who've been under-treated, and others whose illness is not quintessentially biological', yet their treatment has amounted to 'the relentless pursuit of one physical treatment after another'.[43] SSRIs can cause some people to become 'profoundly distressed and agitated', he explains. 'The newer antidepressants were initially presented to us as being highly effective and totally safe, and I think people are feeling that that dream vision isn't holding up.'[44]

In October 2005, a report conducted by the Brain and Mind Research Institute, which the Mental Health Council of Australia labelled as 'damning', showed that Australian mental health services were gravely inadequate and were stretched beyond their capacity.[45] In 2007, a senior consultant psychiatrist and representative of the Royal College of Psychiatrists felt compelled to speak out about Britain's mental health service, saying that hospitals were at crisis point. 'The wards are over-crowded,' he stated, '. . . staff are under immense pressure to get people out because of the number of people coming in . . . It is as bad as it ever has been.'[46]

If the latest psychiatric medications are as effective and as safe as they've been promoted to be, if they really do correct chemical imbalances and get people's brains back to functioning 'normally', then our mental health services should be breathing easy, shouldn't they? Something doesn't add up.

Outside the synthetic environment of clinical trials – often involving fewer than one hundred patients and lasting only a couple of months[47] – there is little evidence that the long- or short-term outcome of depression is changing as a consequence of antidepressant use.[48] In fact, recent sharp increases in antidepressant use have been accompanied by the increased prevalence and duration of depressive episodes[49] and rising levels of sick leave.[50] Naturalistic studies – studies involving the observation of people as they go about their normal activities – have also shown that depressive episodes are more frequent and of longer duration among antidepressant users than among non-users.[51]

What if our current medical treatments for psychological conditions are *contributing* to the pressure on our mental health services? What if a significant proportion of the people using psychiatric services are actually suffering misinterpreted drug-induced side effects that mimic psychiatric illness? Even doctors who swear by the latest antidepressants concede 1 to 2 per cent of patients have a severe negative reaction to them.[52] Two per cent of the estimated two million Britons currently taking these drugs is 40,000 people with severe negative reactions. Even if half of those people had doctors astute enough to realise immediately their medication had caused the severe negative reaction and had taken them off it, there's still the possibility that thousands of people are using mental health services who do not require them. Forty thousand seems a lot of people reacting with significant adversity to medications that were once touted as a revolution in the treatment of depression. That the condition of 40,000 people has been made dramatically worse by their treatment seems almost inconceivable. And in reality, the figures are almost certainly higher than this.

Adverse drug reactions are 'seriously under reported', warns the British Medical Association, making it difficult to ascertain any drug's true potential for adverse effects. 'When a drug is first marketed,' the Association alerts us, ' . . . relatively little may be known about its safety in the population at large.' Hence, the Association is calling for an increase in the reporting of suspected adverse reactions beyond clinical trials, in a bid to protect patients' health and save lives.[53]

There is nothing actually to compel doctors to track or report any adverse effects they think a drug might be causing their patients. 'Doctors just don't report; it's as simple as that,' says psychiatrist and chair of international non-profit organisation Healthy Skepticism* Jon Jureidini. 'They are especially hesitant to report adverse effects associated with psychiatric illness and drugs.'[54]

A recent extensive analysis of the 40-year-old 'Yellow Card' adverse reaction reporting system for medical professionals in the UK suggests only a minority of doctors ever report suspected adverse

---

*An international non-profit organisation with an aim to 'improve health by reducing harm from misleading drug promotion'

drug reactions. A comprehensive survey of the first 20 years of the scheme's operation found that only 16 per cent of doctors working in the NHS had ever sent in a Yellow Card, and that 7.4 per cent of all doctors sent in 80 per cent of all reports.[55] The Australian TGA, via its 2005 *SSRI Adverse Reactions Bulletin*, was keen to point out: 'ADRAC (the Adverse Drug Reactions Advisory Committee) conducted a review of the evidence of suicidal thoughts and behaviour associated with the use of SSRIs in adults. The Committee concluded that, in most adult patients, SSRIs in the treatment of depression are beneficial or cause no harm.'[56] Similarly, in 2004 the UK Committee on Safety of Medicines, or CSM (a branch of the MHRA that is now known as the Commission on Human Medicines) asserted that: 'These drugs are beneficial for the majority of patients with depressive illness and anxiety disorders.' Further, the CSM stated 'that the balance of risks and benefits of all SSRIs in adults remains positive'.[57] But given the current state of affairs with patient monitoring and drug approval processes, how could they possibly be certain about this?

Prescription-drug regulation seems to leave a lot to be desired, right across the board, when it comes to patient safety. If I had succeeded in killing myself, I seriously doubt it would have been reported as an SSRI death. It wasn't as if I took the drug, then did something as blatant as shoot myself immediately or jump in front of a train. It was the panic attacks and the aggression that gave the first clue that something was amiss. By the time I was making serious attempts on my life there were other drugs, other treatments, involved. Had I died, my death would have been regarded, I imagine, as just another unfortunate suicide in mental health.

Epilogue

With such powerful forces at play shaping opinion about mental illness and its treatments, it has never been more necessary to proceed with caution when seeking help with psychological issues. It is important to resist the notion that depression, anxiety or any other mental illness results from a simplistic chemical imbalance in the brain. The idea that this is true and a pill once daily will sort it out and help you carry on is an appealing one – depression sufferers are usually so energy-depleted and confused that the promise of this sort of simple solution seems heaven-sent – but the evidence to support the chemical imbalance theory is far from convincing. It's been around a decade since prominent medical figures such as Valenstein (chapter two) and Mosher (chapter seventeen) warned of the misleading nature of the biochemical imbalance claim, and although some authorities have finally conceded it is time to stop the perpetuation of it, in many arenas it lives on. 'Some patients who suffer from depression need to have the cause analysed, and then any biochemical imbalance corrected with medication,' writes this advice-offering doctor in a late 2008 issue of *The Times*.[1] The truth is, this entirely unsubstantiated hypothesis has been circulated with so much enthusiasm, its inertia is proving extremely difficult to halt.

Also, please don't be swayed by the 'depression is just like diabetes' argument. There are set parameters for healthy levels of sugar in the blood, which can be tested and monitored with simple finger-prick blood testing, the results of which indicate how much insulin is required at each dose. No one knows what a 'normal' level of serotonin – or noradrenalin or dopamine – in the brain is, let alone what constitutes an abnormal level requiring 'correction'. In fact, science has very little understanding of how the brain's serotonin system functions at all.[2]

'I think what we have to tell trainee psychiatrists is that this is a far more complex area than we previously thought,' says Dr Louise Newman, director of the New South Wales Institute of Psychiatry (Australia).[3]

SSRIs are designed initially to increase the availability of the brain's own serotonin, but what happens next still remains a mystery. Whatever it is SSRIs do, some people appear to respond to it favourably, while for others it appears to have devastating consequences. In a 2004 report on the safety of SSRIs, a MHRA-appointed panel acknowledged that: 'The pharmacology of SSRIs and related antidepressants is complex, and their exact mode of action is not entirely clear.' Proposed in the report were four potential differences in the normal biological make-up of individuals that could explain the unpredictable effects of SSRIs from one person to another. These included differences in drug metabolism, brain anatomy, and genetic make-up among individuals. The report concluded that further research is required in order to understand what bearing these factors have on the risk of adverse neuropsychiatric events with SSRIs.[4]

Of late, some researchers have been postulating that SSRIs may be capable of generating the production of new brain neurons (cells that conduct nerve impulses). There is a suggestion that in depressed people there could be a depletion of neurons in a particular area of the brain. Some have ventured to attribute successful treatment with antidepressants to the possibility that the drug has led to a correction of this depletion.[5] However, just as there's never been proof of low brain chemicals in the depressed, neither has there been any of depleted neurons in the brain. I wonder, are we on the verge of seeing the brain chemical deficiency theory of depression superseded by a brain anatomy deficiency theory, based on foundations as shakey as its predecessor? I suppose time will tell.

Much has been posited about how these drugs may be helping those who appear to benefit, but only one thing remains a certainty, as articulated by Yale researcher Professor Ronald Dunman years on from the aforementioned 2004 MHRA-commissioned report: 'Even though we've had these drugs available now for [many] years . . . it's still unclear what the mechanism of action is.'[6]

Rather than perceiving a helpful antidepressant effect as the result of a 'rebalancing' or 'correction' of any description, Dr Joanna Moncrieff, senior lecturer in social and community psychiatry at University College London, explains quite simply: 'It's more accurate to understand psychiatric drugs as inducing abnormal states, analogous to how we use recreational drugs to induce euphoria or social disinhibition.'[7]

It may be encouraging to know that depression is a condition with a high rate of spontaneous remission.[8] In the majority of cases, depression is a result of stressful life events and when these are resolved depression usually follows suit.[9]

Over recent years antidepressants have been prescribed increasingly freely for cases of mild depression. As many as two thirds of the antidepressants prescribed by UK GPs have been for depression of this nature.[10] In 2004, the National Institute for Clinical Excellence (NICE) reviewed its guidelines to recommend to doctors that for mild depression treatments other than antidepressants – such as counselling or cognitive behavioural therapy (CBT)[*] – should initially be explored.[11] Psychiatrist Jon Jureidini, chair of non-profit organisation Healthy Skepticism, points out the many costs of over-zealous antidepressant prescribing. Not only are there the risks of adverse outcomes, costs to the individual and to the taxpayer, but most pertinently Jureidini observes the 'opportunity costs – the lost chances for clinicians and patients to invest time and resources into alternative treatments and activities'. He adds: 'It is too easy to screen for and diagnose mental illness. It is more demanding, but more productive, to seek out mental strength in our suffering patients to help them get back on track. To make suffering into a diagnosis can help, but it can also hinder the productive exploration of ordinary distressing feelings, the expression and understanding of which might lead to significant growth.'[12]

Currently however, there's a big problem for those seeking treat-

---

[*]Cognitive behavioural therapy (CBT) is a form of psychotherapy in which the patient is taught self-help strategies to challenge unhelpful or unhealthy thoughts, feelings and behaviours. It can be used to treat a wide range of psychological conditions.

ments such as counselling and CBT in the UK, with demand exceeding supply to an enormous degree. Right now, on average, a patient will wait eighteen months before getting to see a therapist. Recently the British Government has taken steps towards rectifying this, announcing that by 2010, 3,600 more therapists will be available throughout England: a move projected to reduce the NHS waiting period for psychological therapies to two weeks.[13]

If you do decide to take an antidepressant on your doctor's advice, be realistic about its limitations. A recent US nationwide study found that only 30 per cent of depression sufferers gained significant relief from initial treatment with an SSRI.[14] This was followed by research at the Universtiy of Hull that found that SSRIs and similar drugs provided relief for none but the most severely depressed.[15]

And most importantly, of course, be aware it might make you worse. I would strongly recommend keeping a detailed diary of your state of mind before and during treatment. Tell someone close to you that you've started on the medication so they can be on the lookout for any questionable changes in your behaviour – if you are adversely affected you will most likely lack the insight to pass judgement on your own actions. Remember, contrary to what the drug companies and some doctors would have you believe, these drugs begin to take effect almost straight away, so if any adverse effects emerge that weren't present before, suspect the drug as a cause.

Of course, the decision to take or not take a medical treatment for your emotional issues must ultimately be yours – I would never wish a person be denied the relief a medication might bring them – but each and every one of us deserves to be able to base this decision on the facts, not just on drug company marketing dressed up as medical science. With an issue as important as this one, I think we all deserve that right.

To quote once more from David Healy's logical and balanced perspective: 'The solution for me and for the people who need [anti-depressants] is to know what the risks really are . . . If we are informed what the risks are, then we don't say, "It couldn't be the drug," and increase the dose, which is just the wrong thing to do.' Knowing the full picture, he adds, could mean the difference between life and death.[16]

I didn't come through my experience unscathed. The diabetes will never go away; my left hand, even after two reconstructive operations, will never be quite right; and my left inner forearm will stay marred with telling scars. Reams of medical records characterise me as mentally unstable, potentially prohibiting me from doing such things as entering certain professions or ever adopting or fostering a child.

My marriage, though far less affected than it could have been, is also not without its scars. Nige sometimes has to fight the temptation to mistrust me based on the things I did while on medication. I often have to suppress an unreasonable urge to be angry with him for having not intervened and done something to help me. For the most part we stay conscientiously focused on the future, a task that gets easier and easier with time; it's our best insurance against the past corroding what we've managed to hang on to.

Many friendships were hit hard, particularly those that began only after I was medicated. Some of these friends backed away from me because of my treatment of them. With others it was I who began distancing myself once I was medication-free – there was something horribly troubling about being around people who could remember more about the person I'd become while medicated than I could myself.

My friendship with Dee fell apart, but for neither of these reasons. Both Dee and I did all we could to sustain our bond, but, increasingly, once I was off medication it was as if we were two strangers with little in common, forced to spend time together. Nothing was ever said; our friendship just died a natural death. I was shattered to lose her, and spent a lot of time wondering what more I could have done to prevent it. Then one day, when I came across some photos of the medicated me, a person I could barely recognise, it became clear: my friendship with Dee could never really be because the person she'd befriended never really was.

Even more upsetting than losing Dee was losing my close friend Celeste. When Celeste had taken from me as much as she could tolerate, she simply severed contact. I'd really like to be able to say that I fully understand, that her actions and those of others like her were completely justified given the circumstances, but it just isn't that easy.

It's near impossible to accept responsibility for the actions of someone masquerading as you. Sometimes the injustice of wearing the blame for the damage inflicted by that drug-born personality that possessed my body is really hard to deal with.

Thankfully, though remarkably, not all friendships were lost. For those who remain my friends, for those who returned when the 'real me' had done the same, I know I am truly blessed.

Mum's steadfast support only intensified as I emerged the other side of this crisis. She became as determined as I was to understand what had caused me to be so ill and has been right there with me as I've slowly unravelled the truth. In spite of the ordeal, and possibly even because of it, my relationship with Mum is stronger than ever.

Jemima's temperament eventually evened out beautifully all on its own – she was never shown to have any physical ailment, as was suggested early on. She showed marked improvement at around five months when she could sit up on her own, then further improvement when at nine months she could crawl. By the time she could walk and talk she was a delight: a contented, sociable, confident little extrovert. My theory is that she was raring to go from the moment she was born and her persistent crying was an expression of her frustration at having such a mismatch between her physical capabilities and her mental will.

Despite all she witnessed, all she was caught up in, Jemima appears to have no conscious memory of any of it, which is consistent, I suppose, with the theory that cognitive memory only develops after three years of age – all the bedlam had ceased by the time she had reached that age. Though her hardy and self-assured character gives me hope she has escaped any emotional harm, I'd be a fool to think she hasn't been affected at least on some level. Her fierce protectiveness of me is probably testament to this and the fact that she can hardly bear to leave me on my own. 'What if something happens to you, Mummy?' she said to me one day. 'What if I'm not there to save you?'

For years I couldn't so much as entertain the notion of having another child, despite that being mother of multiple children was how I'd envisaged myself since childhood. The fear was not that I would uncontrollably slide into some desperate postnatal emotional state; I had no more reason to fear that than the next woman. It was a bullying pack of 'what ifs' that had Nige and I denying our plans for family: what if I was to once again have a fractious child? What if I was once again to become beside myself with sleep deprivation? What if once again parenting with scant family support threatened to get the better of me? And the most formidable of them all, that made those preceding it terrifying rather than just troubling: What if any, all of these, or a myriad of other highly possible, highly normal early motherhood difficulties were to cause me to need to *reach out for help*?

But over time, that my experience would rob me of my second child on top of all else became something too painful to live with. To boot; it was an injustice to which I did not have to yield, a wrong I could yet right. But, what a risk, given all that could be inferred from what was medically recorded about my supposed ability – or lack thereof – to cope with mothering. Nevertheless, by the very beginning of 2008, resulting from a maternal yearning to challenge the greatest of cautions and fears, I would once again have taken the plunge, giving birth to another baby girl.

As she approaches 18 months of age, there's been natural curiosity about how things have been for me this time around. The answer is far too complex completely to deal with in brief, but to satisfy what I imagine most people are hoping to ascertain: have there been urges to self-mutilate, or to end it all? Episodes of mania? Panic attacks? Bizarre personality changes?

No. Nothing even close.

Does that mean I've breezed through, having been awarded the idyllic experience I'd anticipated when expecting Jemima? Not at all. 'Just wait and see,' said many, 'with your first so highly strung your second will be a dream.' But, they were wrong, and clearly sharing much of Jemima's make up, Abigail has been uncannily like her.

There've been moments when the sudden and copious losses that swarm pretty much anyone in early motherhood have seemed hellbent on dragging me down: loss of sleep, freedom, figure, fitness, finances, and independence. Loss too of the ability to achieve so many taken-for-granteds: eating at leisure, bathing at will, styling hair, applying make-up, dressing in anything too good to be sullied several times a day. The list continues. Indeed, at times it could feel like I'd exchanged my life for my baby's. But I've made it sure-footedly through, lucky to have established empowering coping strategies – some borrowed from Buddhist philosophy, for example – that have enabled one small success to feed another, one small triumph to create a foundation for the next, allowing my sense of confidence, accomplishment and self-reliance to grow exponentially. Lucky also to have had enough experience to know the tough times will eventually pass, and the maturity, wisdom and internal fortitude to take on board the advice my intuition approved, and to reject that which it didn't. And, so importantly, the ability to recognise that any rough patches, especially in those intense early months, were, I am now convinced, normal responses to stressors unparalleled by any other human experience.

How uniquely elating it's been to be present – physically and mentally – for Abi's first smile, to witness her sit, cut her first tooth, crawl, walk, utter 'mamma'. And yet concurrently saddening, as it all brings with it refreshed awareness that such events missed with Jemima shall remain that way.

By all odds, somewhere amidst my time as a psychiatric patient I probably should have died, but by some incredible fortune I lived. And now I'm telling my tale, in the hope others will recognise their story in mine and I can help to deliver some lives back to their rightful owners. To all those reading this who are taking psychiatric medications, or have a loved someone taking psychiatric medications for chronic depression, bipolar mood disorder, or any other psychiatric disorder, I urge you now to think back: did the crux of the issues develop after the initiation of a psychiatric drug? If so, then it just might be that the drug is to blame.

Notes

One

1. A. Mant, V. A.Rendle, W. D. Hall, P. B. Mitchell, W. S. Montgomery, P. R. McManus and I. B. Hickie,'Making New Choices about Antidepressants in Australia', *Medical Journal of Australia*, vol. 181, issue 7, S21–S24, viewed 10 August 2005, www.mja.com.au/public/issues/181_07_041004/man10822_fm.html

2. M. Andrews, 'GPs prescribe anti-depressants even though they believe other approaches might be more effective, research claims', *Psychminded*, 26 April 2005, viewed 25 August 2008, http://www.psychminded.co.uk/news

3. Viewed 29 August 2004, www.beyondblue.org.au

4. 'The treatment of depression in adults', Booklet, National Institute for Health and Clinical Excellence, April 2007

5. R. Moynihan and A. Cassels, *Selling Sickness*, p. 31–2

6. W. Hall, A. Mant and P. Mitchell, et al.,'Association Between Antidepressant Prescribing and Suicide in Australia, 1991–2000: trend analysis', *British Medical Journal*, vol. 326, 2003, pp. 100–8, cited in Moynihan and Cassels, *Selling Sickness*, p. 32

Two

1. E. S. Valenstein, *Blaming the Brain: the truth about drugs and mental health*, p. 100

2. Ibid., p. 100–1

3. J. R. Lacasse and J. Leo, 'Serotonin and Depression: a disconnect between the advertisements and the scientific literature', *PloS Medicine*, vol. 2, issue 12, November 2005, viewed 20 June 2006, http://medicine.plosjournals.org/perlserv/?request=get-document&doi=10.1371%2Fjournal.pmed.0020392

4. Valenstein, *Blaming the Brain*, p. 165

5. D. Healy, *Let Them Eat Prozac: the unhealthy relationship between the pharmaceutical industry and depression*, p. 280

6. Viewed 8 August 2008,www.pfizer.com.au/Conditions/Depression.aspx

7. Healy, *Let Them Eat Prozac*, p. 11–12

8. Ibid., p. xiv

9. 'Depression – why does it happen?', Royal College of Psychiatrists website, http://www.rcpsych.ac.uk/mentalhealthinformation/mentalhealthproblems/depression/depression.aspx

10. L. Bishop, *Postnatal Depression: families in turmoil*, p. 43–7

11. C. Medawar,'The Antidepressant Web: marketing depression and making medicines work', *International Journal of Risk & Safety in Medicine*, 1997, vol. 10, issue 2, pp. 75–126, viewed 11 November 2005, www.socialaudit.org.uk/docs/adweb.doc

12. Valenstein, *Blaming the Brain*, p. 97

13. Ibid., p. 70

14. G. Jackson, *Rethinking Psychiatric Drugs*, p. 81

15. Healy, *Let Them Eat Prozac*, p. 27

16. Jackson, *Rethinking Psychiatric Drugs*, p. 72

Four

1. Healy, *Let Them Eat Prozac*, p. 178

2. Ibid., p. 240–2

3. Valenstein, *Blaming the Brain*, p. 99; Medawar,'The Antidepressant Web', *International Journal of Risk & Safety in Medicine*, 1997

4. Valenstein, *Blaming the Brain*, p. 99

5. 'Worsening Depression and Suicidality in Patients Being Treated with Antidepressant Medications', US Food and Drug Administration Public Health Advisory, 22 March 2004, viewed 2 April 2004, www.fda.gov/cder/drug/antidepressants/AntidepressantsPHA. htm;'Use of SSRI Antidepressants in Children and Adolescents', TGA Adverse Drug Reactions Bulletin, October 2004, viewed 8 November 2004, www.tga.gov.au/adr/adrac_ssri.htm; D. Fergusson, S. Doucette, K. Cranley Glass, S. Shapiro, D. Healy, P. Herbert, B. Hutton,'Association Between Suicide Attempts and Selective Serotonin Reuptake Inhibitors: a systematic review of randomised controlled trials', *British Medical Journal*, vol. 330, 19 February 2005, p. 396, viewed 18 November 2005, www.bmj.bmjjournals.com/cgi/content/ abstract/330/7488/396

6. 'Stronger Warning for SSRIs and Other Newer Antidepressants Regarding the Potential for Behavioural and Emotional Changes, Including Risk of Self-harm', 26 May 2004, viewed 21 February 2006,www. hc-sc.gc.ca/dhpmps/medeff/advisories-avis/prof/2004/zoloft_2_hpc-cps_e.html; Didham et. al.,'Suicide and Self-harm Following Prescription of SSRIs and Other Antidepressants: confounding by indication', *British Journal of Clinical Pharmacology*, vol. 60, issue 5, November 2005, pp. 519–25, viewed 1 November 2005, www.ncbi.nlm.nih. gov/entrez/query.fcgi?cmd=Retrieve&db=PubMed&list_uids=162360 42&dopt=Citation

7. Diagnostic Criteria from DSM-IV-TR™ , American Psychiatric Association, Washington DC, 2000, pp. 169–72; *MIMS Annual*, Medimedia Australia, Sydney, June 2003, section 3, p. 337 and 342

8. 'FDA Issues Public Health Advisory on Cautions for Use of Antidepressants in Adults and Children', US Food and Drug Administration Public Health Advisory, 22 March 2004, viewed 2 April 2004, www. fda.gov/bbs/topics/ANSWERS/2004/ANS01283.html

9. 'Worsening Depression and Suicidality in Patients Being Treated with Antidepressant Medications', US Food and Drug Administration Public Health Advisory, 22 March 2004

10. Healy, *Let Them Eat Prozac*, pp. 182–87; Breggin and Cohen, *Your Drug May Be Your Problem*, p. 55

11. 'FDA Issues Public Health Advisory on Cautions for Use of Antidepressants in Adults and Children', US Food and Drug Administration Public Health Advisory, 22 March 2004

12. J. Davies,'Jagged Little Pills', *The Bulletin*, 26 May 2004, viewed 18 Jan 2005, www.bulletin.ninemsn.com.au/bulletin/site/articleIDs/ 169F283BE2E8784 DCA256E9D00707567

13. 'Psychiatric Drugs: chemical warfare on humans', interview with Robert Whitaker, 27 August 2005, viewed 20 July 2006, www.icspp.org/index.php?option=com_content&task=view&id=132&Itemid=70

14. C. Medawar and A. Herxheimer, 'A comparison of adverse drug reaction reports from professionals and users', *International Journal of Risk & Safety in Medicine*, vol. 16, 2003/2004, p. 6

15. Ibid., p. 14

16. Ibid.

Five

1. 'Alert Over Taking Prozac During Pregnancy', *Sydney Morning Herald*, viewed 12 January 2004, www.smh.com.au/articles/2003/08/03/1059849278453.html?oneclick=true

2. T. James, 'First Trimester Antidepressant Risk', *Australian Doctor*, 15 September 2005, viewed 24 September 2005, news.australiandoctor.com.au/articles/41/0c036641.asp 150

3. 'Antidepressant Stillbirth Link', BBC News, 7 April 2006, viewed 10 April 2006, www.news.bbc.co.uk/1/hi/health/4886762.stm

4. 'FDA Alert, Increased Risk of Neonatal Persistent Pulmonary Hypertension', July 2006, viewed 25 July 2006, www.fda.gov/cder/drug/InfoSheets/HCP/paroxetineHCP.pdf

5. Ibid.

6. 'Worsening Depression and Suicidality in Patients Being Treated with Antidepressant Medications', FDA Public Health Advisory, 22 March 2004, viewed 15 April 2004, www.fda.gov/cder/drug/antidepressants/AntidepressantsPHA.htm

7. 'Antidepressants and Suicidal Thoughts and Behaviour', Pharmacovigilance Working Party Report 2008, viewed 8 September 2008, http://www.hma.eu/uploads/media/PAR_suicidal_thoughts_in_antidepressants.pdf

8. 'Recommendations from the PhVWP Antidepressants and suicidal thoughts and behaviour SPC wording agreed in January 2008', viewed 8 September 2008, http://www.hma.eu/uploads/media/PI_wording_suicidal_thoughts_in_antidepressants.pdf

9. TGA Adverse Reactions Bulletin, 'Suicidality with SSRIs: adults and children', August 2005, viewed 20 September 2005, www.tga.gov.au/adr/aadrb/aadr0508.htm#1

10. Healy, *Let Them Eat Prozac*, pp. 179–90

11. B. Wyld, 'Drug Trial Stopped After Link to Suicide', *Sydney Morning Herald*, 14 December 2004; J. Groopman, 'The Pediatric Gap', *The New Yorker*, viewed 10 March 2005, www.newyorker.com/fact/content/?050110fa_fact

12. Jackson, *Rethinking Psychiatric Drugs*, p. 123

Six

1. Jackson, *Rethinking Psychiatric Drugs*, p. 199

2. Viewed 11 November 2005, www.healyprozac.com/GhostlyData/default.htm

3. 'Stronger Warning for SSRIs and Other Newer Antidepressants Regarding the Potential for Behavioural and Emotional Changes, Including Risk of Self-harm', 26 May 2004, viewed 21 February 2006, www.hc-sc.gc.ca/dhpmps/medeff/advisories-avis/prof/2004/zoloft_2_hpc-cps_e.html

4. *Patients Rights: a self-help guide to the Mental Health Act*, 5th edition, Mental Health Legal Centre inc., 2000, p. 23

5. Ibid., p. 28

6. MIND *Making sense of ECT* booklet, viewed 10 September 2008, http://www.mind.org.uk/Information/Booklets/Making+sense/ECT. htm#What_do_I_need_to_know_before_I_have_ECT_

7. Breggin, *Toxic Psychiatry*, p. 241–2

8. Ibid., p. 244–5

Seven

1. Zoloft consumer medicine information leaflet, viewed 15 August 2008, http://www.pfizer.com.au/ProfessionalsProductDetails. aspx?ProductID=5e432201-7c85-4e69-8c54-7eaa4336c339

2. Adweb discussion board, viewed 10 October 2005, www.socialaudit.org.uk/_disc//messages/23/23.html?SundayOctober920051148pm

3. R. Kelley,'How to Quit the Cure', Newsweek, 8 August 2005, viewed 20 September 2005,www.msnbc.msn.com/id/8769536/site/ newsweek/

4. 'Practice Guidelines for the Treatment of Borderline Personality Disorder,' American Psychiatric Association, viewed 22 May 2005, www.psych.org/psych_pract/treatg/pg/borderline_revisebook_5.cfm#a

5. D. Becker, *Through the Looking Glass: women and borderline personality disorder*, Westview Press 1997, cited in L. Kerr,'The "Borderline" as the Sociocultural Origin of the Borderline Personality Disorder, and Psychiatry', *Ethical Human Psychology and Psychiatry*, vol. 6, no. 3, fall/winter 2004

Eight

1. 'FDA Issues Public Health Advisory on Cautions for Use of Antidepressants in Adults and Children', FDA Public Health Advisory, 22 March 2004, viewed 15 April 2004, www.fda.gov/bbs/topics/ANSWERS/2004/ANS01283.html; Lieberman et al.,'Comparative Efficacy and Safety of Atypical and Conventional Antipsychotic Drugs in First-episode Psychosis: a randomized, double blind trial of olanzapine versus haloperidol', *American Journal of Psychiatry*, vol. 160, 2003, pp. 1396–1404, cited in Jackson, *Rethinking Psychiatric Drugs*, p. 204

2. A. Firestone, 'Management of Akathisia', *British Medical Journal*, vol. 324, 7 August 2002, viewed 5 November 2005, www.bmj.bmj-journals.com/cgi/elettters/324/7352/1506

3. P. Sanchev, *Akathisia and Restless Legs*, Cambridge University Press, 1996, cited in Y. Lucire,'New Drugs, New Problems', *The Australian Journal of Forensic Sciences*, 2005, vol. 37, p. 9–25

4. H. Steck,'Le Syndrome extrapyramidal et diencephalique au cours des traitements au Largactil et Serpasil', *Annales Medico-Psychologiques*, vol. 112, 1954, pp. 737–44, cited in Healy, *Let Them Eat Prozac*, p. 14–15

5. Healy, *Let Them Eat Prozac*, p. 15

6. M. Teicher, C. Glod and J. Cole,'Antidepressant Drugs and the Emergence of Suicidal Tendencies', *Drug Safety*, vol. 8, issue 3, March 1993, p. 186–212

7. A. Rothschild and C. Locke,'Reexposure to Fluoxetine after Serious Suicide Attempts by Three Patients: the role of akathisia', *Journal of Clinical Psychiatry*, 1991, vol. 52, pp. 491–3, cited in Breggin, *The Antidepressant Fact Book*, p. 87

8. Teicher et al., 'Antidepressant Drugs and the Emergence of Suicidal Tendencies'

9. Healy, *Let Them Eat Prozac*, p. 185–7

10. Breggin, *Toxic Psychiatry*, p. 12–13

11. D. Williams, 'Bitter Pills', *Time Magazine*, 21 November 2005, p. 55

12. Breggin and Cohen, *Your Drug May Be Your Problem*, p. 77

13. Ibid., p. 46; Breggin, *The Antidepressant Fact Book*, p. 34

14. Breggin and Cohen, *Your Drug May Be Your Problem*, p. 46–7

15. Jackson, *Rethinking Psychiatric Drugs*, p. 179

16. Breggin and Cohen, *Your Drug May Be Your Problem*, p. 78

17. *MIMS Annual 2005*, section 3, p. 333

18. Breggin and Cohen, *Your Drug May Be Your Problem*, p. 78

19. Jackson, *Rethinking Psychiatric Drugs*, p. 240–3

20. Ibid., p. 246

21. Ibid., p. 239–40

22. *MIMS Annual 2003*, section 3, p. 294

23. Breggin and Cohen, *Your Drug May Be Your Problem,* p. 79

24. Straus et al., 'Antipsychotics and the Risk of Sudden Cardiac

Death', *Archives of Internal Medicine*, June 2004, vol. 164, p. 1293–7, viewed 24 May 2006, www.ncbi.nlm.nih.gov/entrez/query.fcgi?cmd= Retrieve&db=PubMed&list_uids=15226162&dopt=Abstract

25. Geddes et al.,'Atypical Antipsychotics in the Treatment of Schizophrenia: systematic overview and meta-regression analysis', *British Medical Journal*, vol. 32, 2 December 2000, p. 1371–5, viewed 14 June 2006, www.bmj.com

26. Letter from D. Healy, *PLoS Journals*, 27 April 2006, viewed 10 May 2006, www.medicine.plosjournals.org/perlserv/?request=read-

27. Jackson, *Rethinking Psychiatric Drugs*, p. 214

28. S. Kapur, 'Psychosis as a State of Aberrant Salience: a framework linking biology, phenomenology and pharmacology in schizophrenia', *American Journal of Psychiatry*, vol. 160, 1 January 2003, p. 13–23, viewed 15 December 2005,www.ajp.psychiatryonline.org/cgi/contents/full/160/1/13

29. Valenstein, *Blaming the Brain*, p. 145

30. J. Joseph, *The Gene Illusion*, p. 81–2

31. Joseph, *The Missing Gene*, p. 222

32. K. Kendler, 'A gene for …: the nature of gene action in psychiatric disorders', *American Journal of Psychiatry*, vol. 16, July 2005, pp. 1243–52, cited in Johnson, *The Missing Gene*, p. 221

33. J. Joseph, *The Missing Gene*, p. 222

34. *MIMS Annual*, CMPMedica Australia Pty Ltd, June 2005, section 3, p. 434

Nine

1. Diagnostic Criteria from DSM-IV-TR™ , p. 171–2

2. Ibid., p. 179–86

3. Ibid., p. 187–9

4. T. L. Bettinger, S. C. Mendelson, P. G. Dorson and M. L. Crismon, 'Olanzapine-induced Glucose Dysregulation', *The Annals of Pharmacotherapy*, 2000, vol. 34, p. 865–7

5. 'Zyprexa Side Effects' reports, viewed 20 January 2004, www. zyprexasideeffectslawyer.com/html/reports.html

6. 'Warning about Hyperglycemia and Atypical Antipsychotic Drugs', FDA Patient Safety News, June 2004, viewed 20 September 2005, www.accessdata.fda.gov/scripts/cdrh/cfdocs/psn/printer.cfm?id=229

7. A. Berenson, 'U.S. Wonders if Drug Data Was Accurate', *New York Times*, 25 April 2007, viewed 18 June 2007, http://www.nytimes. com/2007/04/25/business/25zyprexa.html?_r=1&oref=slogin

8. M. Cronin Fisk and E. Lopatto, 'Lilly Trained Sales Force to Ignore Drug's Risks', *Bloomberg Press*, 31 July 2008, viewed 20 August 2008, http://www.bloomberg.com/apps/news?pid=20601103&sid=aN URtByTt7Yk&refer=us

9. Ibid.

10. Ibid.

Ten

1. *Cutting Edge, 'Selling Sickness'*, Paradigm Productions, broadcast on SBS television, Sydney, 2004

2. Ibid.

3. D. Fergusson, S. Doucette, K. Cranley Glass, S. Shapiro, D. Healy, P. Herbert and B. Hutton, 'Association Between Suicide Attempts and Selective Serotonin Reuptake Inhibitors: a systematic review of randomised controlled trials', *British Medical Journal*, vol. 330, February 2005, p. 396–9

4. A. Gardner, 'Report Raises New Concerns About Antidepressants' Suicide Link' *Healthday News*, 7 July 2006, viewed 17 July 2006, www. health.msn.com/centers/mentalhealth/articlepage.aspx?cpdocum entid=100140415

5. 'FDA Medwatch', 12 May 2006, viewed 16 May 2006, www.fda. gov/medwatch/safety/2006/safety06.htm#paxil

6. 'Suicide Warning Issued for Young Paxil Users', 12 May 2006, viewed 14 May 2006, www.edition.cnn.com/2006/HEALTH/05/12/ paxil.suicide.risk.ap/

Eleven

1. Diagnostic Criteria from DSM-IV-TR™ , p. 204

2. Ibid., p. 170

3. Ibid., p. 171–2

4. R. Peyre, H. Verdous and M. Bourgeois, 'Fluvoxamine: study of treatment effect on a group of 189 hospitalised patients with

depression', *Encephale*, 1992, vol. 18, issue 1, pp. 73–4, cited in P. Breggin,'Fluvoxamine as a Cause of Stimulation, Mania, and Aggression with a Critical Analysis of the FDA Approved Label', *International Journal of Risk and Safety in Medicine*, 2001, vol. 14, p. 71–86

5. R. Howland,'Induction of Mania with Serotonin Reuptake Inhibitors', *Journal of Clinical Psychopharmacology*, 1996, vol. 16, p. 425–7, cited in Breggin,'Fluvoxamine as a Cause of Stimulation'

6. D. Ebert, R. Albert, A. May, A. Merz, H. Murata, I. Stosiek and B. Zahner,'The Serotonin Syndrome and Psychosis-like Side Effects of Fluvoxamine in Clinical Use: an estimation of incidence', *European Neuro-Pharmacology*, 1997, vol. 7, p. 71–4, cited in Breggin, 'Fluvoxamine as a Cause of Stimulation'

7. Breggin, 'Fluvoxamine as a Cause of Stimulation'

8. Jackson, *Rethinking Psychiatric Drugs*, p. 128

9. *MIMS Annual*, Medimedia Australia

10. Breggin, *The Antidepressant Fact Book*, p. 46–8

11. Breggin,'Fluvoxamine as a Cause of Stimulation', p. 73

12. Ibid.

13. Breggin, *The Antidepressant Fact Book*, p. 48

14. '*Antidepressant Blamed for Killing*', 7.30 Report, ABC TV, Sydney, 2001

15. '*Expert Warns of Deadly Side Effects of Anti-depressants, Stateline*, ABC TV, Sydney, 28 May 2004, transcript viewed 10 January

2005, www.abc.net.au/stateline/wa/content/2004/s1119845.htm

16. K. Conners,'Antidepressants: can they turn kids into killers?',
Press & Sun Bulletin, 20 February 2005, viewed 7 October 2005,
www.nl.newsbank.com/nlsearch/we/Archives?p_action=doc&p_
docid=1086D4AE118EFD81&p_docnum=1&s_accountid=AC010510
0703582601964&s_orderid=NB0105100703581301937&s_dlid=DL0
105100703584902005&s_username=rbeddoe

17. P. Breggin,'An Examination of Eli Lilly and Company's Conten-
tions that the BMJ Prozac Documents Were Never Missing and Have
No Significance', 12 January 2005, viewed 28 June 2006, www.
breggin.com/Eli%20LillyWithheld%20Prozac%20Documents—
website%20version.pdf

18. 'Antidepressants', *Press & Sun Bulletin*, 20 February 2005

19. Jackson, *Rethinking Psychiatric Drugs*, p.9

20. Ibid., passim

21. Ibid., p. 25

22. Ibid., p. 28

23. Ibid., p. 29

24. Ibid., p. 40

25. Antonuccio et al.,'Psychology in the Prescription Era: building
a firewall between marketing and science', *American Psychologist*,
December 2003, p. 1031, cited in Jackson, *Rethinking Psychiatric
Drugs*, p. 40

26. D. Stipp,'Trouble in Prozac', *Fortune magazine*, 28 November

2005, viewed 27 June 2006, www.money.cnn.com/magazines/fortune/
fortune_archive/2005/11/28/83 61973/index.htm

27. A. Gardner, 'Report Raises New Concerns'

28. Ibid.

29. Jackson, *Rethinking Psychiatric Drugs*, p. 39–40

30. E. H. Turner et al., 'Selective Publication of Antidepressant Trials
and Its Influence on Apparent Efficacy, *New England Journal of Medicine*, vol. 358, issue 3, 17 January 2008, p. 252–260

31. J. Moncrieff,'Is Psychiatry for Sale?', *Healthy Skepticism international news*, January 2004, viewed 16 May 2006, www.healthyskepticism.org/news/issue.php?id=1

32. Jackson, *Rethinking Psychiatric Drugs*, p.16

Twelve

1. Breggin, *The Antidepressant Fact Book*, p. 58–9

2. 'Practice Guidelines for the Treatment of Borderline Personality
Disorder', American Psychiatric Association, October 2001, viewed
10 November 2005, www.psych.org/psych_pract/treatg/pg/borderline_revisebook_index.cfm

Thirteen

1. Breggin and Cohen, *Your Drug May Be Your Problem*, p. 137–9

2. D. F. Zullino, D. Delessert, C. B. Eap, M. Preisig and P.
Baumann,'Tobacco and Cannabis Smoking Cessation Can Lead to
Intoxication with Clozapine or Olanzapine', *International Clinical*

Psychopharmacology, May 2002, vol. 17, issue 3, p. 141–3

3. Jackson, *Rethinking Psychiatric Drugs*, p. 228

Fifteen

1. *MIMS Annual*, June 2005, section 3, p. 335 and 387

2. '*The Secrets of Seroxat*', *Panorama*, BBC1, London, October 2002

Sixteen

1. *MIMS Annual*, June 2005, section 3, p. 393

2. Ibid., p. 378

3. Rapid Responses, vol. 324, 7 August 2002, viewed 5 November 2005, www.bmj.bmjjournals.com/cgi/elettters/324/7352/1506

4. Medawar and Herxheimer, 'A comparison of adverse drug reaction reports from professionals and users', p. 12

5. D. Healy, 'Halting SSRIs', viewed 14 November 2005, www. mind.org.uk/NR/rdonlyres/59D68F19-F69C-4613-BD40-A0D8B38D1410/0/DavidHealyHaltingSSRIs.pdf

6. Ibid.

7. '*The Secrets of Seroxat*', *Panorama*

8. A. Young and A. Curry, 'Physicians' Knowledge of Antidepressant Withdrawal Effects: a survey', *Journal of Clinical Psychiatry*, 1997, vol. 58, 57, p. 28–30, viewed 20 May 2006, www.ncbi.nlm.nih. gov/entrez/query.fcgi?cmd=Retrieve&db=PubMed&list_uids=921949 1&dopt=Abstract

9. 'The Secrets of Seroxat', Panorama

10. Medawar,'The Antidepressant Web: marketing depression and making medicines work'

Seventeen

1. MIMS Annual 2003, section 3

2. Valenstein, Blaming the Brain, p. 99

3. Ibid.

4. Jackson, Rethinking Psychiatric Drugs, p. 76

5. John Horgan, The Undiscovered Mind, p. 37

6. Loren Mosher's letter of resignation from the American Psychiatric Association, 4 December 1998, viewed 27 October 2005, www.mosh-ersoteria.com/resig.htm

7. MindMatters,'Understanding Mental Illnesses', pp. 20–1, viewed 9 August 2008, www.cms.curriculum.edu.au/mindmatters/resources/pdf/booklets/mental_ill17_29.pdf

8. MindMatters,'Understanding Mental Illnesses', pp. 30–44, viewed 9 August 2008, http://cms.curriculum.edu.au/mindmatters/resources/pdf/booklets/mental_ill30_44.pdf

9. Ibid., p. 34

10. Ibid., p. 35

11. MHRA press release,'Safety Review of Antidepressants Used by Children Completed', 11 December 2003, cited in Jackson, Rethinking

Psychiatric Drugs, p. 118

12. Report of the CSM working group on the safety of selective serotonin reuptake inhibitor antidepressants, 6 December 2004, p. 1, viewed 31 May 2006, www.mhra.gov.uk/home/ idcplg?IdcService=GET_FILE&dID=1391&noSaveAs=1&Rendition =WEB

13. FDA Public Health Advisory, 'Suicidality in Children and Adolescents Treated with Antidepressant Medication', 15 October 2004, viewed 31 May 2006, www.fda.gov/cder/drug/antidepressants/ SSRIPHA200410.htm

14. Breggin, *The Antidepressant Fact Book*, p.17

15. Viewed 7 January 2006, www.bipolar.com.au

16. B. Mintzes, 'Disease Mongering in Drug Promotion: Do Govern- ments Have a Regulatory Role?', *PloS Medicine,* vol. 3, issue 4, April 2006

17. Ibid.

18. M. Day, 'UK drug companies must disclose funding of patients' groups', *British Medical Journal*, vol. 332, 14 January 2006, viewed 19 September 2008, http://www.bmj.com/cgi/content/ full/332/7533/69-a?etoc

19. R. Baker,'Beating the blues: mental health takes industry pills', *The Age*, 8 August 2006

20. Moynihan and Cassels, *Selling Sickness*, p. 32–3

21. Inaugural Conference on Disease-Mongering, University of New- castle, Queensland, Australia, 11–13 April 2006

22. *Australian Choice Magazine*, June 2004, viewed 20 April 2006, www.choice.com.au/viewarticleasonepage.aspx?id=104325&catId=10 0231 &tid=100008&p=1

23. R. Moynihan and D. Henry,'The Fight Against Disease-Mongering: generating knowledge for action', *PLoS Medicine*, vol. 3, issue 4, April 2006

24. Moynihan and Cassels, *Selling Sickness*, chapter 2

25. Healy,'The Latest Mania: selling bipolar disorder', *PLoS Medicine*, vol. 3, issue 4, April 2006, viewed 30 April 2006

26. Moynihan and Cassels, *Selling Sickness*

27. V. Parry,'The Art of Branding a Condition,' *Med Mark Media*, vol. 38, 2003, p. 43–9, cited in 'The Fight Against Disease-mongering'

28. J. Coe, 'Healthcare: the lifestyle drugs outlook to 2008, unlocking new value in well-being', *Reuters Business Insight*, London, 2003, p. 243, cited in 'The Fight Against Disease-mongering'

29. Moynihan and Cassels, *Selling Sickness*, p. 38–9

30. Healy, *Let Them Eat Prozac*; Jackson, *Rethinking Psychiatric Drugs*, p. 39

31. M. Larkin,'Whose Article is it Anyway?', *The Lancet*, 10 July, 1999, p. 136, cited in Jackson, *Rethinking Psychiatric Drugs,* p. 39

32. Pfizer expert report,'Sertraline Hydrochloride for Obsessive Compulsive Disorder in Paediatric Patients', approved 20 October 1997, cited in Healy, *Let Them Eat Prozac*, p. 119

33. J. Lenzer and N. Pyke,'Was Traci Johnson Driven to Suicide

by Antidepressants?', *Independent*, 19 June 2005, viewed 10 August 2005, www.news.independent.co.uk/uk/health_medical/story. jsp?story=648010

34. Interview with Sidney Wolfe MD, 'How independent is the FDA?', *Frontline*, PBS TV, November 2003, viewed 25 September 2008, http://www.pbs.org/wgbh/pages/frontline/shows/prescription/hazard/independent.html

35. D. Batty, M. Hodgson, N. Watt, 'Drug companies must reveal more data after Seroxat results withheld', *The Guardian*, 6 March 2008, viewed 25 September 2008, http://www.guardian.co.uk/society/2008/mar/06/health.health

36. *Four Corners*, ABC TV, Sydney, 11 April 2005, viewed 25 April 2005, www.abc.net.au/4corners/content/2005/s1343195.htm

37. J. Graham,'Top Mental Health Guide Questioned', *Chicago Tribune*, 20 April 2006, viewed 30 April 2006, www.chicagotribune.com/news/nationworld/chi-0604200194apr20,1,3690657.story?coll=chi-newsnationworldhed&ctrack=1&cset=true

38. A. Nazareno, 'Pharmaceutical Companies Have Been Ill for a Long While', *San Antonio Express*, 17 August 2005, viewed 20 September 2005, www.mysanantonio.com/business/stories/MYSA091705.health.EN.2131ea98.html

39. Healy, *Let Them Eat Prozac*, p. 230

40. 'Suicide Label Unlikely to Squeeze Glaxo Sales', 12 May 2006, viewed 16 May 2006,www.money.cnn.com/2006/05/12/news/companies/paxil/

41. Healy, *Let Them Eat Prozac*, p. 230

42. R. Whitaker,'Anatomy of an Epidemic: psychiatric drugs and the astonishing rise of mental illness in America', *Ethical Human Psychology and Psychiatry*, vol. 7, no. 1, Spring 2005

43. Williams, 'Bitter Pills', *Time magazine*, p. 52

44. C. Nadar,'Antidepressants: first nine days a risk', *The Age*, 22 July 2004, viewed 10 May 2006, http://www.theage.com.au/articles/2004/07/21/1090089219002.html?oneclick=true

45. A. Cresswell and S. Marris,'Neglect of Mental Health a "Disgrace"', *The Australian*, 20 October 2005, viewed 7 November 2005, www.theaustralian.news.com.au/common/story_page/0,5744,16976046%255E23289,00.html

46. R. Smith, 'Psychiatric wards at crisis point, says doctor', *Telegraph.co.uk*, 18 August 2007

47. Fergusson et al.,'Association Between Suicide Attempts and Selective Serotonin Reuptake Inhibitors', p. 399

48. J. Moncrieff and D. Cohen,'Do Antidepressants Cure or Create Abnormal Brain States?,' *PLoS Medicine*, 6 June 2006, viewed 9 June 2006, www.medicine.plosjournals.org/perlserv/?request=getdocument& doi=10%2E1371%2Fjournal%2Epmed%2E0030240

49. S. B. Patten,'The Impact of Antidepressant Treatment on Population Health: synthesis of data from two national data sources in Canada', November 2004, cited in Moncrieff and Cohen,'Do Antidepressants Cure or Create Abnormal Brain States?'

50. J. Moncrieff and J. Pomerleau,'Trends in Sickness Benefits in Great Britain and the Contribution of Mental Disorders,' *Journal of Public Health Medicine*, vol. 22, p. 59–67, cited in Moncrieff and

Cohen,'Do Antidepressants Cure or Create Abnormal Brain States?'

51. S. B. Patten,'The Impact of Antidepressant Treatment on Population Health: synthesis of data from two national data sources in Canada', November 2004, cited in Moncrieff and Cohen,'Do Antidepressants Cure or Create Abnormal Brain States?

52. D. Williams, 'Bitter Pills', *Time Magazine*, 21 November 2005, p. 50

53. 'Drug reactions "must be reported"', *BBC News*, 11 May 2006, viewed 25 September 2008, http://news.bbc.co.uk/go/pr/fr/-/2/hi/health/4759571.stm

54. Davies, 'Jagged Little Pills', *The Bulletin*, 26 May 2004

55. Medawar and Herxheimer, 'A comparison of adverse drug reaction reports from professionals and users', p.15

56. TGA Adverse Reactions Bulletin,'Suicidality with SSRIs: adults and children', August 2005

57. Questions and answers on findings of CSM Expert Working Group, viewed 29 August 2008, http://www.mhra.gov.uk/Safetyinformation/Safetywarningsalertsandrecalls/Safetywarningsandmessagesformedicines/CON1004259

Epilogue

1. T. Stuttaford, 'Depression your questions', *Times Online*, 22 September 2008, viewed 10 October 2008, http://www.timesonline.co.uk:80/tol/life_and_style/health/mental_health/article4801635.ece

2. Breggin, *The Antidepressant Fact Book,* p. 42

3. D. Williams, 'Bitter Pills', *Time Magazine*, 21 November 2005, p. 50

4. Report of the CSM Working Group on the safety of selective serotonin reuptake inhibitors, 6 December 2004, viewed 26 June 2006, www.mhra.gov.uk/home/idcplg?IdcService=GET_FILE&dID=1391& noSaveAs=1&Rendition=WEB

5. F. Balzac, *Neuropsychiatry reviews*, vol. 8, issue 7, July 2007, viewed 8 July 2008, http://www.neuropsychiatryreviews.com/07jul/ neurotrophic.html

6. *Neuropsychiatry reviews*, July 2007

7. D. Williams, 'Bitter Pills', *Time Magazine*, 21 November 2005, p. 52

8. J. Robotham,'Beyond the Blues', *Sydney Morning Herald*, 25 March 2006, viewed 10 April 2006, www.smh.com.au/news/national/ beyond-the blues/2006/03/24/1143083999610.html

9. Black Dog Institute depression information, viewed 29 July 2006, www.blackdoginstitute.org.au/depression/explained/types.cfm

10. J. Jureidini in *Dying for a Cure* (Australian edition), Random House Australia, Sydney, 2007, p. vi

11. 'GPs get new antidepressant rules', *BBC News*, 6 December 2004, viewed 10 October 2008, http://news.bbc.co.uk/2/hi/health/4071145.stm

12. Jureidini in *Dying for a Cure* (Australian edition), p. viii

13. 'More funds for talking therapies', *BBC News*, 10 October 2007, viewed 26 September 2008, http://news.bbc.co.uk/2/hi/ health/7037400.stm

14. 'A Deadly Emotional Disease', *Harvard Magazine*, July/ August 2006, viewed 17 July 2006,www.harvardmagazine.com/on-line/070648.html

15. 'Antidepressants "little effect"', *BBC News*, 26 February 2008, viewed 26 September 2008, http://news.bbc.co.uk/2/hi/health/7263494.stm

16. A. Gardner, 'Report Raises New Concerns about Antidepressants' Suicide Link', *Healthday News*, 7 July 2006, viewed 17 July 2006, www.health.msn.com/centers/mentalhealth/articlepage.aspx?cpdocumentid=100140415

Bibliography and further reading

Citations refer only to books. All details of journal articles and websites viewed can be found in the Notes.

Marcia Angell, *The Truth About the Drug Companies*, Random House, New York, 2005

Lara Bishop, *Postnatal Depression: families in turmoil*, Halstead Press, Sydney, 2000

Peter Breggin, *The Antidepressant Fact Book: what your doctor won't tell you about Prozac, Zoloft, Paxil, Celexa and Luvox*, Perseus Publishing, Massachusetts, 2001

Peter Breggin, *Toxic Psychiatry: why therapy, empathy and love must replace the drugs, electroshock and biochemical theories of the 'new psychiatry'*, HarperCollins, London, 1993

Peter Breggin and David Cohen, *Your Drug May Be Your Problem: how and why to stop taking psychiatric medications*, Perseus Publishing, Massachusetts, 2000

David Healy, *The Antidepressant Era*, Harvard University Press, Massachusetts, 1999

David Healy, *Let Them Eat Prozac: the unhealthy relationship between the pharmaceutical industry and depression*, New York University Press, New York, 2004

John Horgan, *The Undiscovered Mind: how the brain defies explanation*, Orion Books, London, 2000

Grace Jackson, *Rethinking Psychiatric Drugs: a guide for informed consent*, Authorhouse, Bloomington, 2005

Jay Joseph, *The Gene Illusion: genetic research in psychiatry and psychology under the microscope*, PCCS Books, Ross-on-Wye, 2003

Jay Joseph, *The Missing Gene: psychiatry, heredity, and the fruitless search for genes*, Algora Publishing, New York, 2006

Jacky Law, *Big Pharma: exposing the global healthcare agenda*, Avalon Publishing Group, New York, 2006

Charles Medawar and Anita Hardon, *Medicines Out of Control: antidepressants and the conspiracy of goodwill*, Aksant Academic Publishers, Amsterdam, 2004

Ray Moynihan and Alan Cassels, *Selling Sickness: how drug companies are turning us all into patients*, Allen & Unwin, Sydney, 2005

Elliot Valenstein, *Blaming the Brain: the truth about drugs and mental health*, Free Press, New York, 1998

Robert Whitaker, *Mad in America: bad science, bad medicine, and the enduring mistreatment of the mentally ill*, Basic Books, Massachusetts, 2003

Helpful Internet Sites

www.ahrp.org
Website of the Alliance for Human Research Protection. 'The AHRP is a national network of lay people and professionals dedicated to advancing responsible and ethical medical research practices, to ensure that the human rights, dignity and welfare of human subjects are protected, and to minimise the risks associated with such endeavours.'

www.antidepressantawareness.com
A members-only online forum designed for discussion on psychiatric medications by those who have experienced using them first hand. Friends and/or family members of those using psychiatric medications are also welcome.

www.antidepressantsfacts.com
An independent collection of news stories, journal articles and more – all relating to the continually emerging information regarding antidepressants.

www.breggin.com
Dr Peter Breggin's own website.

www.comingoff.com
An excellently informative website providing up-to-date information about psychiatric medication, how it functions and the withdrawal

process. This site has been created by people who have themselves taken psychiatric medication and experienced its withdrawal, and clinicians who have been involved in supporting this process.

www.drugawareness.org
Founded by Dr Ann Blake Tracy, director of the International Coalition for Drug Awareness (ICFDA) and author of the book *Prozac: panacea or pandora?* The ICFDA states its aim is to 'address the world's most pervasive and subtle drug problem – prescription drugs. We are dedicated to educating the people of the world regarding the potential harmful and life-threatening short- and long-term effects of these drugs, along with the serious problems associated with the unethical marketing techniques of pharmaceutical companies and the off-label prescribing of these drugs by many physicians.' This site includes a discussion board.

www.ect.org
This site is a comprehensive collection of information about ECT, developed by a recipient of the treatment. Includes discussion board.

http://fiddaman.blogspot.com
A blog site run by UK antidepressant campaigner Bob Fiddaman. Here Bob shares his own experiences with taking and withdrawing from *Seroxat*. Bob is an active campaigner with success in gaining respected attention from the MHRA regarding improvements in antidepressant side-effect warnings.

www.healthyskepticism.org
An international non-profit organisation chaired by Dr Jon Jureidini. Healthy Skepticism invites 'health professionals and everyone with an interest in improving health' to share in its aim to 'improve health by reducing harm from misleading drug promotion'.

www.healyprozac.com
Professor David Healy's website 'explores threats to public safety and

academic freedom surrounding the SSRI group of drugs'. This site contains scanned versions of actual trial transcripts from three major legal cases involving SSRIs and suicide and homicide. The site also presents 'correspondence surrounding issues to do with ghost-writing, efforts to draw attention to the hazards of these drugs and the dramatic changes taking place in academia as an increasing proportion of clinical research is privatised'.

www.icspp.org

The website of the International Centre for the Study of Psychiatry and Psychology. A professional organisation 'concerned with the impact of mental health theories on public policy and the effects of therapeutic practices upon individual well-being, personal freedom, and family and community values'. ICSPP strives to 'inform professions, the media and the public about the potential dangers of drugs, electroshock, psychosurgery, and the biological theories of psychiatry'.

www.mhra.gov.uk

The website of the Medicines and Healthcare Products Regulatory Agency. Along with information on medicine safety this site has a provision for patients to report their own suspected adverse drug reactions. Go to the 'Safety information' section on the homepage and follow the links to 'Reporting suspected adverse drug reactions'.

www.mind.org.uk

The leading mental health charity in England and Wales, working 'to create a better life for people with experience of mental distress'. It offers a wealth of quality information on understanding and dealing with mental health issues.

www.patients-association.org.uk

A London-based charity established to 'promote the voice of patients in healthcare'. This site invites patients to share their experiences with the health system with a view to working with the NHS and other healthcare providers in improving services.

www.paxilprogress.org
A discussion board with testimonials of people's experiences with *Seroxat* (*Paxil*) and other SSRIs.

www.plos.org
The Public Library of Science (PLoS) is a non-profit organisation of scientists and physicians committed to making the world's scientific and medical literature a public resource. PloS journals are available for anyone to read, distribute, or use for their own research.

www.ssri-uksupport.com
UK-based SSRI support site. Full of information regarding SSRIs. Includes chatroom, discussion board and links to related sites.

www.thomasjmoore.com
Thomas J. Moore is a healthcare authority and author. His book *Prescription for Disaster* focuses on the risks of the most widely used prescription drugs.

About the Author

Rebekah Beddoe was prescribed antidepressants for suspected post-natal depression shortly after the birth of her first child. Within days her mental health was spiralling out of control. Approximately two years on, still taking an antidepressant as well a host of other drugs, she began studying professional writing with a view to describing her experiences of living with a major mental health problem. In a sharp twist, what started out as a documented insight into a life besieged by chronic mental illness became this book, *Dying for a Cure*. Rebekah, now in her thirties and fully restored to health, lives in Melbourne, Australia, with her husband, two children, and a very spoilt golden retriever.